THE PROFESSIONAL ENGINEERING CAREER DEVELOPMENT SERIES

ENGINEERING PROFESSION ADVISORY GROUP

The Barnes & Noble
Professional Engineering Career Development Series

MEASUREMENTS AND CONTROL APPLICATIONS FOR PRACTICING ENGINEERS

Joel O. Hougen
Department of Chemical Engineering
The University of Texas

Distributed exclusively by CAHNERS BOOKS
89 Franklin Street, Boston, Mass., U.S.A. 02110

 For information address Cahners Books, 89 Franklin Street, Boston, Mass., 02110.

LIBRARY OF CONGRESS CATALOG CARD NUMBER: 74-170127

Preface

This book has been written to assist practicing engineers in solving problems which they encounter in existing processing facilities. It is directed to today's engineers and today's problems.

Those who are motivated to make existing systems perform as intended will find herein a general approach by which the uncertainties obstructing problem solution can be removed. The reader may be surprised to learn that these uncertainties may be reduced almost to the vanishing point. He is therefore virtually assured of success in the solution of almost any technical problem associated with an existing process.

Because the approach applies to existing facilities, the extent which the optimum possible solution approaches the ideal will be dictated by the performance characteristics of the processing apparatus which must be used, the processing technology employed, and economic factors associated with the solution and current operation.

Emphasis is almost completely directed towards the empirical approach to problem solution. In this respect, the book is unique. Current literature, most of which is devoted to theoretical approaches, has given little attention to this aspect.

Any problem associated with the operating performance of an existing processing plant can be solved satisfactorily by techniques existing today. Procedures and methodology have been developed which, if systematically and carefully applied, will always assure success. There is no need to feel one is pioneering anew each time a plant study is to be made. Trails have been blazed and the pathway is wide, clear, and well-marked. The objectives of this book are to present these procedures and methodologies and to offer encouragement and guidance to those interested in venturing along these pathways.

The procedures by which problem solution is achieved are logical and straightforward. It is a traditional approach which engineers of an earlier vintage have used and relied upon. It is the empirical approach. The procedures to be described herein differ only in degree from the earlier ones. Advances in instrumentation and measuring methods have made it possible to obtain more and improved information and thus gain a better understanding of physical processes. Testing procedures play an increased role.

Data-processing capability has increased manyfold in recent years. Information previously impossible or most difficult to obtain can now be acquired almost with impunity. The results are a vastly increased ability to acquire basic information and a widely extended capability to interpret and develop useful knowledge for the solution of particular problems.

The steps required to solve a problem associated with an existing plant are:

(1) define the problem,
(2) develop alternate strategies for solution,
(3) select the most acceptable strategy,
(4) design the required system, and
(5) verify the solution.

This is certainly a time-honored approach and appears simple enough. The most difficult step is the first one, *problem definition*. The problem must be adequately defined if the solution is to be found. "Definition" means the acquisition of an understanding of the process of plant behavior. This implies the understanding of the relationships between pertinent independent and dependent variables, including those that are independent of time and, in some cases, those which include time responses as well. That is, both static and dynamic descriptions will be included in the definition.

Contents

Introduction

Procedures for designing satisfactory feedback and feedforward control systems for most continuously processing operations have been available for some time. If these procedures are followed, the designer is assured of a control system which, following minor adjustments in the field, will perform as predicted.

In the development of a process control system the following steps are taken.

(1) Obtain a quantitative description of the static and dynamic performance of the process.

(2) Develop the control strategy.

(3) Determine the form of the control function which is required.

(4) Obtain quantitative static and dynamic descriptions of the selected control components so that relationships between their adjustable parameters and the performance of the components are known.

(5) Design the control system. This means selecting and adjusting the performance of the control components so that they correspond to the needs of the specific process.

Unfortunately, even though the methodology of carrying out each of these steps is well known, it is usually not easy to execute.

For example, if the process is being designed, it will be very difficult to predict its static and dynamic characteristics. (Step 1) If the process or plant exists, these characteristics can be determined by experimentation, but this is an expensive and time-consuming operation even though the techniques for conducting the tests are well-known.

Availability of components and costs sometimes place restrictions on the control functions which can realistically be chosen. (Step 3) This difficulty is not as severe as it was in the past because of the advances in technology and increased variety of control components.

Limitation in choice will exist, however, for one of a number of reasons.

It is true, nonetheless, that systems with predictable performance can be created following the steps outlined above. The task of the designer is to judge the costs involved and the extent of detail required in each step to accomplish an acceptable engineering solution to a particular problem.

The purpose of a control system is to endow the overall system, of which it is a part, with desirable performance. Broadly speaking, the objective is to create a system the dependent variables of which will remain within prescribed limits despite changes which are deliberately or inadvertently introduced.

The "prescribed limits" and nature of likely changes must be specified in advance if a quantitative definition of the control problem is to be made. Currently, this is rarely done in a rational manner either by process designers or by those responsible for the control-system design. Part of the difficulty is precisely because of this dichotomy in plant design: The process design is produced by one group, while the control systems are specified by another group. The two functions, process design and control-system design, must eventually be considered together if an overall *designed* system is to be realized.

Another reason for the lack of precise specifications for control is the paucity of knowledge of the behavior of processes in response to various inputs. Skills in prediction are simply not sufficiently reliable despite the very large amount of work devoted to 'model building.'

The result is that specifications which are given tend to be quite arbitrary, unrealistic and sometimes trivial.

The following examples will illustrate the significance of these latter remarks.

Suppose the objective is to specify the requirements for designing a reflux drum level control system for a distillation column. A typical arrangement is shown in Figure 1-13.

The size of the reflux drum will probably be such that overhead liquid product rate can be maintained for some specified time despite sudden curtailment in column overhead vapor or vice-versa. Overhead product pump, lines, and control valve will be selected to handle perhaps 125-150 percent of design flow. Thus, the capability and basic size of the pertinent components (pumps and valves) are established without regard to the control problem.

It makes little sense, therefore, to specify that the level should be maintained within two inches, for example, of a reference value, even if the maximum sudden changes in drum influent or effluent were known which is generally not the case. The control-system designer can, however, predict the probable excursions of level which would result if a given control system were incorporated using the specified processing components.

In this instance, since maintenance of level within close tolerances is of secondary importance, this hindsight type of control-system synthesis may be satisfactory. Where a high-performance control system is not required, design criteria can be relaxed.

As another example, consider a rotary kiln in which some kind of pyrochemical reaction is being conducted. Assume that two fuels (pulverized coal and gas) are used, and that the availability of the gaseous fuel is subject to rather sudden changes. Assume further that, whereas primary air for combustion is controllable, the supply of secondary air can change rapidly by virtue of changes in hood or cooler pressure which change the amount of leakage into the preheater and elsewhere. Figure 1-11 shows the process arrangement.

For the sake of fuel economy and maintenance of uniformity of operations, suppose it is proposed that the excess air in the kiln effluent gases should be maintained at some minimum value. An oxygen analyzer would probably serve as the detector in this case.

Since it is specified that all the available gaseous fuel must be used, even though its supply may be subject to change, it is apparent that changes in solid fuel must be made to compensate for changes in gaseous fuel.

The residence time of gases in the kiln is relatively short—perhaps only a few seconds; therefore changes in excess air in the effluent appear very rapidly after a change in air entering the system. Variations in either primary or secondary air will be reflected in changes in excess air within a very short period of time.

A scheme for regulating the excess air by regulating the rate of pulverized coal to the kiln in response to changes in excess air might appear to be logical. Whether such a scheme is feasible depends upon the response characteristics of the coal mill. Whereas excess air can vary rapidly (seconds), it has been found that the effluent coal from a pulverizer can be altered only relatively slowly (minutes) in response to a change in rate of coal feed.

It becomes apparent that the response characteristics of the coal pulverizer rules it out as a device for *directly* controlling the excess air in the kiln effluent if a responsive system is desired.

Obviously, compensating changes in solid fuel must be made if constant energy input is to be maintained. However, to maintain constant excess air requires manipulating inputs capable of producing a more rapid compensating response than the disturbances. In this case, direct regulation of primary air flow, or indirect regulation of secondary air flow via inlet draft pressure regulation, appear to be logical approaches to the short time problem.

These two examples will serve to illustrate that realistic control specifications and schemes cannot be formulated without a knowledge of the performance characteristics of the processing apparatus which will be involved as well as consideration of noncontrol aspects of the problem.

The importance of time relations has been intimated in the above discussion. Response to 'sudden' changes and the response of systems in 'seconds' or 'minutes' has been mentioned. Indeed, time relations are the essence of automatic control. If processes and process inputs were time invariant, there would be no need for control systems. It is precisely to attenuate time-varying responses caused by disturbances which may also be time varying and to maintain outputs at desired values in spite of changes in inputs that control systems are installed. If processes experienced no changes or disturbances of any kind, there would be no need for control devices.

A primary function of a control system is to confer upon the complete ensemble (process plus control system) properties which will enable pertinent process variables to be maintained within prescribed limits despite changes in independent operating variables and/or uncontrolled inputs or disturbances.

1
Strategy of Process Control

A sound strategy must be developed before a control system can be designed. Knowledge of the process, control components and objectives is required. Merely attaching control hardware to a process, the performance characteristics of which are unknown, has a low probability of success if the demands are at all critical.

Strategies of control are derived heuristically. Theory can lend some guidance and judgment, of course, but, in the main, the basic strategy is evolved after an intuitive understanding of the process is acquired. This implies a rather intimate knowledge of plant performance.

There are a number of basic principles which are useful in developing a control strategy. These will be illustrated through a discussion of several case studies.

EXAMPLE 1. Pressure control of a gas-producing system provided with centrifugal exhaust blower.

A process diagram for this system is shown in Figure 1-1. One control scheme is also shown. Reactants and energy were supplied to the reactor which produced liquid and vapor products. The vapor products were further processed in order to recover more liquid products.

The volume of the processing equipment was about four times that of the reactor. The average residence time of the gases in the reactor was about 5 seconds and about 25 seconds for the remainder of the system. The normal pressure drop from reactor to blower suction was approximately 10 inches of water and the maximum pressure rise developed by the blower 20 inches of water. The stripped gas was withdrawn by a centrifugal exhauster which discharged to a manifold collecting material from other similar processes. The endo-

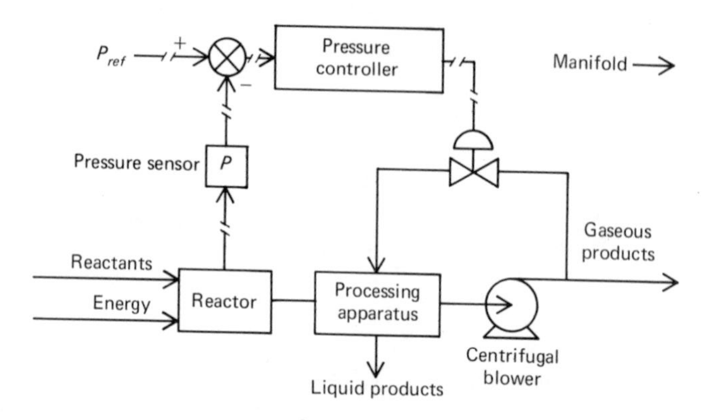

Figure 1.1. Original plan for controlling pressure of a gas-producing reaction system.

thermic reaction was sustained by the addition of energy. Because of the difficulty of supplying reactants at a uniform rate and because of variations in the rate of energy supply, the rate of gas production was subject to rapid and random changes. While energy could be measured, it could not be closely regulated. For example, the rate of energy could vary as much as 50 percent in a matter of seconds.

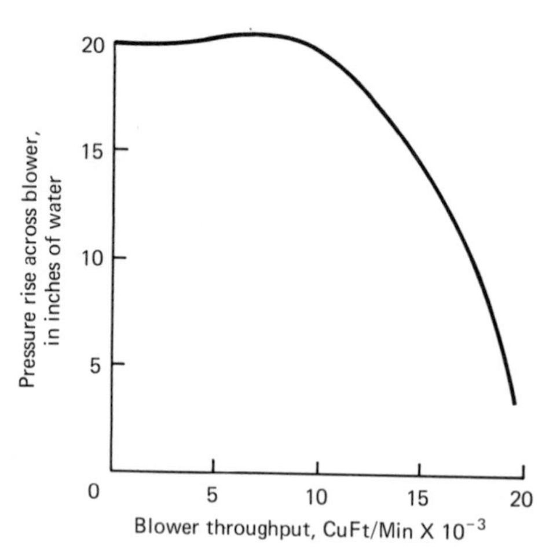

Figure 1.2. Characteristics of a centrifugal blower.

Obviously the pressure in the reactor was subject to rather large and sudden changes, following rather closely the pattern of gas production.

The objective was to design a control system capable of maintaining the pressure in the reactor within about one-half inch of water around a desired steady state. Because of fouling of the gas conduits, the resistance to the flow of gas through the process changed with time. Changes in the manner of operation could also alter the resistance to flow.

The following facts applied to the control-system design.

(1) Changes in reactor pressure caused by variation in the rate of energy input and disturbances in the reactor were very rapid and could be rather large.

(2) The pressure in the collecting manifold was subject to relatively rapid and large changes owing to variation in the flow of the various supplies to it.

(3) For a given gas production and resistance to flow, there was a

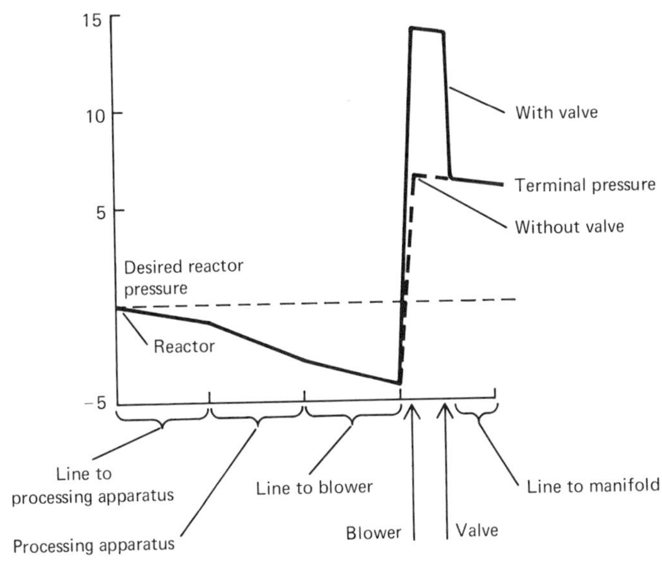

Figure 1.3. Pressure gradient through process for a given state of operation.

unique value of blower suction required to assure the desired reactor pressure.

(4) The performance characteristic of the terminal blower was somewhat as shown in Figure 1-2.

It is instructive to sketch a static (or steady state) pressure gradient in order to emphasize critical points between reactor and manifold. This is shown in Figure 1-3.

Assuming constant reactor operation, it is apparent that pressure changes can be induced at the reactor by changes in manifold pressure. That is, if manifold pressure were suddenly increased, the entire hydraulic gradient would shift upwards. The higher the flow, the less the flow changes for a given change in pressure drop. However, as flow rate increases, the pressure gradient across the blower decreases rapidly.

Regulation of the speed of the blower would be impractical. If the drive were an electric motor, the cost of a speed-control system would be high. In addition, the inertia of the rotating members

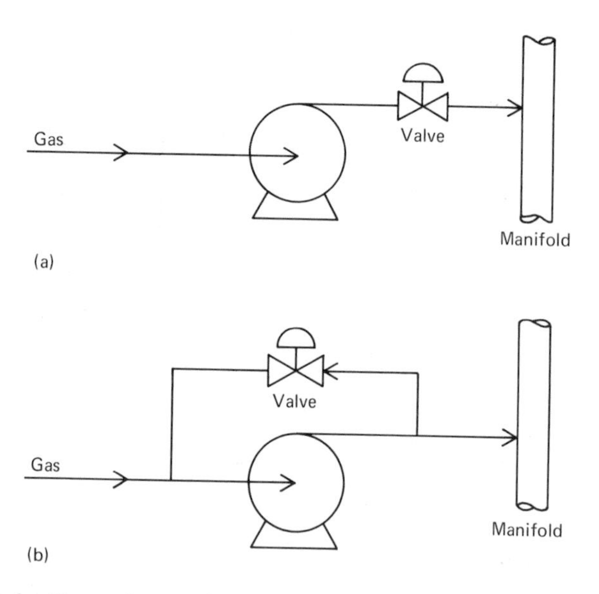

Figure 1.4. Two schemes for regulation of flow through centrifugal blowers. (a) discharge throttling of centrifugal blower, (b) recycle throttling of centrifugal blower.

would probably restrict the dynamic response severely. This would also be true if a steam turbine were used as the driver.

The usual scheme in these situations is to throttle the blower suction or discharge or to throttle a by-pass stream from the blower discharge back to suction or to some point in the process upstream from the blower suction. Figure 1-4 illustrates two methods of regulating flow which could be used.

The by-pass technique has the disadvantages of causing the blower to operate at higher total throughput so that discharge pressures tend to be low. Pressure disturbances arising in the discharge line (mani-

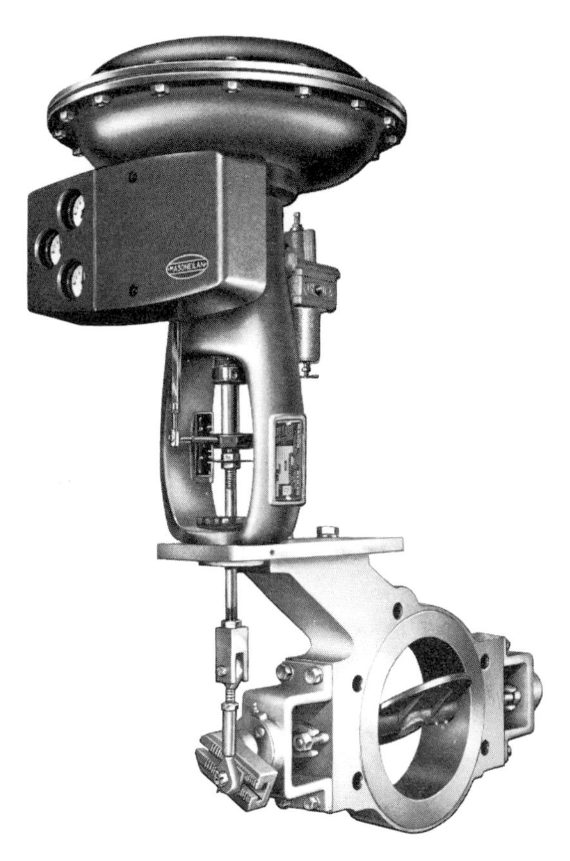

Figure 1.5. Cutaway view of butterfly valve. (Courtesy of Worthington Controls)

fold in this case) are readily transferred across a valve or blower which operates with a low-pressure gradient across it.

This can be seen by examining an equation which describes the performance of valves commonly used to throttle gases, especially at low pressure. These valves use a plate or vane which rotates on a central axis and are called *butterfly* valves. Figure 1-5 shows a typical design.

Over most of the normal useful operating range of butterfly valves (10–65 percent open), the flow can be related to the percent that the valve is open, the density, and the pressure drop across the valve as follows:

$$W = Ke^{kd}\sqrt{\Delta P_v \rho}$$

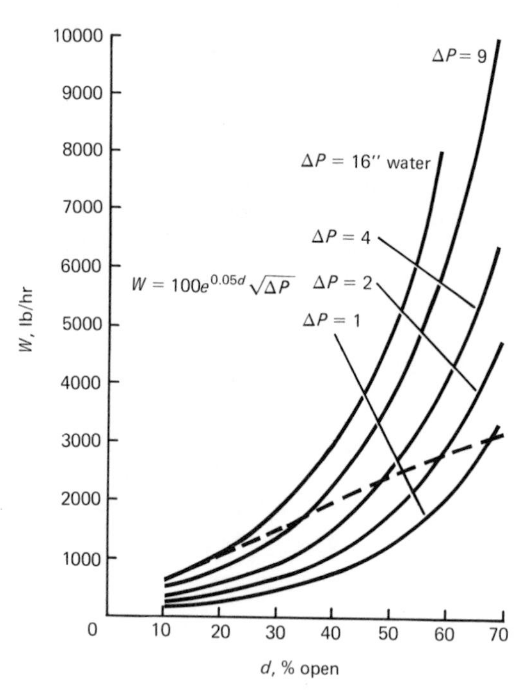

Figure 1.6. Typical performance of a butterfly valve (W versus d).

where

W = mass flow rate,
ΔP_v = pressure drop across the valve,
ρ = density of gas,
d = percent opening of the valve,
K = empirical constant dependent upon the nominal size of the valve, and
k = empirical constant, which is not strongly dependent upon valve size but does depend on vane shape and pressure-tap locations.

Figure 1-6 is typical of the behavior of a butterfly valve handling a gas of given density. Figure 1-7 gives the same information showing mass flow rate versus ΔP_v at constant valve positions.

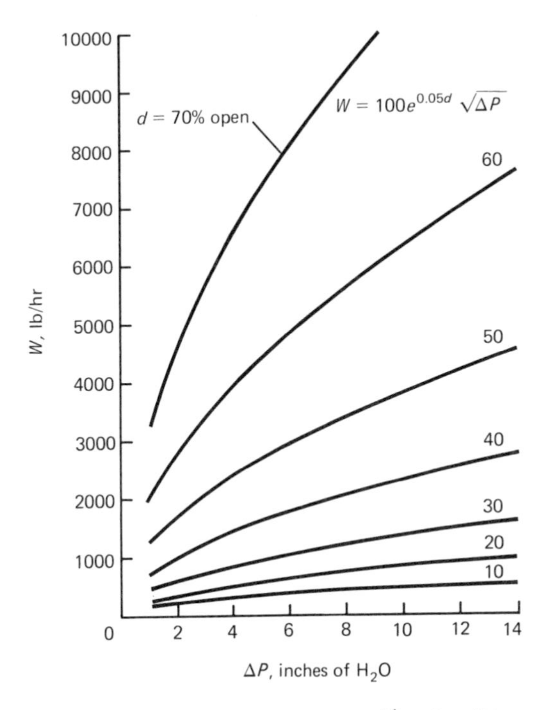

Figure 1.7. Typical performance of butterfly valve (W versus ΔP).

For given gas and flowing conditions, the variation of flow with pressure drop at constant valve opening can be estimated as

$$\left(\frac{\partial W}{\partial \Delta P_v}\right)_d = \frac{K'}{\sqrt{\Delta P_v}} .$$

This indicates that, as the pressure drop becomes higher, the change in flow rate is lower for a given change in pressure gradient. This is borne out in Figures 1-6 and 1-7. This means that, as the pressure drop across the valve increases, the *attenuation* of pressure disturbances arising from the discharge side will be increased; that is, these disturbances will be increasingly diminished.

For these reasons, suction or discharge throttling of centrifugal blowers is the preferred method if precise pressure control of systems of which these devices are a part is to be achieved.

In actual practice, as the valve opens, the available pressure gradient across it usually diminishes since an increasing pressure gradient must develop in the connecting conduit. An operating line such as shown (dotted) in Figure 1-6 is typical. The more linear this actual relationship is, the easier the design of the associated control system. Whether suction or discharge throttling should be used may be a matter of choice or convenience. Where blower capacity is limited, discharge throttling may be required, but, if power consumption must be considered, suction throttling may be attractive. In the above example, discharge throttling was preferred with the arrangement as shown in Figure 1-8. This leads to the first principle of control strategy.

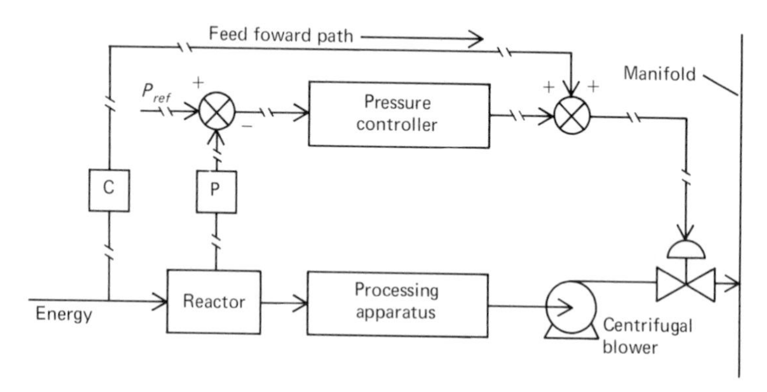

Figure 1.8. Final scheme for control of pressure in gas-producing reactor.

I. Use control apparatus to achieve isolation from disturbances.

The hydraulic gradient of the process, using discharge throttling, will be (for one given condition) as shown in Figure 1-3, and a corresponding plausible control arrangement as shown in Figure 1-8.

Without specific performance data describing the process and control components, it is not possible to proceed further with a control-system design. Since this example is based on a study of a real plant of similar configuration, a review of some of the salient features of that study is appropriate. The reasons for the final strategy will become more apparent.

An alternate control scheme is shown in Figure 1.1. This scheme is inferior to that shown in Figure 1.8 for the reasons stated above. Isolation from the manifold is not achieved, and disturbances can (and indeed did) migrate at will from the manifold to the reactor. This condition was especially aggravated by the performance characteristics of the by-pass valve which possessed an extremely poor time response. In this case, the valve failed to move for about three seconds after commanded and did not return to its original position until about ten seconds after the driving signal was restored to its initial value. Since the changes in pressure in the reactor and manifold varied rapidly, pulsating perhaps 20-30 times a minute, it became immediately clear that the valve actuator was completely inadequate.

In addition, it was soon discovered that the original pressure sensor itself was not suitable. Upon applying a known input to the sensor, it was found that the response of the signal to the valve was, like the valve, much too slow. Either condition (inadequate response of sensor or valve) was sufficient to make it impossible to accomplish any semblance of pressure control of the reactor with the original apparatus. This leads to another principle of control strategy.

II. Select control components that are dynamically compatible with the control problem.

The meaning of "dynamically compatible" will become clear later. Let it be sufficient here to say that the time response of the control components should be considerably faster than that of the process to be controlled.

This control problem was solved by replacing the sensor and valve

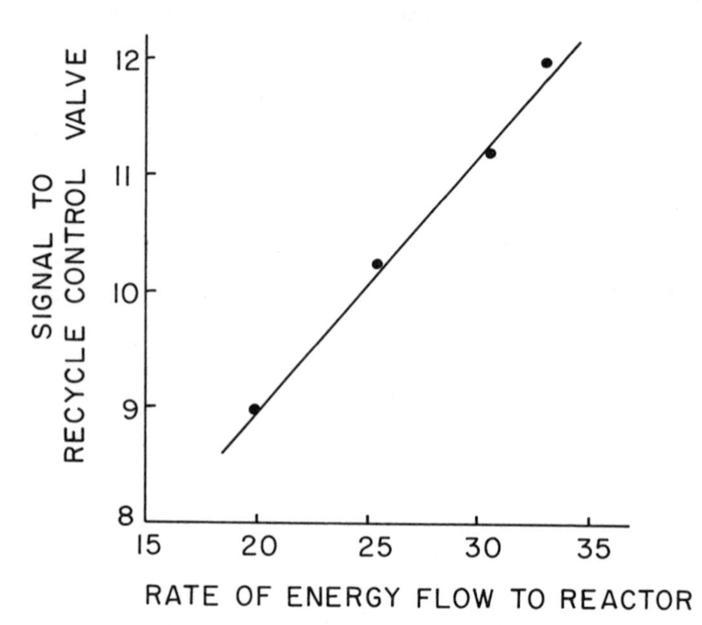

Figure 1.9. Experimentally determined relation between an independent variable (energy rate) and a control signal for a chemical processing system.

with high-performance components (components with rapid response) and using a scheme as shown in Figure 1.8. Design was carried out as will be described later. (See chapter 10.)

One other feature of this study is worthy of mention. A number of static (steady state) tests were made in which the energy input was held at discrete values and the signal to the valve necessary to maintain the reactor pressure at the desired value was observed. The results are shown in Figure 1-9. A simple linear relation was quite unexpected. An application of this result immediately suggested itself: Why not measure the rate of energy input to the reactor and use this to adjust the valve to the position required to maintain reactor pressure at the desired value? The scheme is indicated by the 'feedforward path' in Figure 1.8. An appropriate signal, generated from a measurement of the rate of energy flowing to the reactor, is added to the output of the controller, the sum serving to position the control valve. This leads to a third principle of control strategy.

III. Use relations between inputs (independent variables) and outputs (dependent variables) in a feedforward manner to perform defined control actions.

EXAMPLE II. Pressure control of a gas-producing system using a positive displacement exhaust compressor.

This process had much in common with the previous process, the major difference being the use of a positive displacement type of exhausting compressor. This difference led to a different control scheme and serves to illustrate additional principles of strategy.

Since the capacity of the compressor had to be sufficient to handle somewhat more than the average expected gas production, it was imperative to have some recycling back to suction. This recycle valve was exposed to pressure disturbances developed in the common manifold. To reduce the magnitude of these, compressor discharge pressure control suggested itself. A high performance (rapidly responding) system was required since it was desired that discharge pressure be maintained very constant.

This concept is embodied in a fourth principle of control strategy.

IV. Use high-performance control systems to attenuate disturbances to the process or to achieve isolation from disturbances.

This particular application also produced another salutary effect. By maintaining compressor discharge pressure very nearly constant, the pressure to the recycle valve was likewise kept constant. Hence, the sensitivity of the valve (ratio of flow through valve to fraction open) was kept more constant. (See Figure 1.6.) This demonstrates another principle of control strategy.

V. Use arrangements which tend to maintain constant sensitivity of key control components.

This is a very important principle since components with variable sensitivity (variable steady-state gain) can introduce serious difficulties in control-system design.

Several schemes are possible for controlling this process. However, the control action must establish the appropriate pressure gradient between the reactor and compressor suction so that the gas produced will flow from the reactor and the reactor pressure will be maintained at the desired value. Possible schemes follow:

(1) Adjust the by-pass flow with a controller using reactor pressure as an input. Since the process, in this case, possessed an appreciable, pure delay time (about three times that of the previously discussed system), this technique was ruled out. That is, following a change in recycle flow, the time required for the pressure change to be felt in the reactor was so long that reactor pressure deviations could become intolerable. Figure 1.10 illustrates this scheme. (dashed line.).

(2) Control the compressor suction pressure at a constant value, and throttle a valve in the reactor effluent line (dotted line). This system, although feasible, requires a very high performance control system at both locations as shown in Figure 1.10. The throttling of very large flow rates of gas in an effort to control pressures in a relatively small volume within a few tenths of inches of water is extremely exacting. Moreover, a single failure with the control valve closing could prove catastrophic. A throttle valve at the reactor outlet reduces the effective volume of the system between pressure sensor and valve, thus creating a very responsive system. (The system time constant relating effluent flow and reactor pressure is reduced compared with that if the valve were absent. In this case, the reduction was five-fold.)

Furthermore, there exists a real possibility of adverse interaction between the reactor pressure-control system and the compressor suction pressure-control system; both are very responsive systems. Such a system would require careful design, but is feasible.

(3) Use a small flow of inert gas as an injectant into the reactor for control of rapid fluctuations in pressure. In addition, use the signal from a parallel controller to adjust the reference value of the compressor suction controller. (The latter is termed cascade control.) This scheme is also shown in Figure 1.10 (solid lines) and incorporates several useful strategies. Where an appropriate supply of inert gas is available, it is highly recommended.

A high-performance compressor-suction control system assures that the pressure at this point will always be very close to the reference value. This means that downstream pressure will not interact seriously with reactor pressure. This illustrates a sixth principle of control strategy.

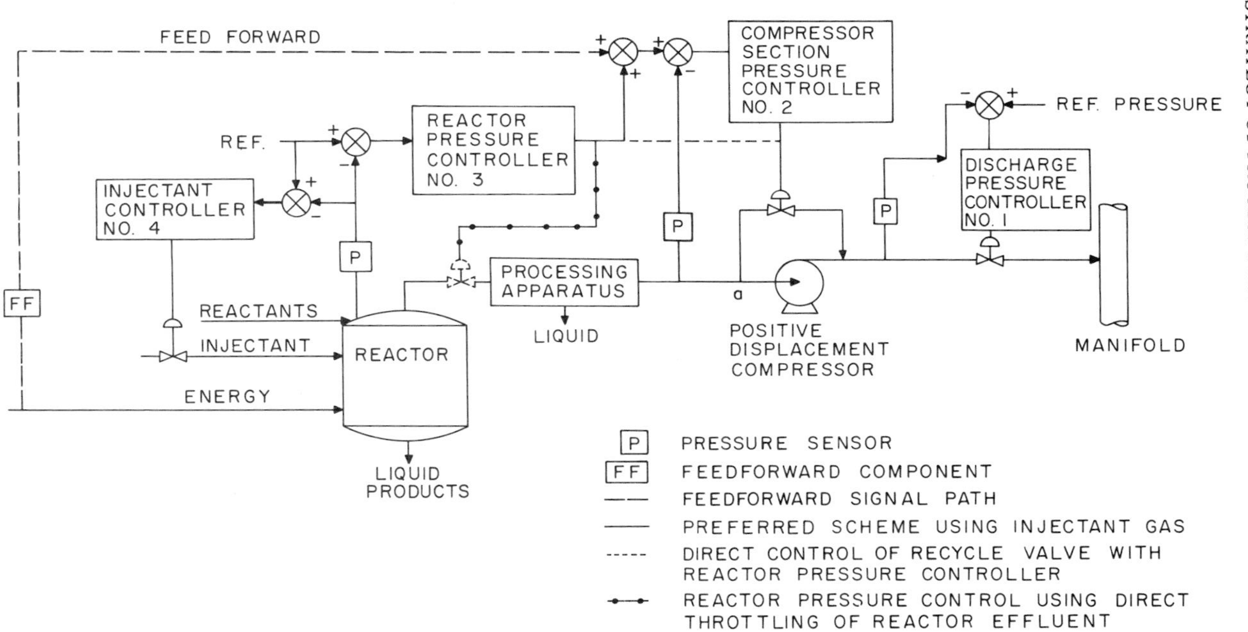

Figure 1.10. Alternate schemes for controlling the pressure of a gas-producing reactor.

VI. Eliminate or reduce interactions or coupling between parts of a process (by means of high-performance control systems).

Throttling a small stream of inert gas for pressure control is easier to accomplish physically and, in addition, is safer—provided, of course, that it is acceptable and an appropriate source is available. This technique illustrates another principle of strategy.

VII. Throttle small streams rather than large streams if the sensitivity of the control action is sufficient and if processing permits.

The pressure of a gaseous system can be changed a few inches of water while the net change in gaseous inventory required to do so is remarkably small. This can sometimes be executed very well by throttling an inert gas stream comprising perhaps no more than 5 percent of the total gas production.

Eliminating the large throttle valve at the reactor outlet illustrates still another principle of strategy.

VIII. Select those arrangements which tend to create large process time constants where this is permissible and advantageous.

With the reactor effluent unrestricted, the effective volume of the system is extended to include the processing apparatus. This gives a less responsive system in respect to the relation between gas production and reactor pressure. The demands on the control-system components are reduced, and design becomes easier.

Whether the above principles can always be applied depends upon practical considerations, but the control engineer should be alert to the possibilities of their application.

Incidentally, the feedforward concept can be applied in this case as well, as indicated by the dot-dash lines in Figure 1.10. A measure of energy flow rate may be used to adjust the set point or reference pressure of the compressor-suction pressure controller to the value required for the given level of gas production. The relationship must be determined empirically.

It is important to realize that the control schemes indicated above constitute strategies but not design. It remains to determine process performance, select control hardware with known characteristics, and to specify the appropriate controller functions such that the final overall system operates as desired with predictable performance. *This constitutes design*.

EXAMPLE III. Kiln control.

A direct-fired kiln can serve as another example where final control strategy is dependent upon the response of system components. Suppose a kiln is fired with gas and pulverized coal, with the latter being preferred because of cost but both being necessary at all times. Suppose further that the supply of gas is variable and that changes must be compensated for by changes in the pulverized-coal feed rate.

The kiln is a cylindrical shell set at a small angle with the horizontal. A typical cement kiln may be 400 feet long and 15 feet in diameter. It is supported on rolls and is rotated at a few revolutions per minute. The kiln is lined with refractory brick. The world's largest kiln is at the Dundee Cement Company plant at Clarkesville, Missouri. It is 570 feet long and over 20 feet in diameter.

Feed, which may be a mixture of granular solids or a wet slurry, is introduced at the high end and moves towards the fired end by virtue of the rotary motion.

Combustion of fuels occurs at the low end where the kiln passes into the hood. Gas velocity is usually quite high, in excess of 100 feet per second, which causes the zone of combustion to extend into the kiln. The dimensions and thermal condition of the flame are determined by the nature of the fuels, excess air and gas velocity.

The feed, moving more or less continuously from entrance to exit, is exposed to varying heat flux. Control is made difficult because feed composition is not always known precisely. Product discharged from the low end is usually cooled with air which becomes heated and is used for combustion. The determination of product quality is one of the major problems associated with kiln operations.

The objectives of the control system are to maintain the quality of the solid effluent from the kiln and yet assure maximum thermal efficiency. In the example to be considered, it is desirable to do this in spite of relatively rapid changes in the supply of gaseous fuel. In order to assure a measure of control over thermal efficiency, it is common practice to attempt to control the excess air in the gaseous effluent. Since changes in gaseous fuel necessitate changes in solid-fuel rate, it might appear that both objectives could be accomplished by regulating coal-firing rate in response to excess air changes. In the steady state, this technique is satisfactory; dynamically, it is not. The response of the flow of pulverized coal from the mill to changes in coal-feed rate will be many-fold slower than the changes in excess air which result from several causes. The coal-mill response corresponds roughly to that of a first-order system with a time constant of several minutes while the response of excess air is largely dependent upon the average residence time of gases within the kiln, a matter of seconds. Therefore, the coal mill, as a control component, is incompatible with the kiln in respect to the control of excess air, (Strategy No. 2) Any attempt to use the feed to the coal mill to compensate for *transients* in the excess air will be doomed to failure. This conclusion can be reached by merely casually considering the physics of the processes; however, a quantitative design requires experimental measurement of the performance characteristics of the physical apparatus.

Figure 1-11 shows a plausible control strategy which could satisfy the overall requirements. The response of the forced-draft throttling system must be very fast, thus minimizing variations in hood pressure. This in turn reduces variations in air intake via leakage at various points. That is, a high-performance hood-pressure control will reduce disturbances and interaction or coupling between different parts of the system (Strategy No. 6). The response of the primary air supply would probably be limited by the response of the O_2 analyzer, and whether the instrument is suitable or not depends upon the rate of uncontrolled changes in the gaseous-fuel supply.

The quality of the product is most difficult to measure and even if it were a function of temperature only, is perhaps the most difficult to obtain. In view of relative time responses, letting this signal regulate the rate of coal firing appears logical. (Strategy No. 2)

Final control strategy and design details depend upon quantitative performance descriptions of the processing and control components as well as the availability of meaningful measurements. Performance data, for the most part, must be obtained by in-plant experimentation.

EXAMPLE IV. Distillation column control.

The literature dealing with the control of distillation columns is profuse. Nonetheless, the experiences gained from an actual experimental study warrant inclusion here.

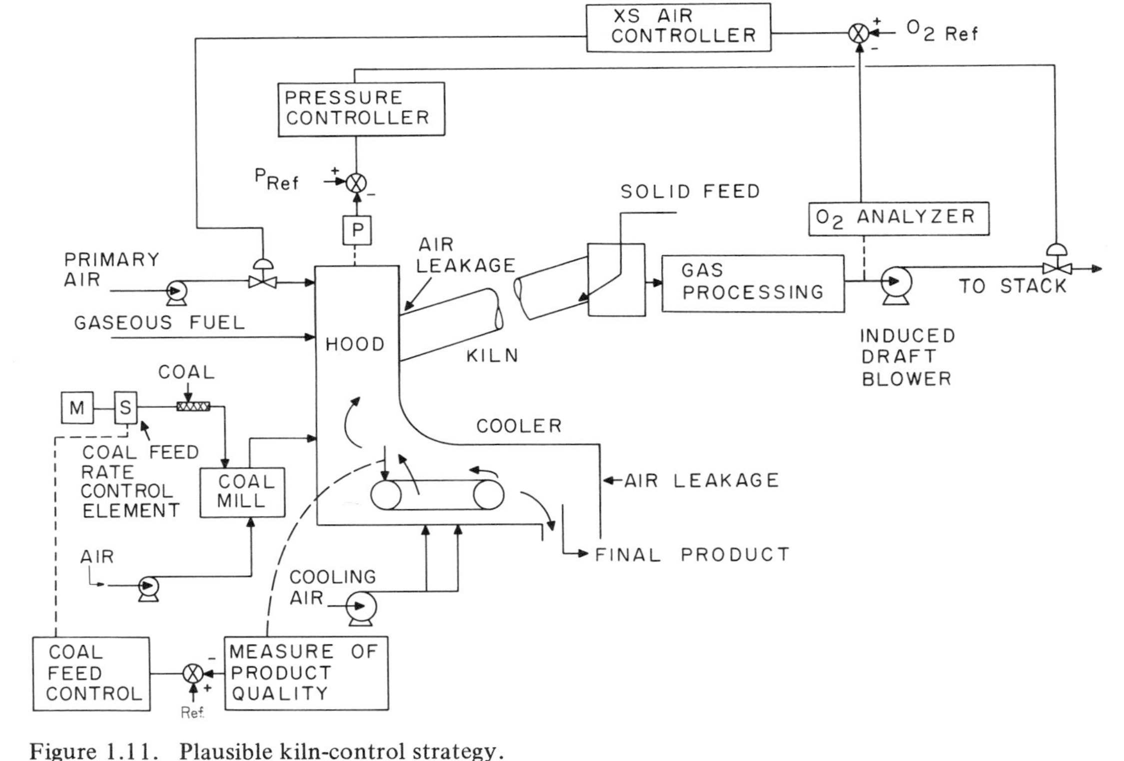

Figure 1.11. Plausible kiln-control strategy.

Distillation can be defined as a process of separation wherein a vapor stream richer in light components is contacted in a continuous countercurrent manner with a liquid stream richer in heavier components whereby the vapor becomes progressively richer and the liquid leaner in light components. The vapor is generated in the reboiler, and the liquid is generated in the condenser. Thermal energy is involved and hence, for control, energy must be regulated by one means or another. For a binary mixture, this interdependency is very well illustrated by the enthalpy-concentration relationships first described by Ponchon and Savarit in 1821 and 1822 which will be discussed later.

The original objective of the study upon which this example is based was to determine if an IBP (Initial Boiling Point) analyzer could be used in a control system to regulate the quality of the bottoms product. The feed consisted of a mixture of numerous hydrocarbons including many isomers. It was important to maintain a close separation in view of the value of the bottoms product which represented the major part of the feed.

The first task was to evaluate the IBP analyzer. This was tested by introducing feed material of high and low initial boiling points, successively. Results showed the instrument to possess a pure time delay of about four minutes. That is, no change in output occurred until four minutes had elapsed after a change in feed composition. The transient response to this step change in feed composition, after the four-minute pure delay time, was found to be similar to a first-order system with a time constant of about five minutes. That is, it required about five minutes for the output signal to attain 62.3 percent of the final value in response to a step change in feed composition. Either of these characteristics, as was demonstrated later, rendered this instrument worthless as a feedback control component (Strategy No. 2).

Further experimental work was directed towards obtaining performance characteristics of the column. Among the interesting observations were that abrupt increases in light components in the feed appeared almost instantly in the overhead, and the column showed almost no changes in the section below the feed. Similarly, abrupt increases in the heavy components were rapidly reflected in bottoms production with imperceptible changes above the feed plate. Further tests showed, not unexpectedly, that the most important controllable input to the column was the reboiler duty (heat-transfer rate in reboiler) and that the most sensitive response to reboiler duty was the pressure drop across the column.

Since previous control of bottoms quality was partially successful by manual regulation of reboiler steam flow in response to a lower-column temperature, there existed some indication that a useful correlation probably existed between such a temperature and product quality. While column-top pressure was controlled by regulating the flow of steam to the vacuum jets, the bottoms pressure was allowed to drift. The use of column pressure drop control suggested itself as a means of making lower-column temperatures meaningful by stabilizing the pressure at this point.

This idea is not new. It was used in France in the early part of the last century and has been used widely since. The interesting facet of this study was the fact that the experimental data pointed this out as a very desirable approach. This is another illustration of the principle of control Strategy No. 4.

The use of reboiler regulation to control column pressure gradient illustrates another useful principle of control strategy.

IX. Manipulate those variables or process inputs to a system that produce the maximum effect on the variable to be controlled.

That it is not always necessary to do this is illustrated by the case where reactor pressure control is achieved by inert gas injection discussed under Example 2. For the distillation column, pressure gradient control was a very effective way to insure a meaningful temperature in the bottom section, enabling a reliable and useful correlation between this and the product quality to be developed.

In the course of this study, it was found that the temperature of the liquid on one specific plate in the upper section responded more to reboiler duty changes than any other. As a result, the temperature at this point was used to regulate the rate of reflux in a conventional manner. This is an example of yet another principle of strategy of control.

X. When several control variables are available, choose the one showing the greatest sensitivity.

The use of a lower-column temperature as a measure of bottoms-product quality illustrates another principle.

XI. Present, in easily understood form, useful indices of performance for operating guides (whether used for control or not).

Figure 1-12 shows the strategy suggested for controlling the column described above. The scheme indicates that the lower-column temperature passes through a component where manual inputs may be inserted. The output of this device is the reference temperature (or set point) for the top temperature regulator acting through the reflux.

Incidentally, it was found necessary to replace the heavily enclosed temperature sensors (thermocouples in heavy wells) by bare elements

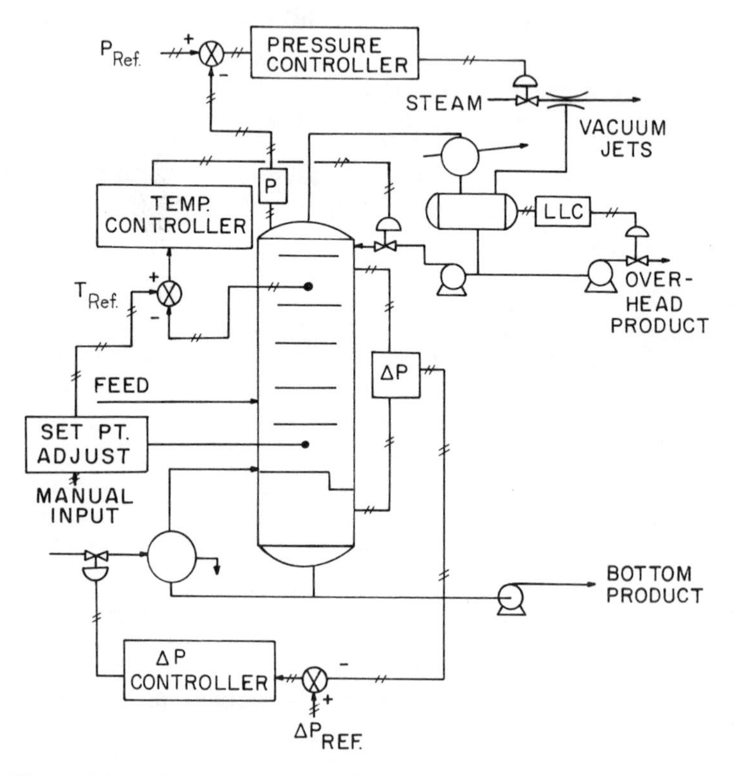

Figure 1.12. Strategy for controlling a distillation process enabling the use of a lower-column temperature for quality control.

in both locations in order to achieve satisfactory results. This is an illustration of the principle that compatible control components are necessary (Principle No. 2).

There are some very important advantages to be gained by controlling the pressure drop across distillation columns. Among these are (1) the column can be operated near its most efficient point for all feed rates since efficiency and vapor loading are closely related, and (2) flooding can be avoided by assuring that the critical pressure drop will not be exceeded.

Disadvantages are that the heat load tends towards a maximum per unit of throughput and that the control system must be designed carefully to avoid excessive energy fluctuations to the reboiler. When appropriately designed, such a control system works very well.

A distillation column can be used to illustrate another principle. Consider the top portion as shown in Figure 1-13. Assume it is desired to control the overhead composition either via temperature control or direct measurement via an analyzer. The input which effects the separation in the top section most greatly is the reflux condenser duty. The greatest control action would therefore be obtained if condenser duty were manipulated directly by throttling the cooling water, varying the condenser surface area (flooded reflux drum technique) or employing a by-pass for the overhead vapor around the condenser. This leads to the next principle of strategy.

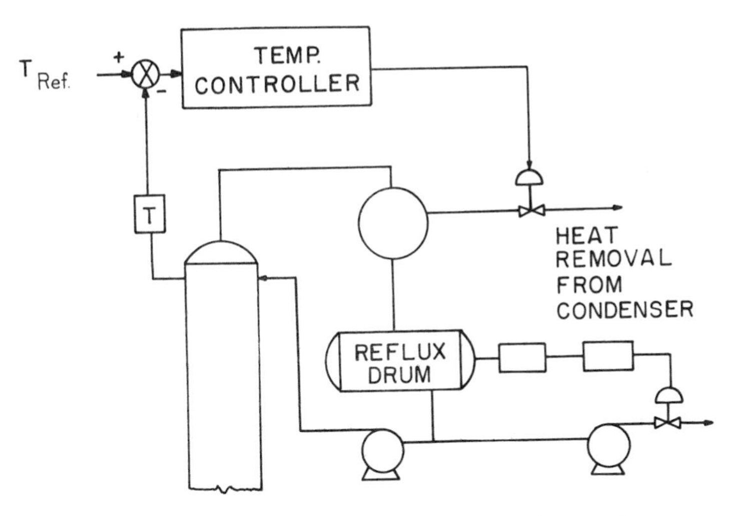

Figure 1.13. Distillation column overhead control.

XII. Apply the control action to the most pertinent part of the process.

Since top composition can be altered more quickly by changing conditions in the top of the column, that is where the action should be applied. Using reboiler duty for this purpose would require the whole column to become involved. As long as the top composition is controlled, what happens in the remainder of the column is of less importance except that malfunctions, such as flooding, should not occur. For overhead composition control, relatively rapid transient alterations in the top section are required. Permanent changes in condenser duty will of course be eventually reflected throughout the system.

Enthalpy-composition relationships are extremely useful for understanding and designing processes where they are applicable. The separation of binary mixtures by fractional distillation is a classic example, the principles being first demonstrated by Ponchon and Savarit. The overall relationships pertaining to a distillation column such as shown in Figure 1-14 are given below for a column separating a binary mixture into two liquid products.:

$$F = D + B \tag{1.1}$$

$$FZ_F = DX_D + BX_B \tag{1.2}$$

$$H_F F = Dh_D + Q_c + Bh_B - Q_B \tag{1.3}$$

The following terms are defined

$$h'_D = h_D + \frac{Q_c}{D} \tag{1.4}$$

$$h'_B = h_B - \frac{Q_c}{B} \tag{1.5}$$

Then (1.3) may be written as

$$H_F F = Dh'_D + Bh'_B . \tag{1.6}$$

The desired relation is obtained by eliminating the mass terms from the three three-term equations. Thus, from (1.1) and (1.2), we get

$$\frac{D}{B} = \frac{X_B - Z_F}{Z_F - X_D}. \tag{1.7}$$

Similarly, from (1.1) and (1.3), we get

$$\frac{D}{B} = \frac{h'_B - H_F}{H_F - h'_D}. \tag{1.8}$$

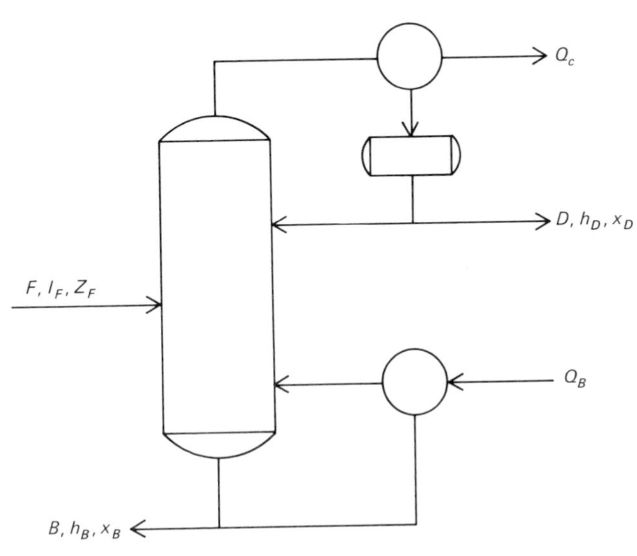

Figure 1.14. Schematic diagram of distillation column and accessories.
Q_c, Q_B—rate of heat removed from condenser and added to reboiler, respectively;
F, D, B—mass flow rates of feed, distillate and bottoms;
H_F, h_D, h_B—enthalpy per unit mass of feed, distillate and bottoms;
Z_F, X_D, X_B—composition of feed, distillate and bottoms in terms of lighter component of binary mixture

The result is a relation involving only concentration and enthalpies (per unit mass of material):

$$\frac{Z_F - X_B}{X_D - Z_F} = \frac{H_F - h'_B}{h'_D - H_F}. \tag{1.9}$$

It can easily be shown that, on a rectilinear graph of enthalpy versus concentration, the corresponding points (Z_F, H_F), (X_B, h'_B) and (X_D, h'_D) lie on a straight line.

If compositions are chosen to refer to the fraction of lighter component, then a diagram such as shown in Figure 1.15 results.

In the *steady state* for a column of fixed design operating at constant plate efficiency and pressure, a change in any of the above

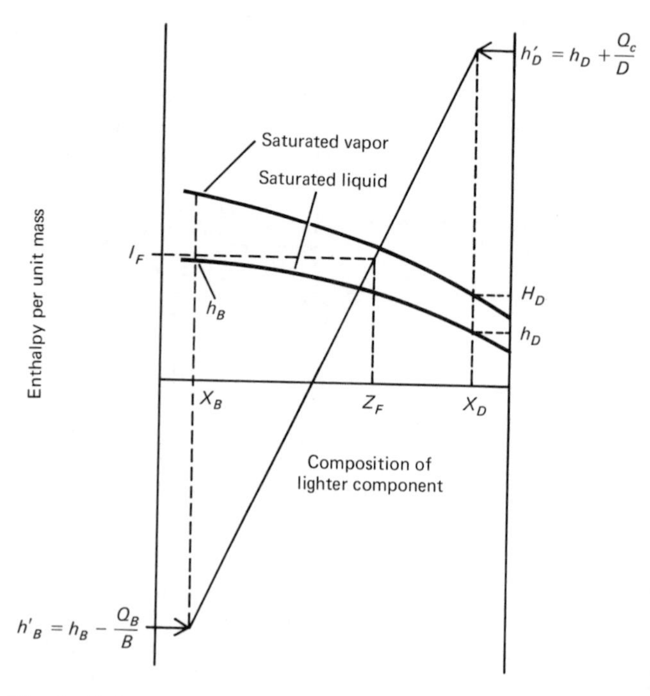

Figure 1.15. Enthalpy-concentration diagram for a binary distillation process.

terms must be accompanied by changes in the others such that a straight line connects the three points. For example, if condenser duty is increased with feed composition and enthalpy constant, the reboiler duty must be increased if terminal compositions are to remain constant.

It is sometimes possible to use relationships such as this in the control strategy, and another principle of strategy is suggested.

XIII. Utilize significant relationships involving process variables to extract information useful in attaining desired operation.

Another way of stating this follows: *Let the process convey information about itself which is useful in implementing a control strategy.*

The above enthalpy-concentration relationship (1.9) applies only to the steady state (static) separation of a binary mixture by distillation under rather special conditions. For multicomponent systems, the *principles* apply, but the relationships are not so useful. The relation tells nothing about the *transient* behavior during which different properties of the system become important. Over brief periods of time, various parts of the system can depart from the steady-state conditions. Control action is used to force the system in the desired direction. Eventually, after all transients disappear, steady operation is again established, and the steady-state relationships must be fulfilled.

EXAMPLE V. Thermal processing.

A given continuous process required the cooling of a liquid intermediate to obtain a solid mass and then further cooling to a temperature suitable for final processing. Figure 1.16 is a schematic diagram of the combined process. In the first operation, it is necessary to extract only sufficient thermal energy to assure complete solidification and sufficient physical strength to enable the transport of the material continuously to the second cooling operation. Because of the nature of the material, it was feasible to measure its temperature only in the liquid state at the inlet to the processing ensemble.

Fortunately, the heat absorbed by the cooling streams could be determined quite accurately via flow and temperature measurements.

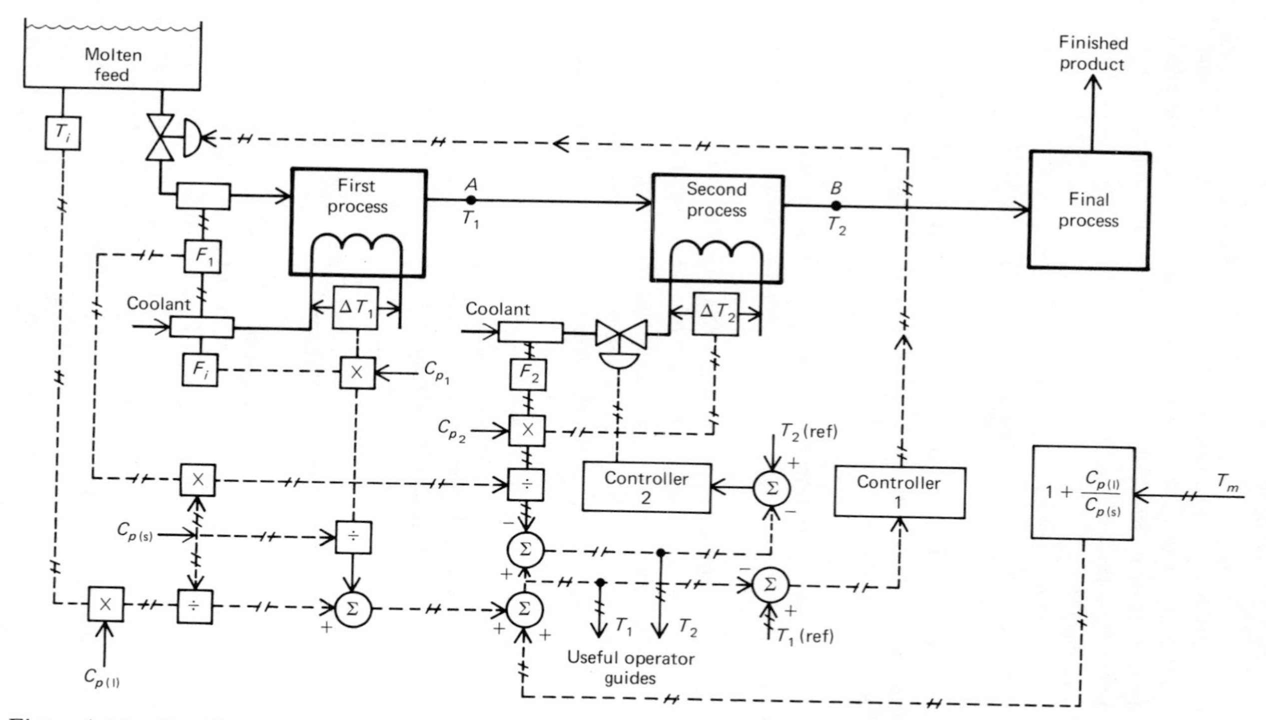

Figure 1.16. Feedforward control strategy for a thermal process.

Measures of the "thermal condition" at points A and B were required if the optimum processing was to be obtained. In this case, maximum throughput was desired. Furthermore, the rate was limited by the heat-removing capacity of the first processing apparatus. A means of maintaining the maximum tolerable temperature was needed or equivalently, assurance of maximum heat removal from the first processing unit consistent with satisfactory product properties at point A.

Such a 'temperature' can be computed from a knowledge of the flow rate of material, the initial temperature, T_1 (which is measurable), the thermal properties of the material being processed (latent heat of fusion and specific heats of the liquid and solid), and the heat removed in processing. That is, the energy balance,

$$C_{p_1} F_1 \Delta T_1 = F_i [C_{p(\ell)}(T_i - T_m) + \lambda + C_{p(s)}(T_m - T_1)],$$

may be used to calculate the desired temperature, T_1:

$$T_1 = \left[1 - \frac{C_{p(\ell)}}{C_{p(s)}}\right] T_m + \frac{C_{p(\ell)}}{C_{p(s)}} T_i - \frac{C_{p_1} F_1 \Delta T_1}{C_{p(s)} F_i} + \frac{\lambda}{C_{p(s)}}.$$

Any heat losses not accounted for by the heat absorbed in the coolant would require an addition to the numerator in the last term. In practice, an *empirically determined factor* by which to multiply the last term would suffice.

Similarly, the thermal condition at B can be computed by an energy balance which yields a measure of the temperature at that point. The heat balance is

$$C_{p(s)} F_i (T_1 - T_2) = C p_2 F_2 \Delta T_2,$$

from which

$$T_2 = T_1 - \frac{C_{p_2} F_2 \Delta T_2}{C_{p(s)} F_i}.$$

Calculated temperatures T_1 and T_2 may be used to guide the plant towards near-optimum conditions. They can also be used as measurements in a fully automatic control system, as shown in Figure 1.16 (dotted lines). This is another illustration of Principles 3, 11, and 13.

Numerous opportunities exist for the application of these simple strategies for industrial process control.

EXAMPLE VI. Chemical reacting system.

As a final example, experiences with another chemical-reaction system will be described. The process is shown in Figure 1.17. Components A and B react to give liquid product P in addition to gases containing an appreciable amount of P which is recovered by subsequent processing. The objective is to obtain maximum production at minimum cost.

As is common with many catalytic reactions, if temperature is too low, very little conversion occurs; if it is too high, reaction is so severe that the desired product is destroyed. Hence, it was not surprising that, following a series of very careful tests (in which energy and material balances closed within two percent), results typical of that shown in Figure 1.18 were obtained. When the ratio of liquid product P to flow of reactant B was plotted against the heat of re-

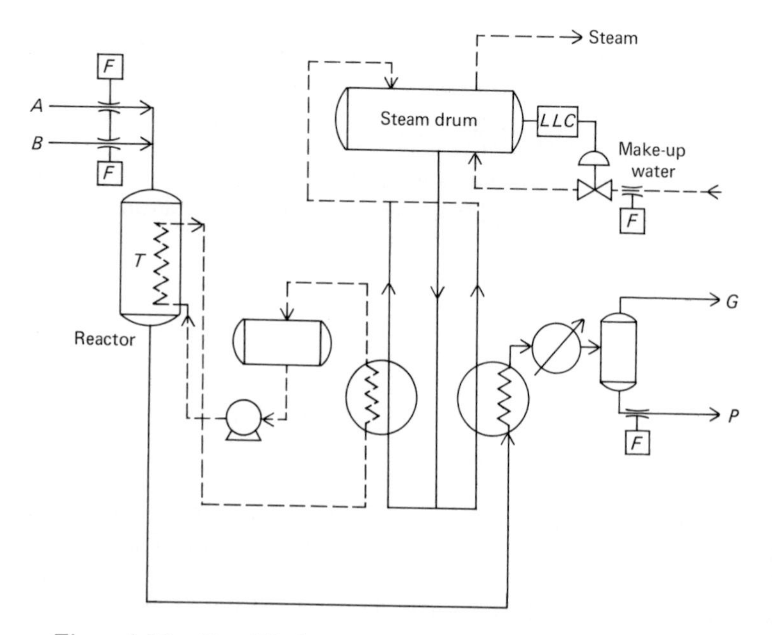

Figure 1.17. Simplified process diagram for a reaction system.

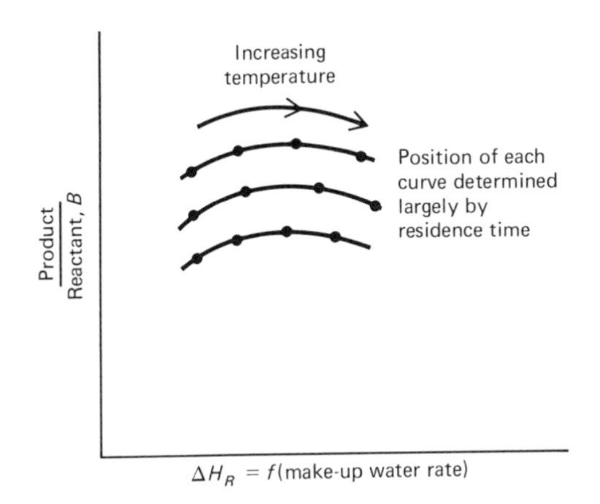

Figure 1.18. Conversion relations for a typical catalytic reactor.

action, as determined from the test data, a maximum point was found for each of a number of different operating conditions.

A study of the energy balances around the system showed that about 85 percent of the heat of reaction was accounted for by the steam generated, the latter being very convenient to measure with a turbine flow meter installed in the make-up water supply. As a result, the same kind of relationship was obtained if water-flow rate was substituted for heat of reaction. Experimental results thus suggested a control arrangement, (Refer to Strategies 3, 11, and 13) whereby adjustments in reactor temperature are made until the ratio of product to critical reactant is a maximum consistent with the desired level of operation and most economical ratio of reactants A and B. The flow of make-up water could serve as a convenient process monitor and could possibly be of assistance in locating the optimum operating point (Strategy 11). The attractiveness of the approach lies in its simplicity and the fact that it eliminates the need for any on-line analyses for purposes of process control.

Since so many chemical processes occur with either evolution or absorption of thermal energy, it would appear that numerous opportunities exist for control strategies similar to this. Simplicity is, however, almost impossible to discover without conducting an experimental study.

There is one principle of control strategy which should be mentioned although it is self-evident:

XIV. Provide control systems which preserve material inventories where these are required for proper operation.

Examples have been presented in the foregoing; control of level in the reflux drum and bottoms of the fractionator shown in Figure 1.12 or the steam-drum level control shown in Figure 1.17.

A corollary strategy is to preserve inventories of *energy*. Perhaps inadvertently in many instances this is done by virtue of temperature control. However, temperature is not a sufficient measure of energy in all cases, and other measures of state will be required such as intimated in Figure 1.15.

As a result of many plant studies, similar to those described above, the following conclusions can be made.

(1) The most satisfactory control system can be designed only after an experimental study of the plant and control components and the development of a sound control strategy.

(2) Theory can be used effectively to quantify the design and to help in the selection of the best strategies, but it is rarely helpful in devising that strategy.

(3) The resulting system will always be relatively simple and easy to construct and to apply on existing plants.

(4) Because of the simplicity, the design of control systems is not difficult, and performance can be predicted.

(5) Experimental studies of plants, if conducted jointly with theoretical studies, will lead to better understanding of process performance, improved design procedures, and more economical operations.

(6) Experimentation produces insights and reinforces intuition from which come new ideas for processing and control. If the experimenter is removed, much of the creativity which has characterized engineering progress will be lost.

2

Organizing the Problem—Block Diagrams

Engineers are accustomed to describing processes by means of process diagrams. In such diagrams, flow of material is represented by a line and discrete components of the plant by a sketch of some kind. Figures 1.11 and 1.12 are illustrations of process diagrams which, in these instances, also show control systems. These diagrams serve to organize and present information so that it is easier to visualize and understand plant performance.

In a similar fashion, information pertinent to control-system performance and the relationship of the control system to the process can be organized. Diagrams useful for this purpose differ from process diagrams because the variables of interest are associated both with the process and control components. The objective is to visualize how the control systems interact with processing apparatus.

The inputs to and the outputs from control components are not necessarily the same as the process variables. A pressure sensor, for example, receives a process pressure as an input, but it may have as an output a mechanical displacement, a voltage or another pressure. Figure 2.1 shows three forms of pressure sensors representative of the above. (A sensing element receives an input associated with energy, the output being some useful effect also associated with energy. Such a device may be called a *transducer.* If the input signal regulates the energy output to a detector provided with an independent energy supply, the device is called a *coducer.* Usually no distinction is made; transducer is the more common term. Concise definitions and illustrations are given in Reference 1.) In these examples, a flexible bellows is used as the *detecting device*.

On the other hand, the input to a control valve is very frequently an air pressure on the diaphragm of an air "motor" while the output is the flow rate of fluid through the valve proper. This is shown in

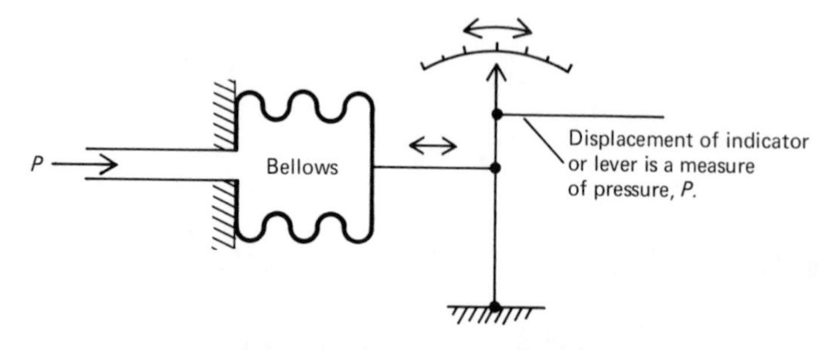

(a) Bellows used as sensor to actuate lever system

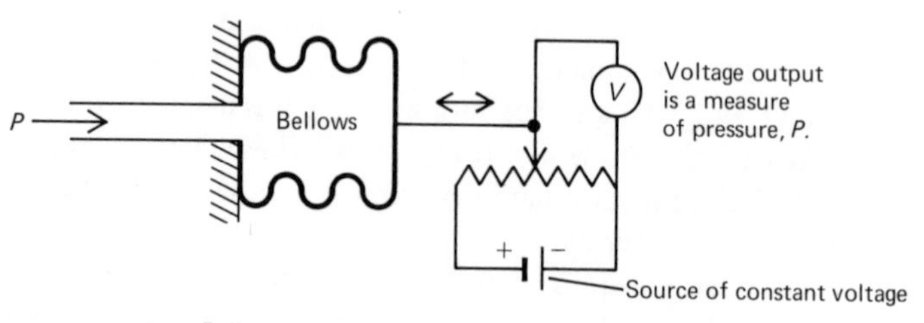

(b) Bellows used to position a potentiometer; the bellows motion produces a voltage signal.

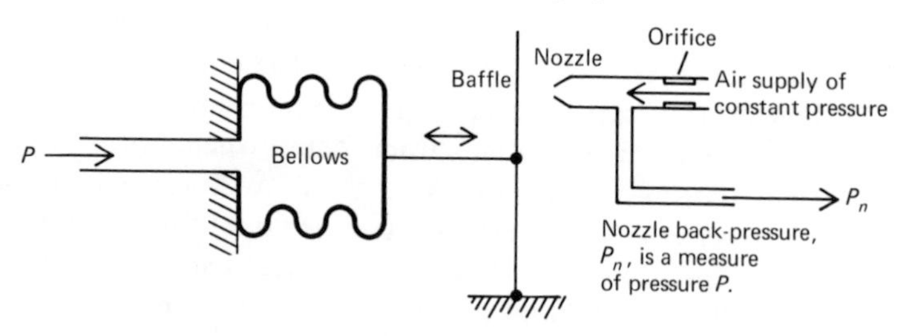

(c) Bellows displacement positions baffle which regulates nozzle back-pressure.

Figure 2.1. Various devices for sensing a pressure signal. (a) bellows used as sensor to actuate lever system, (b) bellows used to position a potentiometer–the bellows motion produces a voltage signal, (c) bellows displacement positions baffle which regulates nozzle back-pressure.

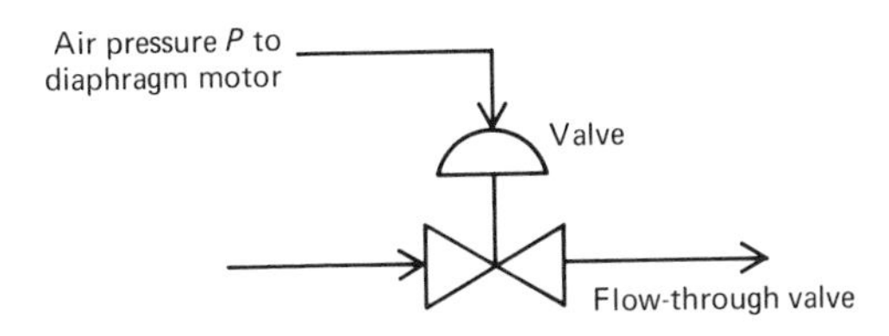

Figure 2.2. Air-operated flow-regulating valve.

Figure 2.2. Here the input is clearly a control-system variable, but the output is a process variable.

A controller usually receives two inputs (as shown in Figure 2.3), the reference value or "set-point" (a measure of the value which it is desired that the controlled variable attain) and a measure of the value of the variable to be controlled. These two "signals" are compared in a *comparator*, the difference becoming the input to the controller mechanism or circuit. The output from the controller may be a signal of the same kind as the inputs, or it may be different. For example, the comparator may compare two voltages, displacements, or air pressures, while the output may be an air or hydraulic oil pressure or a d-c voltage.

For purposes of control-system design, it is convenient to think of all the variables as signals—that is, as *measures* of the variables of in-

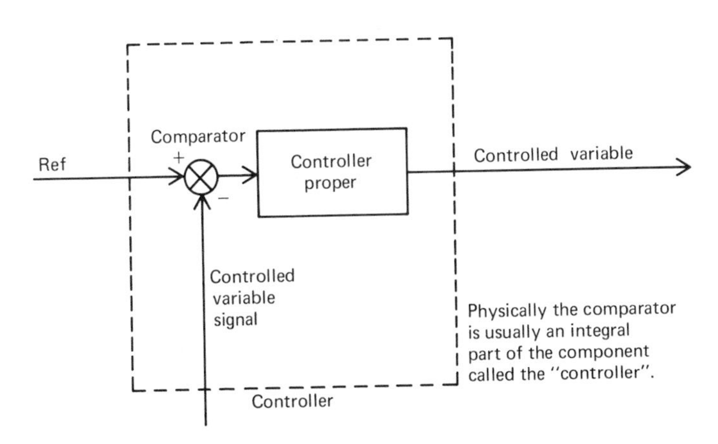

Figure 2.3. Input and output signals associated with a controller.

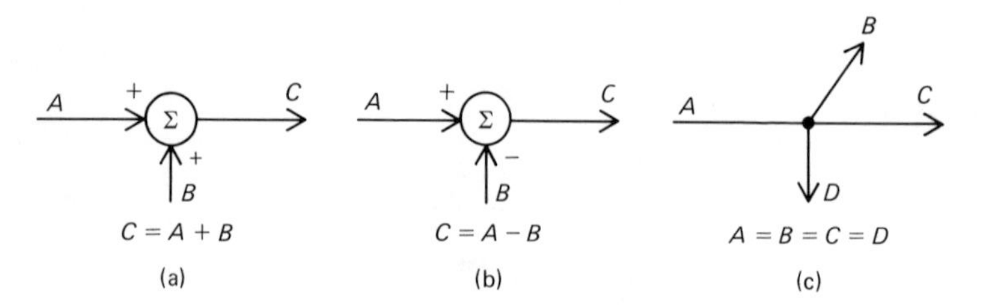

Figure 2.4. Representations for (a) summing, (b) differencing (comparing) and (c) rerouting signals.

terest. The flow-paths of signals to or from control or processing components are shown as lines entering or leaving *blocks,* which represent the components.

Thus, the lines represent measures of variables such as temperature, flow of fluids, flow of energy, composition, density or whatever may be the variable of interest. The blocks represent discrete components, subsystems or even complete systems. Blocks may also represent *mathematical functions.* The major distinction between process diagrams and block diagrams is that the former are intended to show the flow of matter while the latter are principally concerned with the flow of information.

Signals may be added to or subtracted from one another. The symbols for these are shown in Figures 2.4a and 2.4b. Examples of Figure 2.4b, the comparator or differencing point, have appeared in the illustrations of process control systems previously discussed.

Signals, unlike material flows, can be directed from a given point to various destinations without loss in strength. Such a point of origin, called a *pick-off* point, is shown in Figure 2.4c.

Within a block is inserted a symbol which relates the output from the block to the input to that block. Figure 2.5 is illustrative.

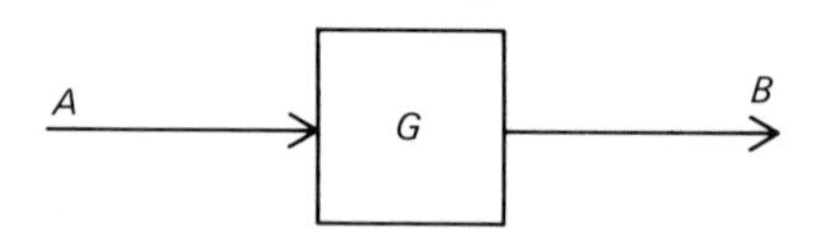

Figure 2.5. Block-diagram representation of a processing or control component or subsystem.

In the broadest sense G may be called the *generalized performance function.* It is that function which, when allowed to operate on an input, produces an output. G could be a constant, a table of data, a graph, or a mathematical function. The relationship is indicated in (2.1),

$$[\text{a function of output}] = G \cdot [\text{a function of input}],$$

or

$$G = \left[\frac{\text{a function of output}}{\text{a function of input}}\right]. \tag{2.1}$$

In special cases, G becomes a well-defined mathematical operator, and the operation becomes one of multiplication.

For purposes of organizing a problem, the signals may be considered as representing measures of the variables of interest such as flow, voltage, current, pressure, composition, etc., as previously stated. A given component, represented by a block, may receive many input signals and produce many output signals. For example, the reactor described in Figure 1.8 has rate of energy, rate of feed stock, and atmospheric disturbances as inputs. Intuitively these appear to be logical inputs since all these inputs will cause changes in outputs such as flow rate of gas, composition of effluent gas, gas temperature and reactor pressure (in this example, changes in products other than gaseous materials were irrelevant to the pressure-control problem and did not require consideration).

There is yet another input which must be considered in this example. This is the action of the terminal valve which produces changes in reactor outputs such as gas flow and reactor pressure. A change in position of the valve produces a change in flow through it, and this, in turn, causes the reactor outputs to change. Figure 2.6 shows the relationships.

It is obvious that all inputs (independent variables) influence in some manner all the outputs (dependent variables), and hence very complex interrelationships between and among independent and dependent variables can be imagined. Rarely, however, do all the possibilities need to be considered. As a matter of fact, most of the relationships of interest become fairly simple.

In this example, the rate of energy to the reactor was not controllable (by virtue of the special type of energy source), but it could be

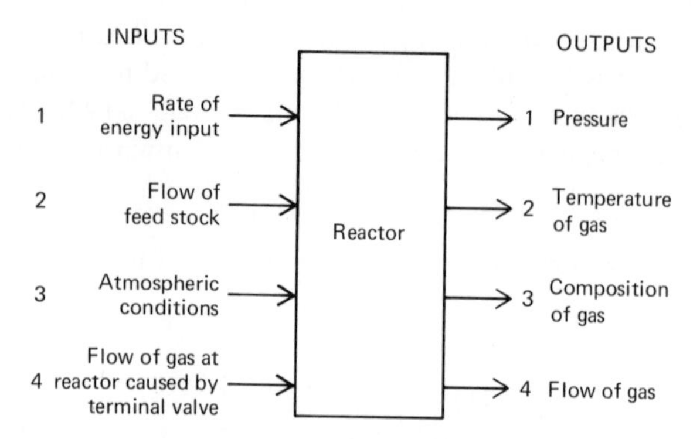

Figure 2.6. Some inputs and outputs associated with a gas-producing reactor.

measured rather easily. Likewise, the flow of feed was not easily regulated, and of course atmospheric conditions were uncontrollable. Of the outputs, only pressure was of immediate concern. Thus, the problem was simplified to a consideration of a single input and a single output as shown in Figure 2.7.

In a similar manner, the terminal valve by itself may be represented as in Figure 2.8a, and the entire valve mechanism, including the valve actuating motor, may be represented as shown in Figure 2.8b.

Finally, the flow changes produced at the reactor by flow changes at the valve may be represented as in Figure 2.9.

The complete chain of components can now be connected, via their signals, to yield the block diagram shown in Figure 2.10.

Since some of the intermediate signals are of no interest (in this

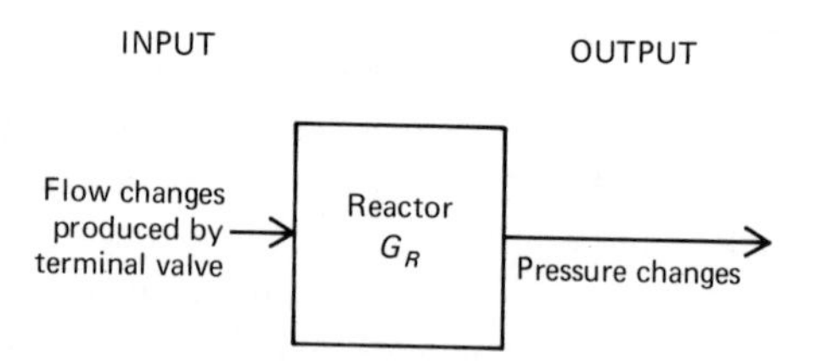

Figure 2.7. Simplified block diagram for reactor pressure control problem.

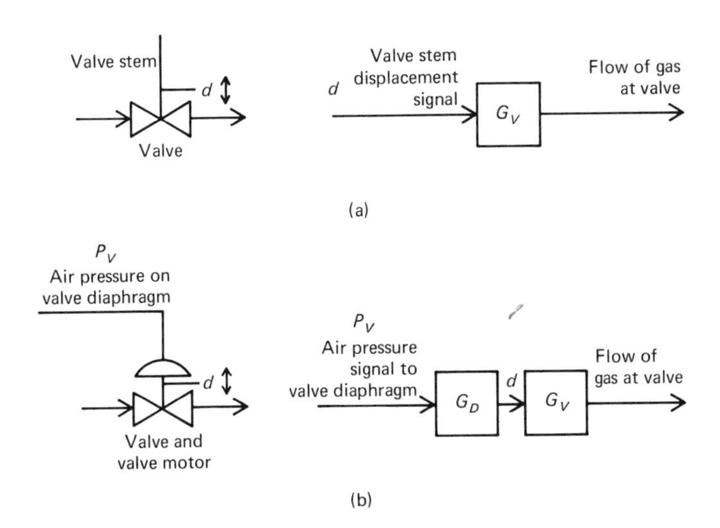

Figure 2.8. Representations of a control valve.

problem), the block diagram may be simplified by combining elements as shown in Figure 2.11. Here G_v and G_p represent the overall relations for the valve and processing systems, respectively.

Continuing with the reactor pressure-control system as an example, the reactor pressure is sensed by a pressure transducer, the output from which, the pressure signal, is compared with the reference pressure at a difference point, and the difference directed to a controller. Figure 2.12 shows this part of the block diagram.

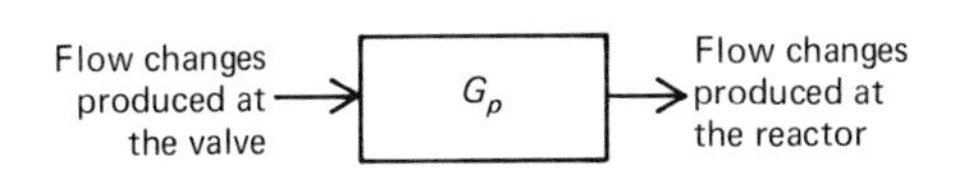

Figure 2.9. Block diagram for gas-throttling and transmission system.

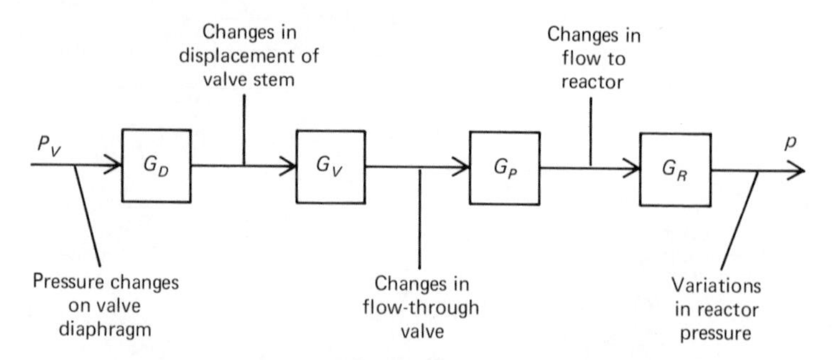

Figure 2.10. Block diagram for a series of components.

The combination of Figures 2.11 and 2.12 gives a complete block diagram for a reactor pressure-control system, Figure 2.13.

Because a signal is fed back to be compared with some reference or desired value, this kind of control is called *feedback* control. The path, including the sensor G_s, is called the feedback path. The path taken by the signal after the comparator is called the *feed-forward* path.

If, for the moment, it is assumed that the functions shown as G's are such that the output of a block is obtained by *multiplying* an input by the G function, the following interesting result is obtained.

$$e = p_{Ref.} - p_s \tag{2.2}$$

$$p_s = G_s p_r \tag{2.3}$$

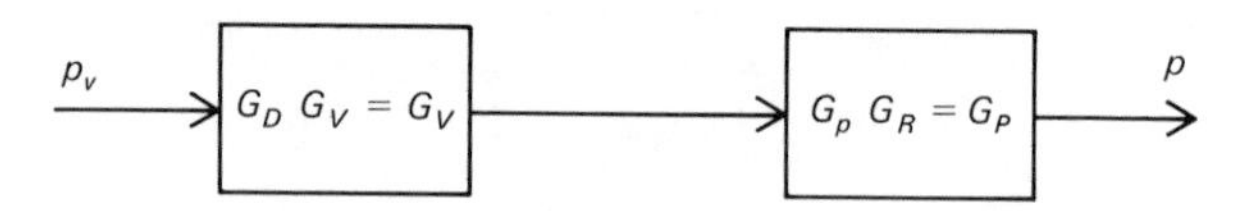

Figure 2.11. Block diagram combining several serial components.

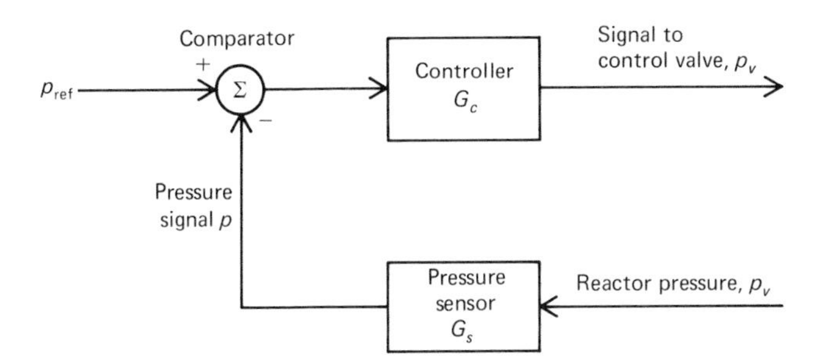

Figure 2.12. Block-diagram representation of sensor, comparator and controller components.

$$p_r = G_c G_V G_p \, e \tag{2.4}$$

Then we eliminate e and p_s and solve for the ratio, $\dfrac{p_r}{p_{Ref}}$:

$$p_r \quad = G_c G_V G_P [p_{Ref} - G_s p_r]$$

or

$$\frac{p_r}{p_{Ref.}} = \frac{G_c G_V G_P}{1 + G_s G_c G_V G_P} \tag{2.5}$$

This form is characteristic of a *closed loop* negative feedback control system of which this is an example. This arrangement is some-

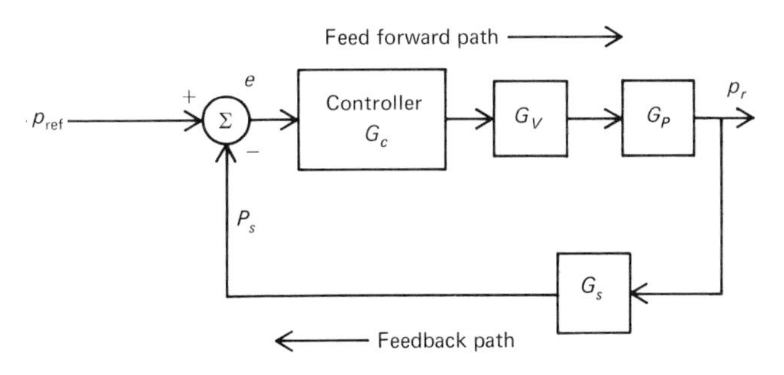

Figure 2.13. Block diagram for a feedback control system.

times called a series compensated negative feedback control system because the controller is placed in *series* with the process rather than, for example, in the feedback path, and the feedback signal is subtracted (negative) from the reference value.

Equation 2.5 shows that the control function, G_c, appears in both numerator and denominator of the p_r/p_{Ref} ratio, and that the nature of the G_c function can greatly influence the overall relationship p_r/p_{Ref}. This gives the opportunity to define the purpose of the controller function, G_c.

The controller function is so chosen that, when combined with the functions representing the performance of the process and other control components, the overall relationship (p_r/p_{Ref} in this case) has desirable properties.

What "desirable properties" are must await explanation. However, one observation is worth a comment. As can be seen from (2.5), if G_c is so large that $G_sG_cG_VG_P$ is very much greater than unity, $1 + G_sG_cG_VG_P \cong G_sG_cG_VG_P$, and

$$\frac{p_r}{p_{Ref.}} \cong \frac{1}{G_s}.$$

If the sensor is perfect, such that $G_s \cong 1$,

$$\frac{p_r}{p_{Ref.}} = 1. \tag{2.6}$$

This, of course, is the object being sought: a direct correspondence between p_r and $p_{Ref.}$

Because of the nature of the functions G_V and G_P, it is not possible to achieve this objective by merely increasing G_c. It usually turns out that, as the magnitude of G_c increases, the closed loop system becomes increasingly oscillatory and eventually unmanageable.

In terms of transient response, the objective of the control function is to create a system with a behavior similar to the curve labelled "satisfactory" in Figure 2.14. As G_c increases, the "overshoot" of the response increases; if G_c is too small, the response becomes "sluggish."

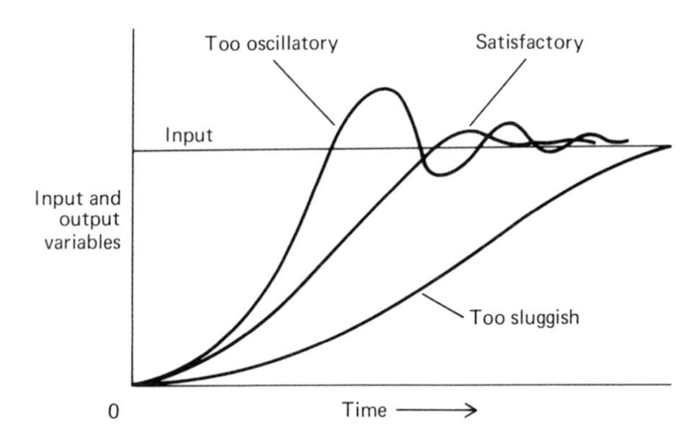

Figure 2.14. Typical transient responses of a system to a step-like forcing.

In general, the G's are complex functions, and their transient behavior is difficult to predict. The above description must suffice at this point.

The fired-kiln process has some especially interesting features which become obvious from its block diagram. Assuming the interaction of signals through common process apparatus, the block diagram appears as in Figure 2.15. Here it is assumed that direct throttling of the primary air in response to the measure of excess air is chosen and that hood pressure control via throttling of the induced draft fan discharge is considered acceptable. Coal firing will be assumed to be controlled by the temperature of the solid product being discharged from the kiln (which in turn is assumed to be an index of product quality).

Three separate negative feedback systems (or loops) are shown in Figure 2.15. All are shown to be interconnected through the block representing the kiln. This means that the outputs, excess air (O_2), solids temperature, and hood pressure are all dependent upon the inputs, primary air flow, coal flow, effluent gas flow and the disturbances. There are thus three controlled inputs and one uncontrolled input (combining all disturbances) and three measurable outputs of concern in this diagram. If it is assumed that all inputs significantly affect every output, a combination of 12 pairs of input-output relations is possible. A list of them follows:

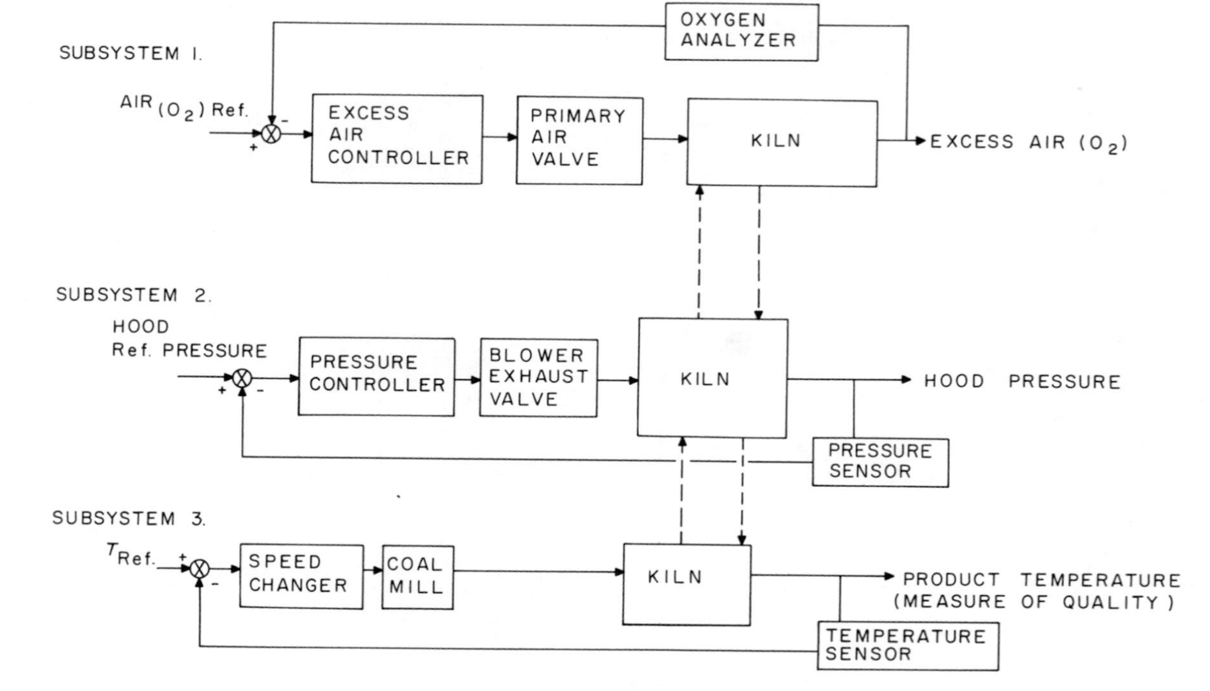

Figure 2.16. Reduction of multiinput-multioutput systems to single input-single output systems by appropriate control strategy.

Input	*Output*
Disturbances	Excess O_2
Disturbances	Hood Pressure
Disturbances	Product Temperature
Primary air flow	Excess O_2
Primary air flow	Hood Pressure
Primary air flow	Product Temperature
Coal flow	Excess O_2
Coal flow	Hood Pressure
Coal flow	Product Temperature
Effluent gas flow	Excess O_2
Effluent gas flow	Hood Pressure
Effluent gas flow	Product Temperature

Systems such as this, with multiple inputs and outputs, are common in chemical engineering operations. If all interrelations are considered, the design of the control system would usually become very difficult. By applying sound strategy, it is almost always possible to eliminate or reduce the interactions between and among various parts of the system.

In the above example, the sensitivity of the relation between hood pressure and displacement of the valve in the discharge duct from the induced draft fan is very high. The response of hood pressure to changes in this throttle valve displacement is also very fast. Accordingly, if a high-performance control system is used for hood pressure control, this system becomes virtually isolated or decoupled from the other systems. ("High performance" implies the ability of the controlled variable to follow rapid changes in the reference value (or command) and to effectively eliminate the influence of disturbances on the controlled variable.)

Responses of excess O_2 in the kiln effluent gas to a change in primary air can also be visualized as being fast. The O_2 analyzer can very likely be the slowest element in this system. For purposes of discussion, let it be assumed that this system is somewhat slower than the hood pressure-control system. If so, then this system will not seriously interact with the hood pressure-control system, the characteristic times being sufficiently separated.

Finally, the coal-firing system, by virtue of the coal mill and product temperature sensor, will be the slowest to respond. This subsystem can therefore be largely decoupled from the other two. The result is shown in the block diagram, Figure 2.16.

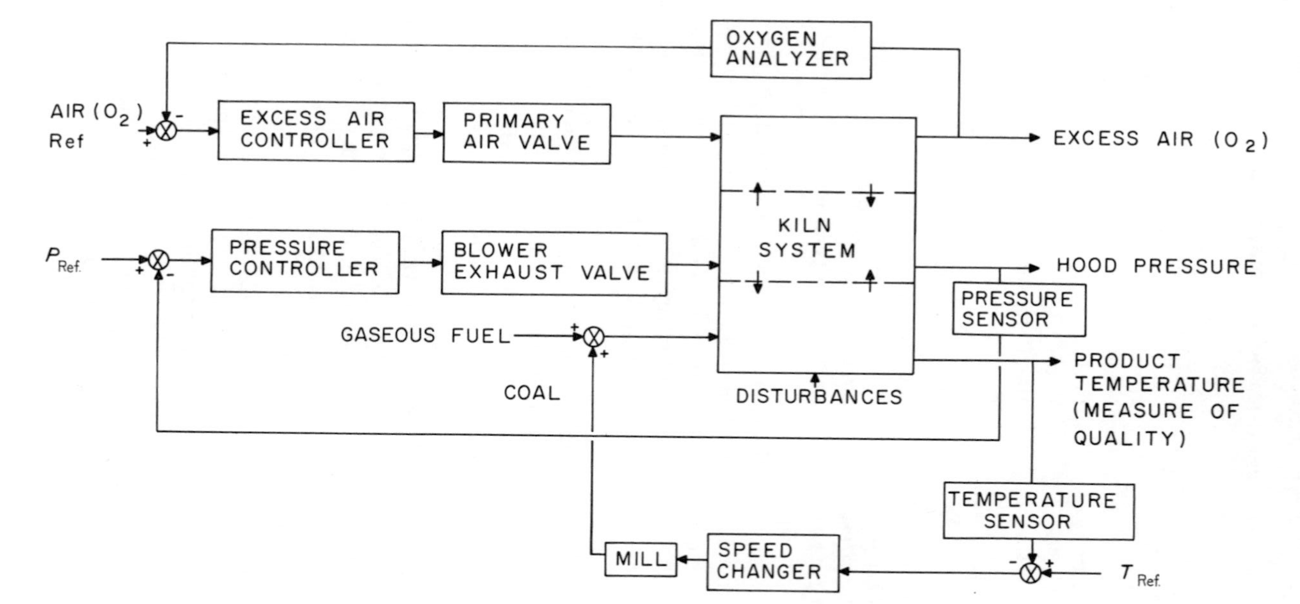

Figure 2.15. Block diagram of fired-kiln and associated processes with a suggested control strategy.

In a similar manner, the block diagram of the process of Figure 1.10 with the preferred control scheme may be shown as a block diagram where the several subsystems are assumed composed of smaller components. This is shown in Figure 2.17.

The pressures, p_1, p_2, p_3, and p_4, are fictitious. One would rarely wish to know the individual functions G_1, G_2, G_3, and G_4 which determine these outputs. The sum of the above pressures gives the true reactor pressure which, after measurement, becomes the reactor pressure signal. Other fictitious signals are p_5, p_6, p_7, and p_8.

If all the interactions required consideration, the study and design of possible control schemes would be a formidable task. Through the application of rational strategies, the task becomes very much simplified.

By controlling the compressor discharge pressure very precisely via Controller G_{c3} in Subsystem 3, the variations in flow through valve G_7 caused by changes in compressor discharge (signal F_1) are made negligible. This also makes Subsystem 3 immune to changes in pressure of the compressor suction p_8. Subsystem 3 can therefore be treated as a single input-single output system, and the control system can be designed on that basis.

Similarly, if the control action in Subsystem 2 is capable of maintaining the compressor suction pressure P_{cs} within close agreement with the reference pressure, P_{cs}(ref), the effect of changes in process pressure p_5 are minimized, and Subsystem 2 becomes essentially a single input-single output system which can be designed independently.

Subsystem 2 contains process elements which are slower than those in Subsystem 3. Specifically, the volume associated with Subsystem 2 is considerably larger than that of Subsystem 3. This makes Subsystem 2 less responsive and provides the separation of time constants between the two systems which permits individual design. Controller G_{c2b}, the compressor suction controller, is shown as cascaded with Controller G_{c2a}. That is, the output of Controller G_{c2a} is the reference or set point for Controller G_{c2b}. The input to Controller $G_{c2a}$is, in turn, the deviation of the reactor-pressure signal from the reactor-pressure reference. The function of Controller G_{c2a} is to provide a slow resetting (integration) of the compressor suction controller reference.

Likewise, Subsystem 1, being less responsive than Subsystem 2 by virtue of the large volume associated with it, can be designed as if it

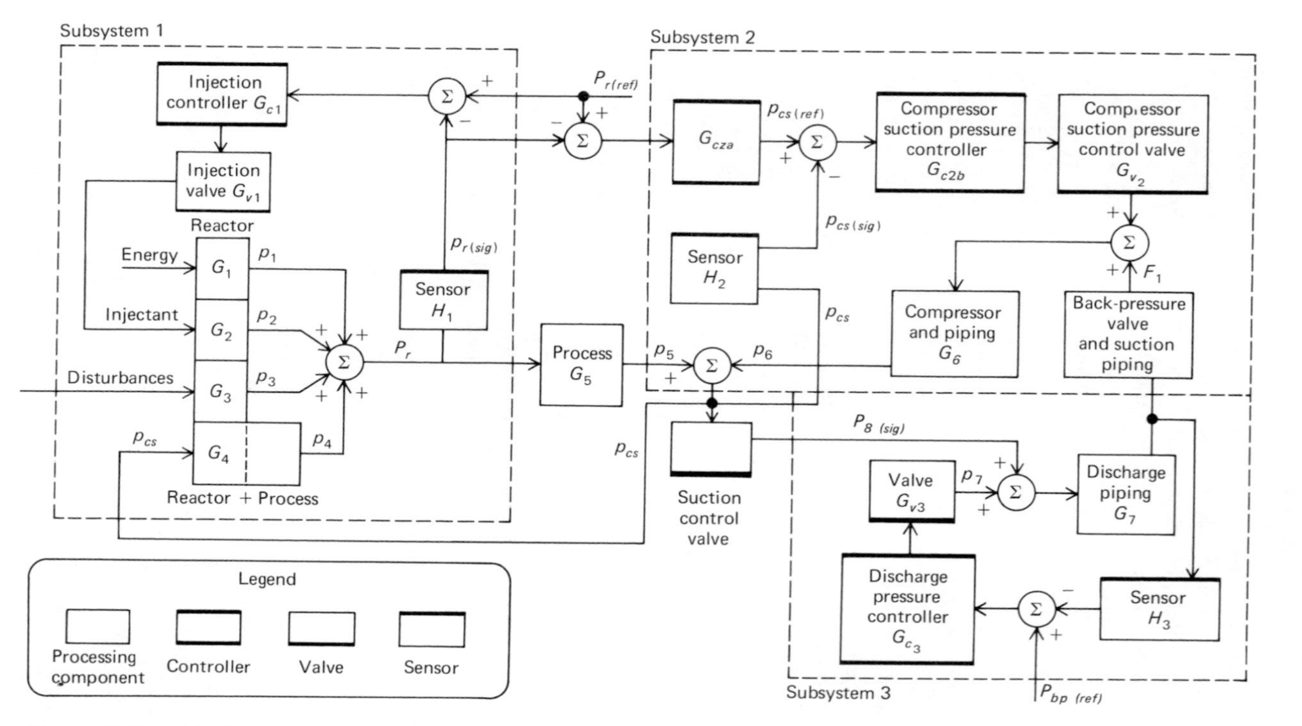

Figure 2.17. Block diagram of reactor pressure-control system.

were a single input-single output system. This simplifies the task of selecting Controller G_{c1} which regulates injectant gas by Valve G_{v1}.

The above statements will become more meaningful once an appreciation of dynamic response is obtained. The object here has been to illustrate the role of block diagrams as a technique to organize a control-system synthesis problem and to point out that, by proper choice of strategy, design problems can be greatly simplified.

References

1. Draper, C. S., Walter McKay, and Sidney Lees. Measurement Systems, vol. 3, part I in *Instrument Engineering.* McGraw-Hill Book Co., New York, 1953.

3
Elements of System Response

Dynamic characteristics are those properties of a physical system which determine its transient response. That is, dynamic characteristics determine the time history of the outputs caused by changes in the inputs. The transient response of several simple physical systems will be used to illustrate the ideas.

An electrical system consisting of a resistor and a capacitor is illustrated in Figure 3.1.

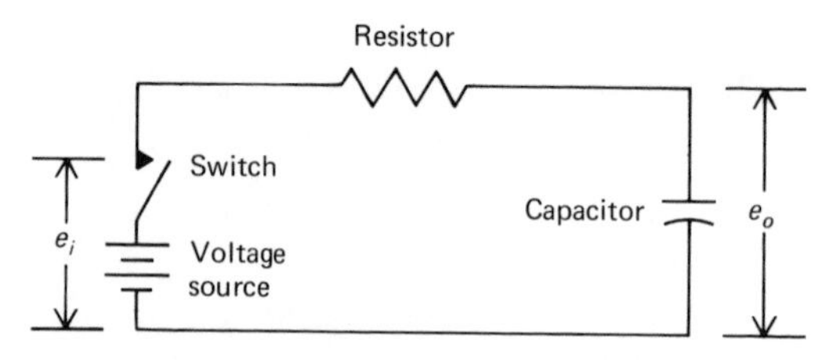

Figure 3.1. A simple resistance-capacitance electrical circuit.

Suppose that, at time zero, the voltage e_o is zero and switch s is closed imposing voltage e_i across the terminals of the circuit and the time response of e_o is observed. Intuitively, the flow of electrons into the capacitor is visualized, and a response such as shown in Figure 3.2 is expected with e_o eventually attaining the value of e_i.

Suppose now the battery is replaced by a device generating a sinusoidal voltage such that $e_i = A \sin \omega t$, where A is the amplitude and ω is the frequency of the oscillation. If ω is very low, it is ex-

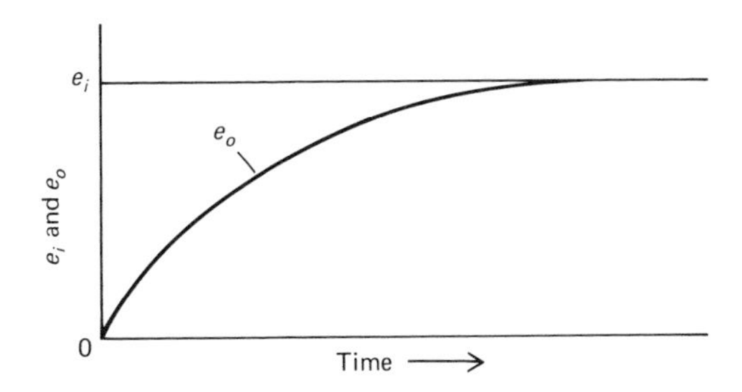

Figure 3.2. Response of RC circuit to step change in input voltage.

pected that the output voltage, e_o, would follow the input faithfully. As frequency is increased to a very high value, it is readily visualized that the changes in the output would be hardly discernible. At intermediate values of frequency, attenuation of the input amplitude would be expected to be somewhere between these limiting values. A result as shown in Figure 3.3 seems reasonable.

Similarly, it is expected that, at very low frequency, the output would be exactly in *phase* with the input. As frequency is increased, it is logical to expect the output to be increasingly out of phase with

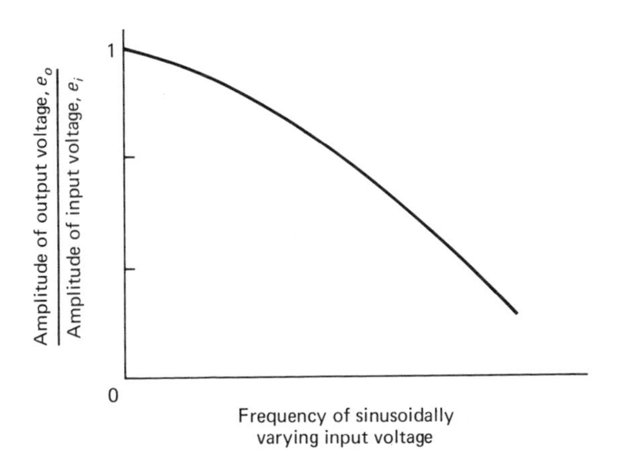

Figure 3.3. Response of simple RC electrical circuit to a sinusoidal input voltage of various constant frequencies.

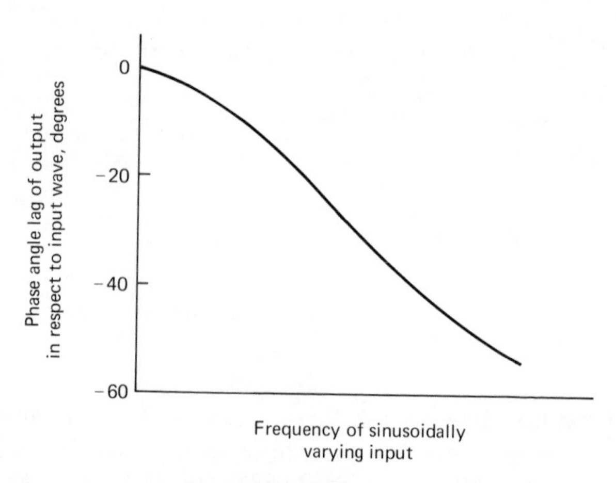

Figure 3.4. Relation of phase of output wave to input for an RC systems being forced sinusoidally.

(behind) the input. A plot of the phase difference between input and output similar to Figure 3.4 is likely.

Taken together, such information defines the *frequency response* of the RC circuit.

As another example, consider a well-stirred vessel into and from

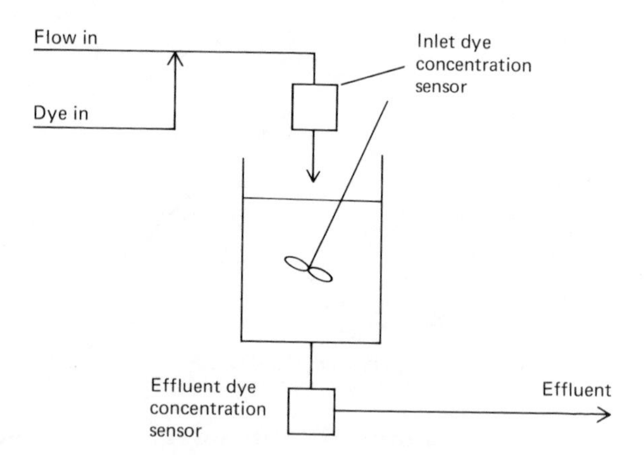

Figure 3.5. A well-stirred tank receiving and discharging liquid at constant rates provided with dye injection.

which a liquid flows at constant rate, as shown in Figure 3.5. Imagine that, starting at time zero, a small constant flow of dye is added to the inlet stream very near the point at which liquid enters the vessel and the concentration in the effluent measured. The vessel contents, being well agitated, will have a uniform concentration at all times. At time zero, the dye concentration will be zero. As time proceeds, the concentration increases but at an ever decreasing rate. Initially the rate of increase is the greatest since concentration in the vessel is lowest. The difference between rate of inlet flow and outflow of dye is obviously greatest at time zero. Eventually, as concentration within the vessel increases, it is expected that the rate of dye leaving will equal its input and no further change in effluent dye concentration will occur. A result entirely analogous with the time history of output voltage shown in Figure 3.2 can be predicted.

Similarly, if the flow of dye is changed in a sinusoidal fashion, it is expected that the amplitude of the changing outlet concentration and the phase lag between input and output wave would be similar to the voltage relations shown in Figures 3.3 and 3.4.

Although the responses of these two systems are similar, the processes taking place are considerably different. In the electrical circuit, the flow of electrons is visualized as being restricted by the resistor, but, once past it, they accumulate on the surfaces of the capacitor material. In the second case, it is assumed the dye is perfectly dispersed by the mixing device so that it is instantly uniformly distributed throughout the liquid in the vessel. After time zero, dye is continuously removed in the effluent, but, since the inlet concentration exceeds that of the feed, the inventory of dye in the vessel increases. Yet, as will be shown, the two responses can be described by analogous mathematical relations.

In both of these cases, the response characteristics are expected to change if the properties of the system are changed. A larger capacitor or a larger vessel volume would, for example, make the systems respond more slowly. Increasing the flow rate of fluid or decreasing the electrical resistance would yield more rapidly responding systems. Changing the magnitude of input voltage or rate of dye injection would, however, not alter the *form* of the responses.

A more complex system is illustrated by the spring-mass-dashpot illustrated in Figure 3.6.

Suppose it is of interest to follow the position, y, of the mass at any time as the upper support is moved vertically along the x scale. If x is moved very slowly, it is expected that y would move an equal

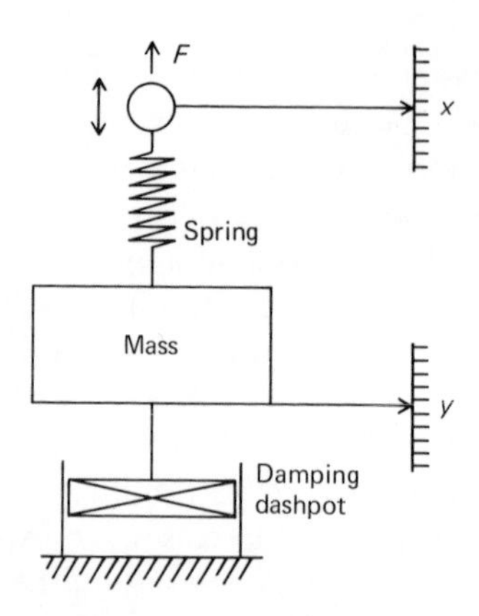

Figure 3.6. Mass-spring-dashpot system with force applied to free end of spring.

amount. If x is moved very rapidly from its initial position, intuitively it is visualized that y will not be able to respond exactly because of the inertia in the mass and the resistance offered by the dashpot. Common experience also indicates that, if the system is lightly damped (small resistance offered by the dashpot), the motion of the mass may be oscillatory. This is caused by an exchange of energy between mass and spring, losses in the kinetic energy of the mass appearing as gains in the potential energy as the mass oscillates.

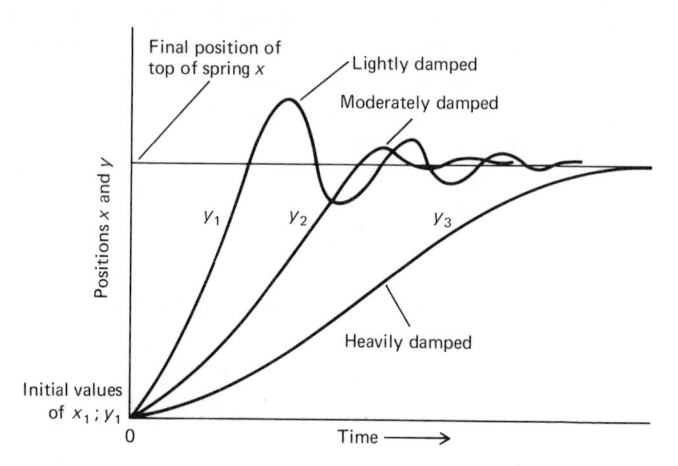

Figure 3.7. Typical responses of mass-spring-dashpot system to step changes in position of free end of spring.

The more damping introduced, the more energy is dissipated in the dashpot, the less conserved, and the less oscillatory the system becomes.

In response to a sudden change in position x, the position of the mass with time would appear as shown in Figure 3.7 for various combinations of damping.

Intuitively, the frequency response of such a system would be expected to show a one-to-one correspondence between y and x at very low frequency; at very high frequencies, y would show little response. At intermediate forcing frequencies, the result cannot be easily estimated. However, it does not come as a surprise to know that it is possible that the amplitude of y may exceed that of x at certain frequencies. Again the characteristics of the frequency response depend upon the nature of the physical system. In this case, as damping action of the dashpot is increased, it will be more difficult to make the system oscillate for a given spring characteristic. Likewise, for a given damping action, the tendency to oscillate increases as the spring becomes stiffer. Common sense indicates that the response will be dependent upon mass, spring stiffness, and extent of damping. Frequency responses as shown in Figure 3.8 are expected.

The above discussion was meant to introduce the ideas of transient response and frequency response in a qualitative way. The time his-

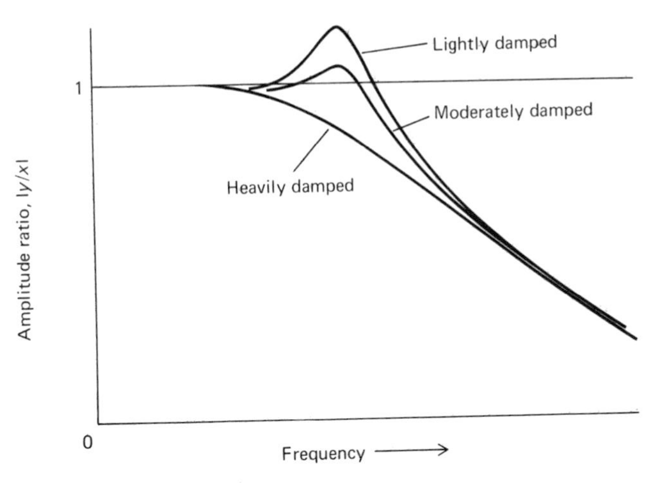

Figure 3.8. Frequency response characteristics of mass-spring-dashpot system.

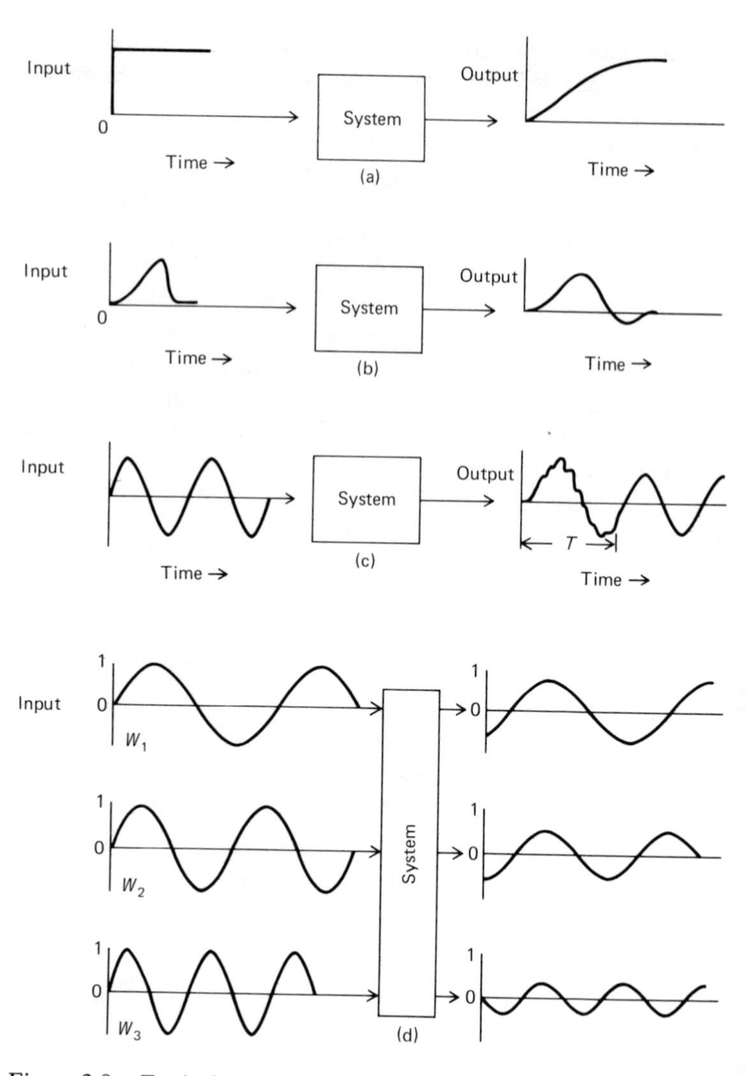

Figure 3.9. Typical system responses to various forcings: (a) transient response to step forcing, (b) transient response to pulse forcing, (c) initiation of frequency response forcing at a given frequency, (d) steady-state sinusoidal responses to forcings of three different frequencies.

tory of responses caused by step-like inputs is illustrative of transient behavior. This kind of forcing is usually called forcing by a constant. The response to a sinusoidal type of forcing is considered to be that which results after the sinusoidal input has been active for a time sufficient to produce a repetitive sinusoidal output. Figure 3.9 illustrates the response to several forcings.

Figure 3.9a is typical of the response of a damped system to a step forcing—that is, a system being forced with a constant.

Figure 3.9b indicates the response of a somewhat lightly damped system to a pulse-like forcing.

Figure 3.9c shows what happens when a system initially at rest is forced sinusoidally. For the first cycle or two, it is seen that the output is irregular, but finally the output becomes a smooth repeating wave of the same frequency as the input. Its amplitude is constant but not necessarily the same as that of the input, and the phase has been shifted (usually) in respect to that of the input. After the transient period T has passed, the output is called the *steady state* response to sinusoidal forcing.

Figure 3.9d attempts to illustrate the changes in amplitude and phase in the steady-state response of a system to sinusoidal forcings of three different frequencies but of constant amplitude.

Approximately the following relations exist.

	Input		*Output*	
Frequency	*Amplitude*	*Phase*	*Amplitude*	*Phase*
ω_1	1	0	0.80	$-45°$
ω_2	1	0	0.60	$-90°$
ω_3	1	0	0.40	$-180°$

If these data were plotted, amplitude and phase of output versus frequency, a diagram such as shown in Figure 3.10 would result. The output phase *lags* that of the input in this illustration.

In Chapters 1 and 2, systems and components were qualified as fast or slow and the compatibility of a component judged on the basis of their time responses relative to the system with which they were to be used.

In terms of the time response to a step type of input (step forcing), components such as sensors or valve actuators become compatible with the process to which they are associated if their time histories compare with that of the process somewhat as shown in

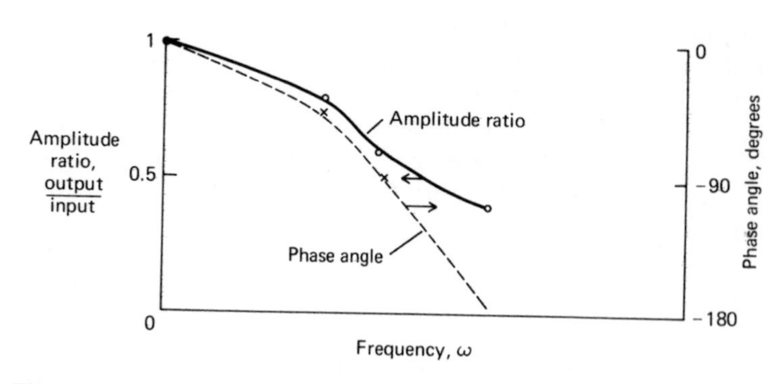

Figure 3.10. Frequency-response data plotted on rectangular coordinates.

Figure 3.11. Very roughly, the time t_1 required for a component to exhibit an output equal to about two-thirds of the final value should be about one-tenth the time t_2 required for an equal fraction change in the response of the process. If the response of the component is slower than this, then it becomes increasingly difficult to design a completely satisfactory control system.

In terms of frequency response, the frequency at which the component's amplitude ratio falls to about 0.7 should be ten times greater than the frequency at which the amplitude of the process is reduced to 0.7. Figure 3.12 illustrates this.

Once again, as ω_2 approaches ω_1, the characteristics of the component becomes of increasing importance in the control-system design. It is good practice to select control components, such as sen-

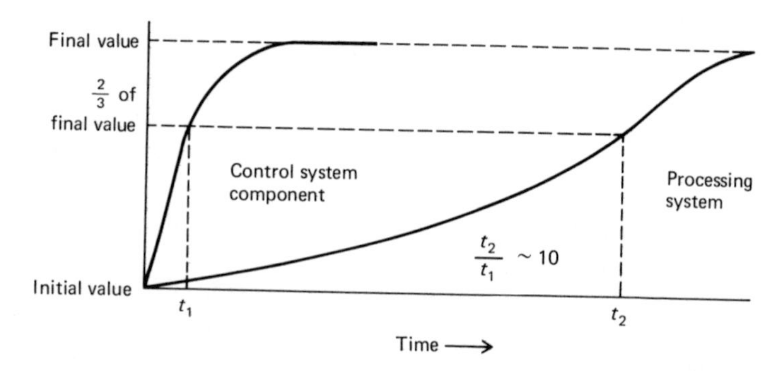

Figure 3.11. Recommended relative transient-response characteristics of processing system and control components.

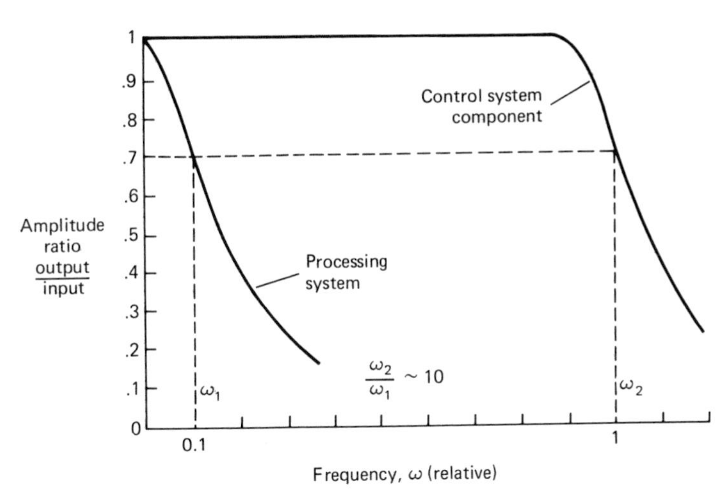

Figure 3.12. Recommended separation of frequency-response characteristics of processing system and control components.

sors and valve actuators, the dynamic characteristics of which are 'separated' from the process somewhat as indicated in Figures 3.11 and 3.12.

Sometimes the output from a system is delayed in its response to an input. This could occur if the gears in a mechanical system possessed backlash or if a magnetic system experienced hysteresis. Chemical processes or fluid systems very frequently exhibit pure time delay or dead time which is somewhat different than backlash or hysteresis.

For example, pneumatic transmission lines or gas processing systems cannot transmit pressure signals under usual conditions at a

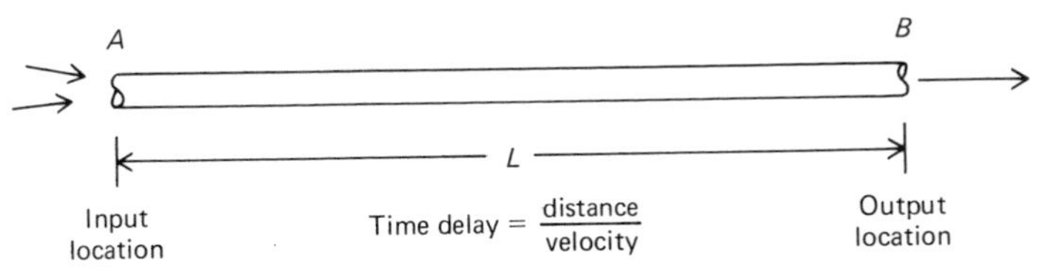

Figure 3.13. Delay time caused by limitations on velocity of signal transmission.

velocity greater than the acoustic velocity in the particular medium. A change in pressure at point B in Figure 3.13 will not be detected until T seconds after a change at point A is introduced:

$$\text{where } T = \frac{\text{distance } \overline{AB}}{\text{acoustic velocity in fluid}}.$$

The response at point B to a pulse change in pressure at A would appear as shown in Figure 3.14.

Similarly, because of imperfect mixing, changes in concentration are delayed if fluids flow through long narrow conduits. For example, the concentration change occurring in the well-mixed vessel (Figure 3.15), into and from which fluids flow, will not be detected at point D until T seconds later where

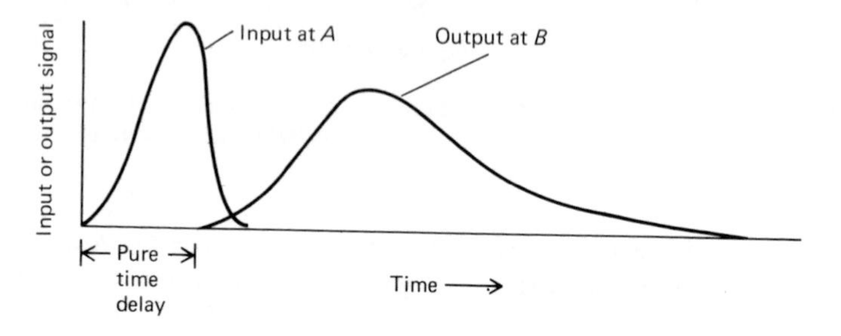

Figure 3.14. Response of a pressure signal in a fluid transmission line.

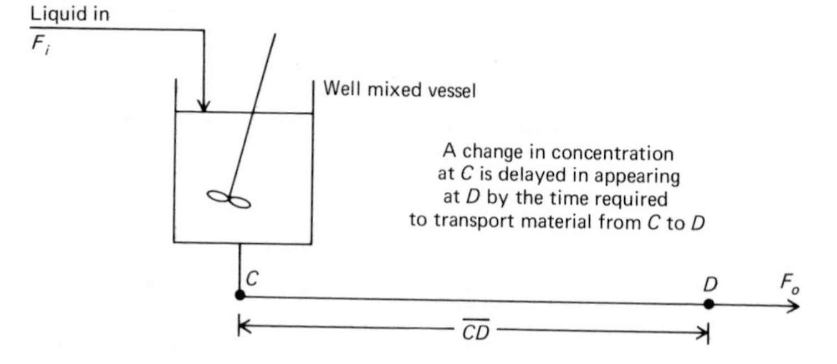

Figure 3.15. A system which exhibits pure delay time or dead time.

$$T = \frac{\text{distance } \overline{CD}}{\text{effective velocity in conduit}}, \frac{\text{ft}}{\text{ft/sec}} = \text{sec.}$$

Almost all processes exhibit pure delay time, however small. It is most difficult to predict but relatively easy to measure if a high-quality data system is used. Care should be taken to distinguish real process delay time from that associated with the poor response and low sensitivity of sensors or measuring systems.

Delay time is one of the most insidious properties of processes contributing to the difficulties of designing process-control systems. Its presence always limits the performance of a controlled system. When the pure delay time exceeds about 10 percent of the value of the major dominant time constant of the process being controlled, performance of a closed-loop negative feedback system begins to deteriorate.

It is good practice and a better investment to reduce pure delay time by process rearrangement, better location of sensors, changes in control strategy, and improved instrumentation rather than to resort to complicated control circuits and functions designed to compensate for it.

4
Simple Systems and Responses

Several systems which have practical relevance will be described. These will yield mathematical descriptions generally referred to as first-order ordinary linear differential equations with constant coefficients.

Solutions to these equations will be derived for various forcing functions by classical methods. The role of operational techniques will be introduced.

Three simple but relatively important physical systems will be analyzed.

The first consists of an open vessel of constant cross-section, A, filled with a liquid to level ν_0 which is permitted to discharge freely through a hydraulic resistance.

The following terms are defined:

ν = level in vessel at any time, t, ft.
ν_0 = initial value of level (at time zero), ft,
F_o = effluent flow rate, cu ft/min,
A = cross-sectional area of vessel,
R = hydraulic resistance defined such that

$$F_o = \frac{V}{R} \text{ or } R = \frac{\nu}{F_o} = \frac{\text{ft.}}{\text{ft}^3/\text{min}} = \text{min/ft}^2$$

($1/R$ = ft^3/min/ft might be considered a conductance).

The process diagram appears in Figure 4.1.

Suppose at time zero the valve is instantaneously opened and flow commences, with no time being required to accelerate the fluid to its

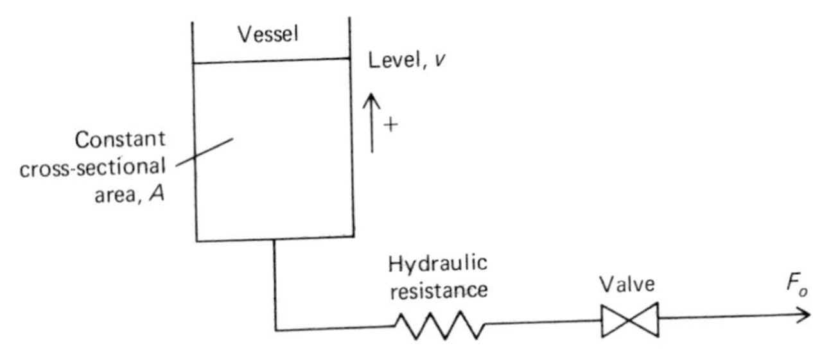

Figure 4.1. Open vessel discharging a liquid through a hydraulic resistance.

terminal velocity in the discharge conduit. With these assumptions,

$$-A\frac{dv}{dt} = F_o.$$

However, since $F_o = v/R$,

$$A\frac{dv}{dt} + \frac{v}{R} = 0. \tag{4.1}$$

It is customary to place this equation in a *standard form* by dividing by the coefficient of the zeroth order term—in this case, $1/R$. Hence,

$$AR\frac{dv}{dt} + v = 0. \tag{4.2}$$

The dimensions of the coefficient of the first-order term must be time, since $AR\ dv/dt$ must have the dimensions of level v.

The product, of which AR is typical, is frequently called the *time constant* of the system or its *characteristic time*—i.e.,

$$AR \equiv \tau \equiv (CT), \text{ with units of time.}$$

Note that τ is derived from the constants of the system: the product of the cross-sectional area of the vessel (a capacitance) and the hydraulic resistance, R, of the effluent conduit.

It should also be noted that viscous flow has been assumed in the efflux conduit so that a *linear* differential equation resulted. If the relationship between level v and effluent flow rate F_o were such that $F_o = K\sqrt{\Delta P}$, the differential equation would have been non-linear.

The solution of (4.2) is readily achieved by the separation-of-variable technique and recognition of the resulting forms.

$$\frac{dv}{dt} = -\frac{1}{\tau}v, \; \frac{dv}{v} = -\frac{dt}{\tau}, \; d(\ln v) = -\frac{1}{\tau}dt.$$

The indefinite integral becomes

$$\int d(\ln v) = -\frac{1}{\tau}\int dt, \text{ or } \ln v = -\frac{1}{\tau}t + C$$

from which

$$v = e^{-t/\tau + c} = e^c e^{-t/\tau} = C_0 e^{-t/\tau}. \tag{4.3}$$

The important observations to be made at this point are the following.

(1) The solution is an exponential decay; i.e., the sign of the exponent is negative.

(2) The rate at which decay occurs is inversely dependent upon the time constant of the system, τ; i.e.,

$$\frac{dv}{dt} = -\frac{1}{\tau}C_0 e^{-t/\tau}.$$

(3) The purely exponential term is modified by a coefficient C_0.

The coefficient C_0 is called the *fitting constant*, since it fits the solution of the particular differential equation to its associated physical system. That is, system specifications are required before C_0 can be evaluated for a particular case. These specifications are embodied in the statements of *initial conditions*.

In this case, only the initial fluid level in the vessel need be specified. Suppose

$$\nu = \nu_0 \quad \text{when} \quad t = 0.$$

Substitution into (4.3) gives

$$\nu_0 = C_0 e^{-0/\tau} = C_0. \tag{4.4}$$

The solution then becomes

$$\nu = \nu_0 e^{-t/\tau}. \tag{4.5}$$

The result may be made nondimensional by dividing by ν_0:

$$\frac{\nu}{\nu_0} = e^{-t/\tau}. \tag{4.6}$$

The term ν/ν_0 is sometimes called the *dependent variable ratio*, *DVR*. The time behavior of *DVR* is shown in Figure 4.2.

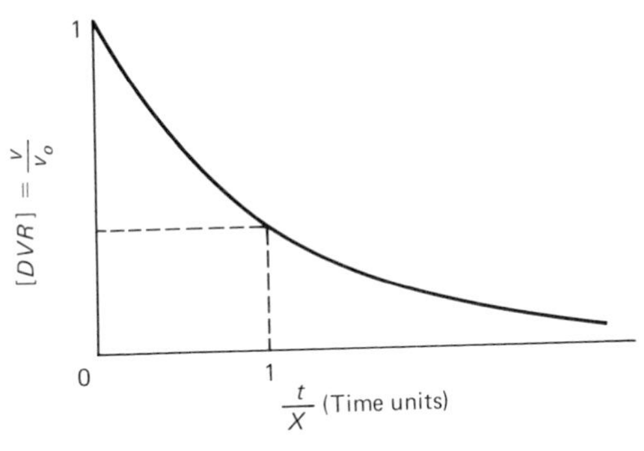

Figure 4.2. Response of first-order linear system with zero forcing; dependent variable ratio versus dimensionless time.

Note that, when $t = \tau$,

$$\frac{\nu}{\nu_0} = e^{-1} = 1/e,$$

and

$$\nu = \nu_0/e = \nu_0/2.72 = 0.368\ \nu_0. \tag{4.7}$$

That is, the time required for ν to diminish to 36.8 percent of the initial value (or to accomplish 63.2 percent of the ultimate change) is equal, numerically, to the time constant.

For the response shown in Figure 4.2, this corresponds to the point where $t/\tau = 1$. If the relation between ν and t is shown on a rectilinear graph, Figure 4.3 is obtained.

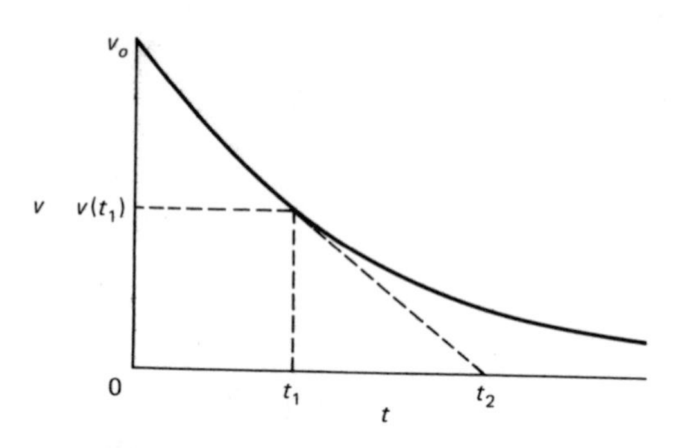

Figure 4.3. Response of first-order linear system with zero forcing; dependent variable versus time.

From Equation 4.5, the slope at point t_1 is

$$\left(\frac{d\nu}{dt}\right)_{t=t_1} = -\frac{\nu_0}{\tau}e^{-t_1/\tau}. \tag{4.8}$$

If the variable is permitted to continue changing at this rate until it reaches zero, a time equal to $t_2 - t_1$ will be required. Therefore, the slope at $t = t_1$ is

$$\frac{-(\nu_1 - 0)}{t_2 - t_1} = \frac{-\nu_0 e^{-t_1/\tau}}{t_2 - t_1}$$

Setting this equal to the slope as found from (4.8) gives

$$\frac{-(\nu_1 - 0)}{t_2 - t_1} = \frac{-\nu_0}{\tau}e^{-t_1/\tau}.$$

and, when we solve for the time interval, we get

$$t_2 - t_1 = \frac{(-v_0 e^{-t_1/\tau})}{\left(\frac{-v_0 e^{-t_1/\tau}}{\tau}\right)} = \tau. \tag{4.9}$$

For first-order equations, of which (4.2) is typical, the above properties exist.

In this example, it was assumed that the valve in the efflux line was opened instantaneously at time equal to zero. The system was released from an initial point and allowed to respond in a manner unrestricted except for the limitations imposed by the resistance of the system. In this case, the system was *unforced;* i.e., no outside motivation except gravitational force was applied.

Suppose the system is altered by permitting a stream of liquid to enter the vessel. Assume that, at time zero, the influent and effluent flow rates are equal so that an equilibrium value of level v_0 exists (see Figure 4.4). Then, at time zero, the rate of input is decreased to a new value by adjusting the valve. What situation now prevails?

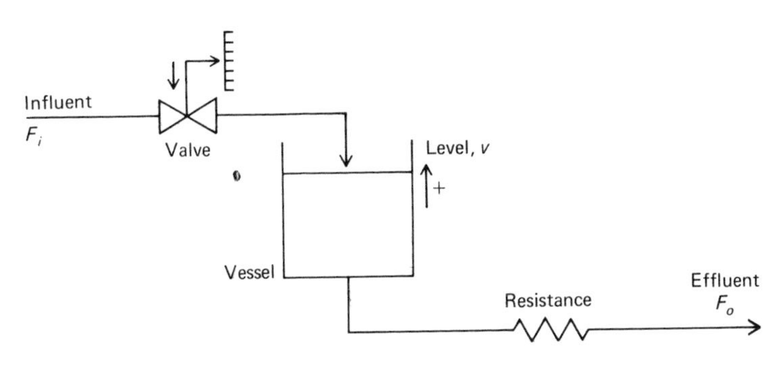

Figure 4.4. Modified flow system.

Again the basic equations can be written, using the previous assumptions, as follows:

$$F_i - F_o = A\frac{dv}{dt}$$

where F_i is the adjusted value of influent.

As before, $F_o = v/R$ so $v/R - F_i = A\ dv/dt$ or

$$AR\frac{dv}{dt} + v = RF_i. \tag{4.10}$$

As compared with (4.2), the left side of (4.10) is now equal to RF_i instead of being equal to zero (unforced case). (It should be noted that RF_i is expressed in units of level v.)

The simple exponential decay type of solution shown above is inadequate in this case, for now the level doesn't need to go to zero but may well approach a new level somewhat less than the initial level, v_0. In fact, at time equal to infinity when $dv/dt = 0$, v approaches RF_i. This value of v is called the *steady state* value, i.e.,

$$v_{ss} = RF_i. \tag{4.11}$$

It is also called the *forced solution*, and, in this case, it is equal to the forcing, RF_i.

Intuitively, an exponential decaying response is also expected, and it is logical to *guess* that an exponential type of solution exists which, following a sufficient length of time, disappears, leaving only the steady-state solution.

Equation 4.10 can be solved directly by the method of separating variables:

$$\frac{dv}{(RF_i - v)} = \frac{1}{AR}\,dt.$$

By letting $RF_i - v = y$ (RF_i is a constant), $-dv = dy$, and

$$-\frac{dy}{y} = \frac{1}{AR}\,dt,$$

from which $ln\ y = ln\ (RF_i - v) = -\dfrac{1}{AR}t + c,$

or

$$v = RF_i - C_0\,e^{-t/\tau}. \tag{4.12}$$

If we use the initial conditions that $v = v_0$ when $t = 0$, it follows that

$$C_0 = RF_i - v_0.$$

Consequently,

$$\nu = (\nu_0 - RF_i)\, e^{-t/\tau} + RF_i. \qquad (4.13)$$

This result satisfies the conditions that $\nu = \nu_0$ (the initial value) when $t = 0$, and $\nu = RF_i$ (the steady state value imposed following the change in valve position) when $t = \infty$.

In addition to the steady-state value, RF_i, this solution differs from (4.5) in the alteration of its fitting constant $(\nu_0 - RF_i)$.

The solution is composed of two parts, a transient part and a steady-state part; i.e.,

$$\nu_{tr} = (\nu_0 - RF_i)\, e^{-t/\tau} = C_0\, e^{-t/\tau},$$

the transient solution, and $\nu_{ss} = \nu_f = RF_i$, the steady-state or *forced solution.* The transient solution is exponential in form while the steady-state or forced solution is of the same *form* as the forcing. (In this case, it is identical with the forcing if the original differential equation is placed in standard form.)

It should be emphasized that, whereas the fitting constant was

$$C_0 = \nu_0$$

(unforced case)

for the unforced case, the fitting constant is altered and depends on the type of forcing when a forcing is imposed

$$C_0 = (\nu_0 - RF_i)$$

(forced case)

It is therefore not possible to determine the fitting constant *unless the forcing is specified.*

In the particular situation described above, where a step change in influent liquid flow rate was assumed, the forcing is a constant. The level is said to be the response to a *constant* or response to a (decreasing) *step function.* Results are shown graphically in Figure 4.5. Notice that, when the system is forced with a constant, no error exists after the transient disappears; that is, the complete solution and forced solution coincide.

Also note that, where forcing is present, the transient component in the solution is of the same *form* as that appearing in the solution

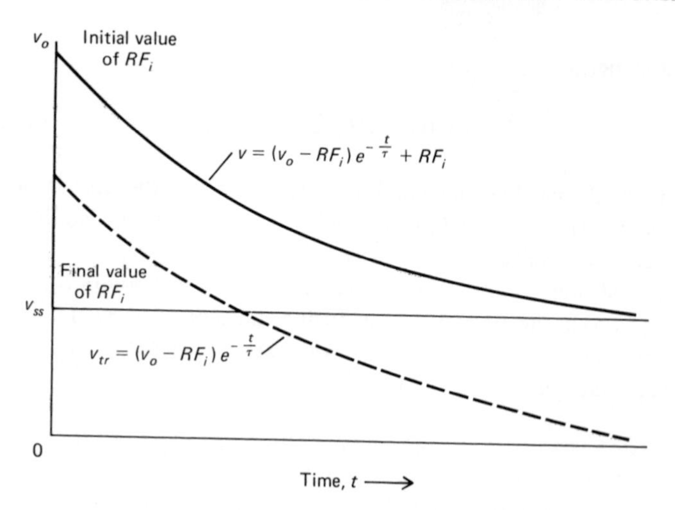

Figure 4.5. Complete solution and transient and forced solution components for a first-order system forced with a decreasing step.

of the unforced case. It seems logical, therefore, to conclude that the *form* of the transient solution of any linear ordinary differential equation with constant coefficients can be found by setting the forcing function equal to zero and solving the remaining equation. Furthermore, it appears that a logical *choice* for this transient solution will be an exponential.

Likewise, it appears that the forced solution (or steady-state solution) will be of the same *form* as the forcing. As will be seen, these conclusions are basically valid and will be clearly demonstrated in the material which follows.

When the forcing function is zero, the differential equation is called a *homogeneous* equation. For example,

$$\tau \frac{dv}{dt} + v = 0$$

is the homogeneous first-order differential equation. The solution to the homogeneous equation yields the *form* of the complementary or transient solution, which is exponential.

When the forcing function is not zero, the equation is said to be *nonhomogeneous.*

The method of *guessing* at the form of the *forced solution* and then finding the required coefficients is called the *method of undetermined coefficients.* It does not always lead to a solution, but, for most cases of engineering interest, it does. The solution obtained is sometimes called the *particular integral.* Usually it is referred to as the forced or steady-state solution.

As another example, consider the electrical circuit shown in Figure 3.1. Relationships are as follows:

$$i = \frac{e_i - e_o}{R}, \; e_o = \frac{1}{C}\int i\,dt \quad \text{or} \quad \frac{de_o}{dt} = \frac{i}{C}.$$

Therefore,

$$\frac{de_o}{dt} - \frac{e_i - e_o}{RC} = 0,$$

from which it follows that

$$RC\frac{de_o}{dt} + e_o = e_i \qquad \text{or} \qquad \tau\frac{de_o}{dt} + e_o = e_i$$

where

$$\tau = RC. \tag{4.14}$$

This is recognized as a first-order ordinary linear differential equation with constant coefficients forced with e_i, which may be a function of time.

Another physical system which can be approximated by a first-order system is a thermal sensing element installed in a flowing medium illustrated in Figure 4.6. If it is assumed that the thermal conductivity of the sensing element is very high so that the temperature of the bulb is everywhere uniform, that the resistance to heat transfer resides entirely in the fluid film surrounding the bulb, and that the temperature gradient across the film is linear, then the following relations may be written:

$Q = -Ak\dfrac{dT}{dx}$, Fourier's law of heat transfer by conduction;

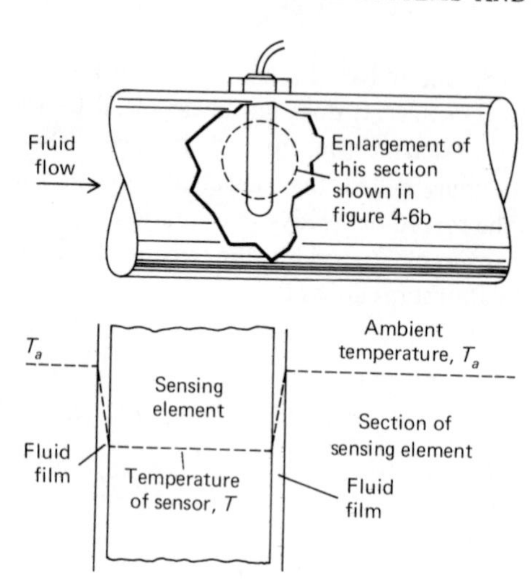

Figure 4.6. (a) Thermal sensing element immersed in fluid stream. (b) Temperature gradients associated with idealized thermal sensor.

$Q = MC_p \dfrac{dT}{dt}$, rate of accumulation of thermal energy in the bulb;

$\dfrac{dT}{dx} = \dfrac{T - T_a}{\Delta x}$, linear temperature gradient across film.

When the above are combined,

$$MC_p \frac{dT}{dt} = \frac{Ak}{\Delta x}(T - T_a) \quad \text{or} \quad MC_p \frac{dT}{dt} + \frac{Ak}{\Delta x} T = \frac{Ak}{\Delta x} T_a.$$

If $k/\Delta x \equiv h$, the film coefficient, then

$$\left(\frac{MC_p}{Ah}\right) \frac{dT}{dt} + T = T_a, \quad \text{or} \quad \tau \frac{dT}{dt} + T = T_a. \tag{4.15}$$

Once again, the first-order differential equation is obtained.

All the above differential equations have been derived without regard to a reference value for the variables except that it has been inferred that each was evaluated with respect to some arbitrary zero. For convenience, it is useful to consider these variables as deviations from some steady-state level.

In the last example, let $T = T' + T_R$ where T_R is a constant reference temperature. Then $dT/dt = dT'/dt$, and the equation becomes

$$\tau \frac{dT'}{dt} + T' + T_R = T_a' + T_R \quad \text{or} \quad \tau \frac{dT'}{dt} + T' = T_a'.$$

Here T' and T_a' are the deviations from the reference value, T_R, which can be arbitrarily assigned. The *form* of the differential equation has not been changed by these substitutions. *Henceforth, unless otherwise stated, the deviation variables will be used with no special designation.*

It is instructive to estimate the magnitude of error which can be expected if the ambient temperature surrounding an idealized temperature sensor changes with time. A realistic situation will be used as an example.

Assume the protecting sheath (well) surrounding a small temperature sensor is cylindrical, made of steel, one inch in diameter, and one foot long (effective length). If the surface area of the end is neglected, the area (of the convex surface only) is $\pi/12$ square feet. The volume is $\pi d^2/4\ (1) = \pi/576$ cubic feet. If a density of 480 pound/feet^3 is assumed, the ratio of mass to area is

$$\frac{M}{A} = \frac{480\pi}{576}\left(\frac{12}{\pi}\right) = 5\ \text{lb/ft}^2.$$

If the heat capacity is 0.1 BTU/lb/°F, then

$$\frac{M}{A} C_p = (5)\,(0.1) = 0.5\ \text{BTU/ft}^2/°\text{F}.$$

If the film heat transfer coefficient takes on various values, the corresponding time constant $\tau = MC_p/Ah$ is shown in Table 4.1.

Suppose now the ambient temperature changes in a linear manner such that

$$T_a = mt, \text{ a ramp forcing.}$$

The *steady state* solution is assumed to be of the same *form* as the forcing; i.e., $T_{ss} = nt + b$.

TABLE 4.1 Time Constants for a Temperature Sensor

Film heat transfer coefficient, h		Time constant, $\tau = \frac{MC_p}{Ah}$
BTU/hr/ft²/°F	BTU/min/ft²/°F	Minutes
12.0	0.2	2.5
120.0	2.0	0.25
1200.0	20.0	0.025

Therefore, $dT_{ss}/dt = n$ and $\tau n + nt + b = mt$. Comparing coefficients gives $n = m$ and $b = -\tau n$ or $b = -m\tau$. The steady-state or forced solution becomes $T_{ss} = mt - m\tau$. The transient solution is of the exponential form, $T_{tr} = C_0 e^{-t/\tau}$ so the total solution is

$$T_{Total} = C_0 e^{-t/\tau} + mt - m\tau. \tag{4.16}$$

At some t, after the transient disappears,

$$T_{Total} = T_{ss} = mt - m\tau.$$

Subtracting the forcing, $T_a = mt$, gives

$$T_a - T_{ss} = m\tau. \tag{4.17}$$

This states that, after sufficient time to permit the disappearance of the transient component, there is a constant error between the ambient temperature and the sensed temperature (temperature signal). The magnitude of this error depends on the time constant, τ, and the rate of change of the ambient temperature, m. This difference is called the *dynamic error.*

The time by which the measured temperature *lags* the true temperature when the true temperature is changing in a ramp fashion can also be calculated. Thus, if $T_{ss} = T_a$, then $T_{ss} = mt_{ss} - m\tau$. But $T_a' = mt_a$ so that, if T_{ss}' and T_a' are the same, $0 = m(t_{ss} - t_a) - m\tau$ or $\tau = (t_{ss} - t_a)$, the time constant. Figure 4.7 illustrates the above. Dynamic errors for a temperature sensor having various time constants being forced at different rates in a ramp fashion are given in Table 4.2.

The magnitude of the dynamic error is rather surprising; for example, a sensor having a time constant of 15 seconds will exhibit a

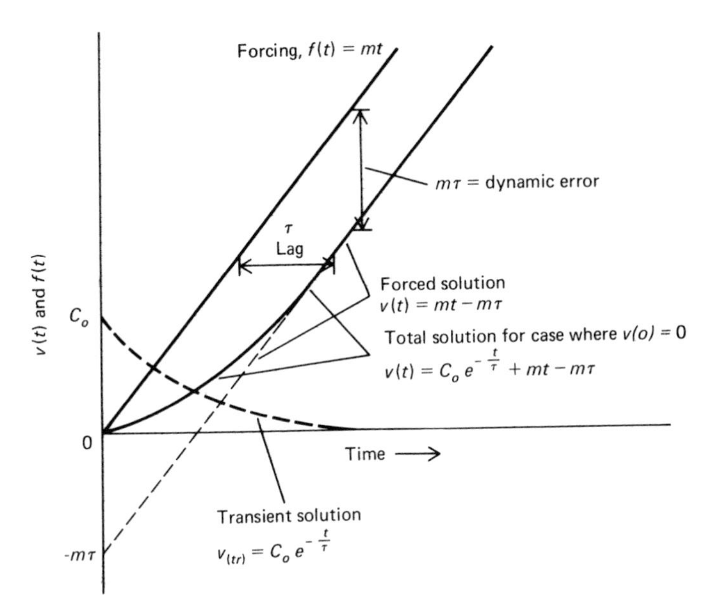

Figure 4.7. Dynamic error and time lag exhibited by a first-order system being forced by a ramp function.

TABLE 4.2 Dynamic Errors of an Idealized Temperature Sensor

τ, Time constant		Rate of forcing, °F/min, m		
		1	10	100
Minutes	Seconds	Dynamic error °F	Dynamic error °F	Dynamic error °F
2.5	150.0	2.5	25.0	250.0
0.25	15.0	0.25	2.5	25.0
0.025	1.5	0.025	0.25	2.5
0.0025	0.15	0.0025	0.025	0.25

dynamic error of 25F if the ambient temperature is changing at the rate of 100F per minute.

The results of these examples show that a first-order system being forced by a constant (either an increasing or decreasing step function) will show no error between the forced solution (steady-state solution) and the forcing. If the forcing is a ramp function, then there exists a constant error between the forced solution and forcing, the magnitude of which is dependent upon the system parameters (τ) and the rate of the forcing.

It is natural to ask what this error might be if the forcing were parabolic and to guess that this error would be a function of time. This is true, and the results are summarized in Table 4.3.

TABLE 4.3 Dynamic Error for First-Order Systems With Various Forcings

Type of Forcing	Forcing function	Forced solution	Dynamic error
Step (constant)	B	B	0
Ramp	mt	$m(t - \tau)$	$m\tau$
Parabolic	mt^2	$mt^2 - 2m\tau t + 2m\tau^2$	$2m(t - \tau)$

The general trend is clear. When the running variable, t, does not appear in the forcing, there is no dynamic error; when the running variable appears raised to a power, the dynamic error is dependent upon the running variable raised to a power one less than that in the forcing.

Solutions to forcings which can be considered combinations of simple forcings such as step followed by a ramp, or ramp followed by a step, can be found by using the principal of superposition which is valid for linear systems.

A forcing of interest is the trigonometric function $A \cos \omega t$. Following the usual procedure, the transient solution is assumed to be of exponential form and the steady-state solution of a form similar to that of the forcing function:

$$v_{tr} = C\, e^{-t/\tau},$$

$$v_{ss} = a \cos \omega t + b \sin \omega t.$$

Since $dv_{ss}/dt = -a\omega \sin \omega t + b\omega \cos \omega t$, substitution into the equation

$$\tau \frac{dv_{ss}}{dt} + v_{ss} = f(t)$$

gives $\tau(-a\omega \sin \omega t + b\omega \cos \omega t) + a \cos \omega t + b \sin \omega t = a \cos \omega t + b \sin \omega t$. It follows that

$$(\tau\omega b + a)\cos\omega t + (-\tau\omega a + b)\sin\omega t = A\cos\omega t$$

and therefore

$$a + \tau\omega b = A \qquad \text{or} \qquad a = A - \tau\omega b$$

and

$$b - \tau\omega a = 0 \qquad \text{or} \qquad a = b/\tau\omega$$

from which

$$b = \frac{A\tau\omega}{1 + (\omega\tau)^2}$$

and

$$a = \frac{A}{1 + (\omega\tau)^2}.$$

The complete solution is

$$\begin{aligned} v &= C\,e^{-t/\tau} + \frac{A}{1 + (\tau\omega)^2}\,[\cos\omega t + \tau\omega\sin\omega t] \\ &= C\,e^{-t/\tau} + \frac{A}{\sqrt{1 + (\tau\omega^2)}}\,[\cos(\omega t - \psi)], \end{aligned}$$

where

$$\psi = \tan^{-1}\tau\omega.$$

C is obtained from a knowledge of an initial condition which is, typically,

$$v = v_0 \qquad \text{when} \qquad t = 0.$$

Thus,

$$C = v_0 - \frac{A}{\sqrt{1 + (\tau\omega)^2}}\cos\psi.$$

Therefore,

$$\nu = \left(\nu_0 - \frac{A \cos \psi}{\sqrt{1 + (\tau\omega)^2}}\right) e^{-t/\tau} + \frac{A}{\sqrt{1 + (\tau\omega)^2}} \cos (\omega t - \psi).$$

The steady-state solution is frequently of greatest interest;

$$\nu_{ss} = \frac{A}{\sqrt{1 + (\tau\omega)^2}} \cos (\omega t - \psi).$$

This response is a sinusoidal function of the same frequency but of different amplitude than the forcing, and is shifted phasewise from it.

The ratio of the amplitude of the output to that of the input is

$$\frac{|\nu_{ss}|}{A} = \frac{1}{\sqrt{1 + (\tau\omega)^2}}.$$

This is frequently denoted as the *dynamic amplitude ratio*, *DAR*. The phase difference between the steady-state response and forcing is ψ, defined as the *dynamic response angle*, *DRA*. Taken together, these properties are referred to as the frequency response of the system. Figure 4.8 shows *DAR* and *DRA* information for a first-

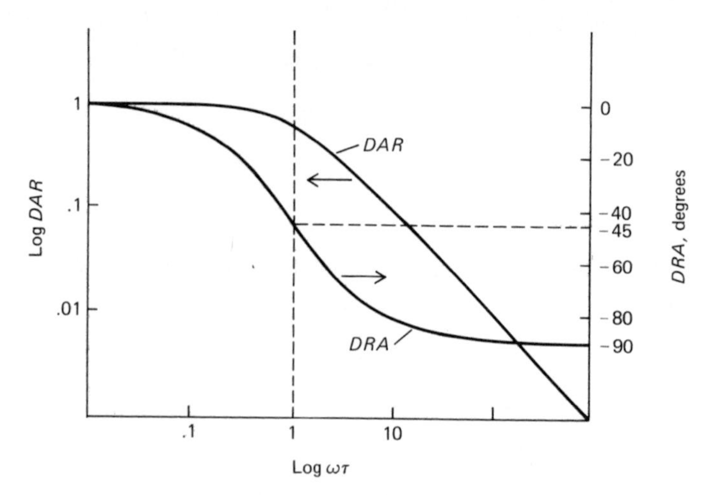

Figure 4.8. Frequency response of a first-order system.

order system with log DAR and DRA, in degrees, plotted versus $\tau\omega$ on a log scale.

It should be noted that, on such a plot where the scale of both logarithmic coordinates are equal, the DAR relation approaches a straight line with a slope of -1 as $\tau\omega$ increases. Furthermore, at high frequency where $\tau\omega \gg 1$,

$$\log DAR = \log \frac{1}{\sqrt{1 + (\tau\omega)^2}} \approx \log \frac{1}{\tau\omega} \approx - \log \tau\, \omega.$$

If this straight-line relationship is extrapolated back to $DAR = 1$ or to where $\log DAR = 0$, at this point $\tau\omega = 1$ or $\tau = 1/\omega$. Also, since $\psi = \tan^{-1} \omega\tau$, where $\omega\tau = 1$, $\psi = -45^\circ$.

A frequency response with these properties is characteristic of first-order linear systems.

It is instructive to consider one more forcing, using the alternate form for the cosine function,

$$A \cos \omega t = A \frac{e^{j\omega t} + e^{-j\omega t}}{2}.$$

Since $e^{j\omega t}$ can be considered as a unit vector rotating about the origin in a counterclockwise (positive) manner and $e^{-j\omega t}$ as a unit vector rotating clockwise, the situation at any given value of the argument, ωt, is illustrated in Figure 4.9. Since the imaginary parts

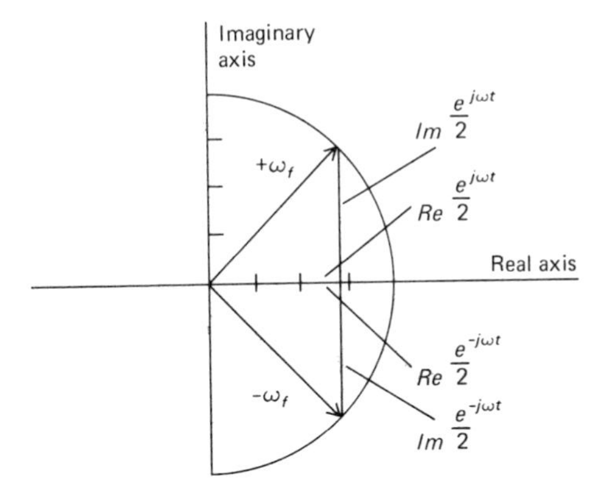

Figure 4.9. Real and imaginary components of the exponential form of the cosine function.

always cancel, the forcing turns out to be 2A $\text{Re}(e^{-j\omega t}/2)$ = 2A $\text{Re}(e^{-j\omega t}/2) = A\ e^{j\omega t}$, the latter being understood to imply the real part.

The *steady-state* solution is assumed to be of the same form as the forcing

$$v_{ss} = G\ A\ e^{j\omega t} \qquad \text{where} \qquad G \text{ may be complex.}$$

Then $dv_{ss}/dt = G\ A\ j\omega e^{j\omega t}$ and $\tau\ G\ A\ \omega j\ e^{j\omega t} + G\ A\ e^{j\omega t} = A\ e^{j\omega t}$. Thus,

$$G = \frac{1}{1 + j\omega\tau} = \frac{e^{-j\psi}}{\sqrt{1 + (\omega\tau)^2}}$$

where

$$\psi = \tan^{-1}\ (\omega\tau).$$

The *steady state* solution then becomes

$$v_{ss} = \frac{e^{-j\psi}}{\sqrt{1 + (\omega\tau)^2}}\ A\ e^{j\omega t} = \frac{A\ e^{j(\omega t - \psi)}}{\sqrt{1 + (\omega\tau)^2}}.$$

This is recognized as

$$\frac{2A\ \text{Re}}{\sqrt{1 + (\omega\tau)^2}}\ \frac{e^{j(\omega t - \psi)}}{2}$$

which is

$$\frac{A\ \cos\ (\omega t - \psi)}{\sqrt{1 + (\omega\tau)^2}},$$

identical with the solution previously derived for the *steady state* response to the forcing $A\ \cos\ \omega t$.

In exponential form, the steady state solution at a given frequency can be considered the sum of two vectors each of length $A/[\sqrt{1 + (\omega\tau)^2}]$, one at an angle of $(\omega t - \psi)$ and the other $-(\omega t - \psi)$. As with the input, the imaginary parts cancel so that the result is the sum of the real parts or

$$2 \text{ Re } \frac{A}{\sqrt{1+(\omega\tau)^2}} \frac{e^{j(\omega t-\psi)}}{2} = \frac{A}{\sqrt{1+(\omega\tau)^2}} e^{j(\omega t-\psi)}.$$

It is clear that, as previously,

$$DAR = \frac{1}{\sqrt{1+(\omega\tau)^2}} \text{ and } DRA = -\tan^{-1}(\omega\tau).$$

The differential equations mentioned above have all been of the form

$$\tau \frac{dv}{df} + v = f(u)$$

where $f(u)$ is the forcing function. If the differential operator p is defined such that $d/dt = p$ and $dv/dt = pv$ then

$$\tau\, pv + v = f(u)$$

or

$$v = \frac{f(u)}{1+\tau p}.$$

This relationship may be represented in block diagram form as in Figure 4.10. This states that the output v is to be obtained by

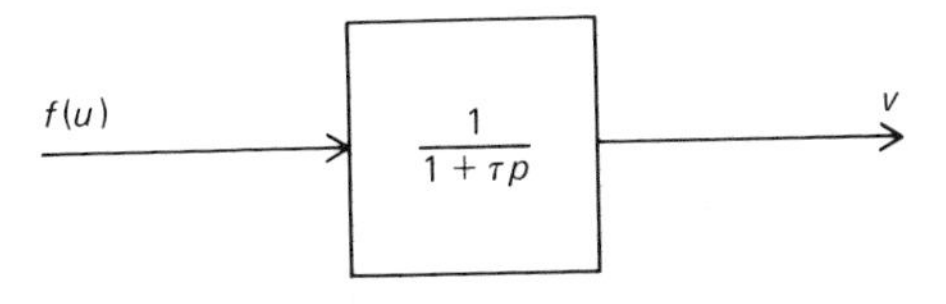

Figure 4.10. Block diagram representation of a first-order system.

multiplying the forcing function (input) by $1/(1+p\tau)$, the operator p being such that this is valid. Assuming for the moment that this is true, by analogy any ordinary linear differential equation with constant coefficients could be thus represented. For example, if

$$a_n \frac{d^n v}{dt^n} + a_{n-1} \frac{d^{n-1} v}{dt^{n-1}} + \ldots + a_o v = b_o u + b_1 \frac{du}{dt} + \cdots + b_m \frac{d^m u}{dt^m} \tag{4.18}$$

then

$$\frac{v}{u} = \frac{b_m p^m + b_{m-1} p^{m-1} + \ldots + b_o}{a_n p^n + a_{n-1} p^{n-1} + \ldots + a_o}$$

The block diagram form representation is shown in Figure 4.11.

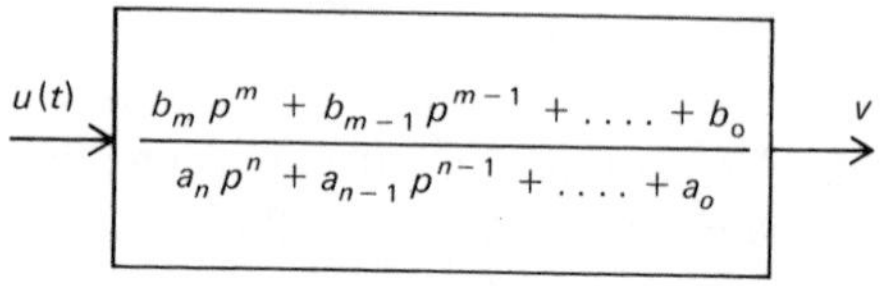

Figure 4.11. Block diagram representation of an nth order system being forced with function consisting of the sum of an independent variable and m of its derivatives.

Whether this kind of representation is valid depends upon the significance of the operator p and the nature of the input and output. The possibility and usefulness of such a concept is merely pointed out at this time.

Because ordinary differential equations are frequently involved when a physical problem is formulated in mathematical terms, attention will be devoted to these. The major concern will be with *linear ordinary differential equations*, further restricted, for the most part, to *ordinary linear differential equations with constant coefficients.* The significance of these restrictions will become obvious later.

It is important to realize that the mathematics associated with these linear differential equations is relatively simple and restricted. Nonetheless, a thorough understanding of only this small segment of mathematics and associated techniques will enable one to observe a pattern in the response of physical systems, and, if this is accomplished, a real 'feel' for process dynamics can be acquired. An engineer's perspective and intuition can be greatly augmented, and his usefulness should thus be considerably increased if he has this knowledge.

It will have been observed in the last examples that three variables are involved, v, u, and t. It is customary to let v represent the **dependent variable** and u the **independent variable**; t is called the running variable. In physical situations, the running variable is usually time, thus the symbol t. The a's and b's in the above differential equation are the *coefficients.*

A usual requirement is to find the response of the system described by the left-hand terms (dependent variable side) as a function of time when the system is forced in the manner described by the right-hand side (independent variable side). The variation of the independent variable with time must be fully specified.

Equation 4.18 is called an *ordinary* differential equation since none of the indicated derivatives are partial. It is a *linear* equation if the following hold true.

(1) The dependent variable, v, and such of its derivatives are of *first degree.*

(2) No products of v and any of its derivatives are present in the equation.

(3) There are no products of derivatives of v.

(4) The above conditions also exist for the independent variable, u.

(5) There are no products between the derivatives of v or u.

(6) The coefficients may be functions of the running variable, t, but they cannot be functions of either v or u.

The *order* of a differential equation, such as (4.18), is determined by the highest derivative; thus, (4.18) is of nth order in the dependent variable and mth order in the independent variable.

The left-hand side of the equation is normally associated with the physical system under consideration. The independent variable, u, describes the *forcing* variable or disturbance entering or acting on the system. In the most general case, the system may be forced not only by the independent variable but by derivatives and integrals of it as well. The right-hand side then becomes the *input forcing function.*

A system designer may be faced with one or all of the following four types of problems.

(1) *The direct analysis problem.* Here the differential equation

describing the physical system is known, the forcing function is also known, and the initial conditions of the system and forcing function are specified. The problem is to find or infer the *response* of the system as a function of time.

(2) *The inverse analysis problem.* The differential equation of the system is known as well as its response as a function of time. The problem is to find what the forcing function is and the initial conditions.

(3) *The performance function analysis problem.* The input forcing function and the response or output function are known, perhaps only as experimental data. It is required to find the performance function (or mathematical form) describing the system which is associated with the particular input and output function. (This is a very common practical problem.)

(4) *The design problem.* Here it is required to determine the characteristics a system must have in order that the response of the system to a specified input forcing function falls within given tolerance limits.

Solutions to ordinary differential equations may be obtained in the following ways.

(1) Guess a solution that satisfies the equation.

(2) Make changes in the variables, and use recognized identities which break the equation into integrals which are known or may be found in tables. (This method includes operational techniques.)

(3) Graphically.

(4) Numerical methods (includes digital machines).

(5) Mechanical differential analyzers.

(6) Electronic computers.

(7) Combinations of all above methods.

There are popular misconceptions concerning the classical methods of obtaining solutions to ordinary differential equations. Among these are the following.

(1) All ordinary differential equations have solutions.

(2) The analytical solution shows all sorts of things of value concerning the variables, these being easily apparent by inspection of the solution.

(3) In the closed solution form (answers which may be expressed in terms of standard mathematical functions), almost everything cancels out at the end, leaving a relatively simple expression.

In answer to 1, it only needs to be stated that only a finite number of mathematical forms are integrable while an infinite number are not. Thus, the probability of being able to solve a differential equation, *written at random,* is zero.

As for item 2, it is generally true that the differential equation tells more about the physical system and its behavior than does the solution. As for 3, some closed forms become quite complicated, making it very difficult to visualize the behavior of the dependent variable in response to changes in the dependent variable.

5
Second-Order Systems

Solutions to higher order linear differential equations with constant coefficients may be obtained by procedures analogous to those used with first-order equations. These will be illustrated by reference to the familiar idealized spring-mass-dashpot system shown schematically in Figure 5.1.

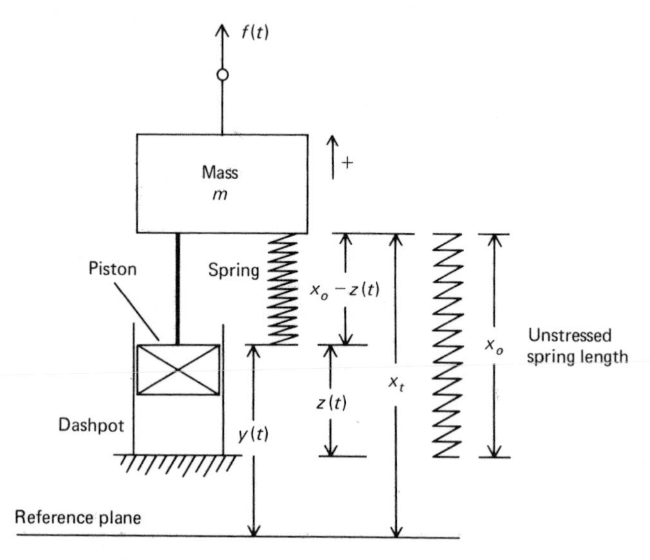

Figure 5.1. Mass-spring-dashpot system.

5.1 SYSTEMS EQUATIONS

With respect to the reference level, the following are defined:

$z(t)$ = net compression of spring at any time, t

$$x(t) = y(t) + x_0 - z(t) \text{ or}$$
$$z(t) = y(t) - x(t) + x_0.$$

The objective is to derive the relation between the position of the mass $x(t)$ at any time as both the force, $f(t)$, and position of the lower extremity of the spring, $y(t)$, vary. In this example, $x(t)$ is the output or dependent variable, and $f(t)$ and $y(t)$ are the independent variables or inputs. A simplified block diagram would appear as in Figure 5.2.

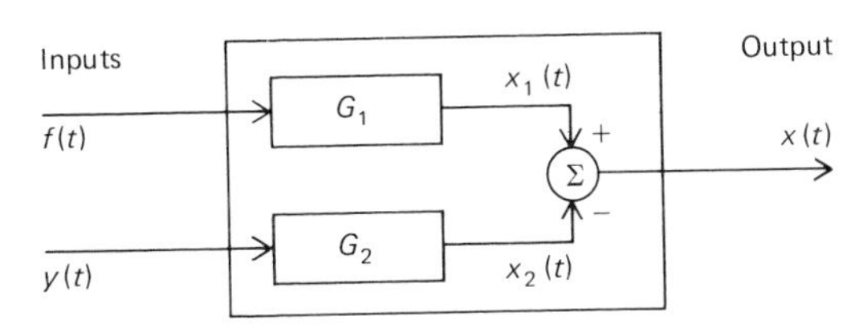

Figure 5.2. Block diagram of mass-spring-dashpot system.

The two internal blocks are shown to indicate that the relation between the input-output pairs, $[x_1(t)]/[f(t)]$ and $[x_2(t)]/[y(t)]$, may be different and that they add to give the combined output $x(t)$, the displacement.

Assuming the validity of Newton's laws of motion, that the spring obeys Hooke's law and that the dashpot imparts viscous damping, the following relationships may be written (for convenience, assume that the supporting spring is under compression and that $f(t)$ is positive and upward).

Downward forces:

(1) Resistance offered by dashpot, $D\, dx/dt$, where D is the damping coefficient of the dashpot.

(2) Gravitational force, mg.

Upward forces:

(1) Force applied to mass from above, $f(t)$.

(2) Force applied from below by the spring under compression = $kz(t) = k[y(t) - x(t) + x_0]$.

The difference between upward and downward forces will be available to give the mass acceleration or to change the momentum of the mass.

$$\Sigma F = \frac{d(mv)}{dt} = m\frac{dv}{dt} = m\frac{d^2 x(t)}{dt^2},$$

provided the mass remains constant. Therefore,

$$m \frac{d^2 x(t)}{dt^2} = \Sigma F_{\text{up}} - \Sigma F_{\text{down}}$$

or

$$m \frac{d^2 x(t)}{dt^2} = f(t) + k[y(t) - x(t) + x_0] - D \frac{dx}{dt} - mg.$$

After rearranging and letting $x = x(t)$

$$m \frac{d^2 x}{dt^2} + D \frac{dx}{dt} + kx = f(t) + ky(t) + kx_0 - mg.$$

In standard form (with the coefficient of x unity),

$$\frac{m}{k} \frac{d^2 x}{dt^2} + \frac{D}{k} \frac{dx}{dt} + x = \frac{f(t)}{k} + y(t) + \left(x_0 - \frac{mg}{k} \right). \qquad (5.1)$$

Note that the forcing function now appears to consist of three parts, $f(t)/k$, $y(t)$, and $(x_0 - mg/k)$, the first two being arbitrary functions of time and the third a constant, $(x_0 - mg/k)$. The latter term is the displacement of the mass at equilibrium with $f(t)$ and $y(t)$ equal to zero. If a new measure of length is chosen such that $X = x - (x_0 - mg/k)$, the equation becomes

$$\frac{m}{k} \frac{d^2 X}{dt^2} + \frac{D}{k} \frac{dX}{dt} + X = \frac{f(t)}{k} + y(t), \qquad (5.2)$$

where X is the displacement of the mass at rest relative to the position occupied when $y(t) = 0$ and $f(t) = 0$. The forcing function now appears as the sum of two independent time-varying forcings. X may be called the deviation variable from which x may be found since $x = X + (x_0 - mg/k)$.

The solution to the differential equation in X consists of two parts: (1) the transient solution, X_{tr}, and (2) the steady state solution, X_{ss}.

The *form* of the transient solution is found as the solution to the homogeneous equation, while the steady-state solution satisfies the forced equation.

(1) For the transient, where X_{tr} is the transient solution component,

$$\frac{m}{k}\ddot{X}_{tr} + \frac{D}{k}\dot{X}_{tr} + X_{tr} = 0. \tag{5.3}$$

(2) For the forced equation, where X_{ss} is the steady-state solution component,

$$\frac{m}{k}\ddot{X}_{ss} + \frac{D}{k}\dot{X}_{ss} + X_{ss} = \frac{f(t)}{k} + y(t). \tag{5.4}$$

Transient Solution Past observation has indicated that the exponential is a good choice for the *form* of the transient solution. Thus, assume $X_{tr} = Ae^{pt}$. Accordingly $\dot{X}_{tr} = Ape^{pt}$ and $\ddot{X}_{tr} = Ap^2e^{pt}$. Substitution into the homogeneous equation gives

$$\frac{m}{k}Ap^2e^{pt} + \frac{D}{k}Ape^{pt} + Ae^{pt} = 0,$$

or

$$Ae^{pt}\left[\frac{m}{k}p^2 + \frac{D}{k}p + 1\right] = 0.$$

Since Ae^{pt} is, in general, never zero, it follows that

$$\frac{m}{k}p^2 + \frac{D}{k}p + 1 = 0,$$

or

$$p_1, p_2 = \frac{-\dfrac{D}{k} \pm \sqrt{\left(\dfrac{D}{k}\right)^2 - \dfrac{4m}{k}}}{(2m/k)} = -\frac{D}{2m} \pm \sqrt{\left(\frac{D}{2m}\right)^2 - \frac{k}{m}}. \tag{5.5}$$

The transient solution must accommodate both possibilities, hence its form becomes

$$X_{tr} = A_1e^{p_1t} + A_2e^{p_2t}, \tag{5.6}$$

where

$$p_1 = -\frac{D}{2m} + \sqrt{\frac{D^2}{4m} - \frac{k}{m}} \tag{5.7}$$

and

$$p_2 = -\frac{D}{2m} - \sqrt{\frac{D^2}{4m} - \frac{k}{m}}\,. \tag{5.8}$$

Notice that the values of p_1 and p_2 depend upon the system parameters, D, m and k. The *fitting contants*, A_1 and A_2, cannot be evaluated without a knowledge of the forcing function and information about the system.

It is important to note that, if the sign of p_1 and p_2 are both negative, a decaying type of transient response is obtained. If the exponential possessed a positive sign, the transient solution would continue to increase with time. Such a solution is called an unstable solution since it describes a physical situation where a variable increases without limit. Whether stability or instability exists is dependent upon the combination of physical parameters of a system. This will be illustrated at a later point.

Forced Solution Next consider the forced solution resulting from the forcing function $[f(t)]/k + y(t)$. Both of these functions, being some function of time, are similar. Little is to be gained by considering them together. In any event, if both are active, solutions to each can be found and the solutions added to give the response to the combination of forcings.

To illustrate the method of finding a forced solution, let $f(t) = 0$ and choose sinusoidal forcing for $y(t)$ such that

$$y(t) = Y \cos \omega t = Y\left[\frac{e^{j\omega t} + e^{-j\omega t}}{2}\right] = Y\,e^{j\omega t} \tag{5.9}$$

where the latter term is meant to indicate the real part of $Y\,e^{j\omega t}$.

Again, the steady state solution is assumed to be of the same form as the forcing; i.e.,

$$X_{ss} = GY\,e^{j\omega t},$$

so that

$$\dot{X} = GYj\omega\, e^{j\omega t}$$

and

$$\ddot{X} = GY(j\omega)^2\, e^{j\omega t}.$$

Substitution in the differential equation gives

$$\frac{m}{k} GY(j\omega)^2\, e^{j\omega t} + \frac{D}{k}\, GYj\omega\, e^{j\omega t} + GY\, e^{j\omega t} = Y\, e^{j\omega t}$$

or

$$\frac{m}{k} G(j\omega)^2 + \frac{D}{k} Gj\omega + G = 1.$$

It follows that

$$G = \frac{1}{\dfrac{m}{k}(j\omega)^2 + \dfrac{D}{k}\, j\omega + 1}$$

$$= \frac{1}{\left(1 - \dfrac{m}{k}\,\omega^2\right) + \dfrac{D}{k}\, j\omega}. \qquad (5.10)$$

This may be written in two different forms:

$$G = \frac{e^{-j\theta}}{\sqrt{\left(1 - \dfrac{m\omega^2}{k}\right)^2 + \left(\dfrac{D}{k}\,\omega\right)^2}}$$

or

$$G = \frac{1}{\sqrt{\left(1 - \dfrac{m\omega^2}{k}\right)^2 + \left(\dfrac{D}{k}\,\omega\right)^2}}, \angle{-\theta} \qquad (5.11)$$

where

$$\tan^{-1}\theta = \frac{\frac{D\omega}{k}}{\left(1 - \frac{m\omega^2}{k}\right)}$$

and $\angle -\theta$ implies "angle of minus θ."

The steady state response becomes

$$X_{ss} = \frac{Y\,e^{j(\omega t-\theta)}}{\sqrt{\left(1 - \frac{m\omega^2}{k}\right)^2 + \left(\frac{D\omega}{k}\right)^2}} = \frac{Y\cos(\omega t - \theta)}{\sqrt{\left(1 - \frac{m\omega^2}{k}\right)^2 + \left(\frac{D\omega}{k}\right)^2}} \; . \tag{5.12}$$

5.2 DAR/DRA

The *dynamic amplitude ratio* is defined as $|X_{ss}/Y \cos \omega t| = |X_{ss}/Y\,e^{j\omega t}|$;

$$DAR \equiv |G| = \frac{1}{\sqrt{\left(1 - \frac{m\omega^2}{k}\right)^2 + \left(\frac{D\omega}{k}\right)^2}}, \tag{5.13}$$

and the *dynamic response angle* is defined;

$$DRA = \angle -\theta = -\tan^{-1}\frac{\left(\frac{D\omega}{k}\right)}{\left(1 - \frac{m\omega^2}{k}\right)} \; . \tag{5.14}$$

Returning to the differential equation,

$$\frac{m}{k}\ddot{X} + \frac{D}{k}\dot{X} + X = y(t),$$

let the operator s denote $\frac{d}{dt}$ and s^2 denote $\frac{d^2}{dt^2}$. Then the equation may be written

$$\frac{m}{k} s^2 X + \frac{D}{k} sX + X = y(t)$$

or

$$\frac{X}{y(t)} = \frac{1}{\frac{m}{k} s^2 + \frac{D}{k} s + 1} .$$

Note that if $s = j\omega$, then

$$\frac{X}{y(t)} = \frac{1}{\frac{m}{k} (j\omega)^2 + \frac{D}{k} (j\omega) + 1} = \frac{1}{\left(1 - \frac{m\omega^2}{k}\right) + j \frac{D}{k} \omega}$$

$$= \frac{1}{\sqrt{\left(1 - \frac{m\omega^2}{k}\right)^2 + \left(\frac{D\omega}{k}\right)^2}} \quad e^{-j\theta} = DAR, \ \underline{/DRA} \tag{5.15}$$

This result is the same as that obtained for the steady-state solution with sinusoidal forcing. Thus it appears that, to obtain the steady-state response to sinusoidal forcing, designated as the dynamic amplitude ratio and dynamic response angle, the differential operator (defined as s, above) is replaced by $j\omega$.

A convenient and popular form of the second order ordinary linear differential equation with constant coefficients is

$$\frac{1}{\omega_n{}^2} \frac{d^2 x}{dt^2} + \frac{2\xi}{\omega_n} \frac{dx}{dt} + x = f(t) \tag{5.16}$$

where ω_n is called the undamped natural angular frequency and ξ is the damping coefficient. The form of the transient solution, as previously shown, is

$$X_{tr} = A_1 \, e^{p_1 t} + A_2 \, e^{p_2 t},$$

where, if $\xi > 1$,

$$p_1, p_2 = -\frac{\dfrac{2\xi}{\omega_n} \pm \sqrt{\left(\dfrac{2\xi}{\omega_n}\right)^2 - \dfrac{4}{\omega_n^{\,2}}}}{\left(\dfrac{2}{\omega_n^{\,2}}\right)} = -\xi\omega_n \pm \omega_n\sqrt{\xi^2 - 1} \tag{5.17}$$

or if $\xi < 1$.

$$p_1, p_2 = -\xi\omega_n \pm j\omega_n\sqrt{1 - \xi^2}\,. \tag{5.18}$$

The choice of expression for p_1, p_2 depends upon the value of the radical.

In terms of the mass-dashpot-spring system, the parameters are

$$\frac{m}{k} = \frac{1}{\omega_n^{\,2}} \quad \text{or} \quad \omega_n = \sqrt{\frac{k}{m}} \quad \text{and} \quad \frac{D}{k} = \frac{2\xi}{\omega_n} \quad \text{so that}$$

$$\xi = \frac{D}{2k}\,\omega_n = \frac{D}{2k}\sqrt{\frac{k}{m}} = \sqrt{\frac{D^2}{4mk}}\,.$$

Notice that ω_n depends only upon the ratio of mass to spring constant but that ξ is a function of D (the dashpot damping coefficient) as well.

If, for the spring-dashpot-mass system, the dashpot were removed (i.e., $D = 0$) and if the mass were initially displaced from some equilibrium position and released, motion in subsequent time would be described by the equation

$$\frac{1}{\omega_n^{\,2}}\frac{d^2X}{dt^2} + X = 0. \tag{5.19}$$

A solution can be found by inspection; $X_{tr} = A \sin \omega t$. Substitution into the homogeneous equation gives

$$-\frac{A\omega^2}{\omega_n^{\,2}} \sin \omega t + A \sin \omega t = 0,$$

or

$$A\left[1-\frac{\omega^2}{\omega_n{}^2}\right]\ \sin \omega t = 0. \tag{5.20}$$

For this result to be generally true requires that $\omega = \omega_n$ which indicates that the undamped second-order system will oscillate with frequency ω_n at constant amplitude. This is why ω_n is called the undamped natural angular frequency.

On the other hand, if the transient solution is assumed to be exponential *m* i.e., $X_{tr} = A\ e^{pt}$, then

$$\frac{Ap^2\ e^{pt}}{\omega_n{}^2} + A\ e^{pt} = 0 \quad \text{or} \quad p^2 = -\omega_n{}^2 \quad \text{or} \quad p = j\omega_n$$

and

$$X_{tr} = A\ e^{j\omega_n t} = A\ \cos \omega_n t = X_0\ \cos \omega_n t$$

which satisfies the equation when the initial value of X is X_0.

Sinusoidal Forcing A second-order system when forced sinusoidally will exhibit a dynamic amplitude ratio dependent upon system parameters–in particular upon the value of ξ, the damping coefficient. As inferred in Chapter 3, if the damping is small enough (value of ξ less than unity), the amplitude of the output could conceivably exceed that of the input. The value of forcing frequency at which the peak value of DAR occurs can be found by the usual method of finding maxima:

$$DAR = \left|\frac{1}{\dfrac{(j\omega)^2}{\omega_n{}^2} + \dfrac{2\xi}{\omega_n}(j\omega) + 1}\right| = \frac{1}{\sqrt{\left(1-\dfrac{\omega^2}{\omega_n{}^2}\right)^2 + \left(\dfrac{2\xi}{\omega_n}\omega\right)^2}}$$

$$= \frac{1}{[(1-\beta^2)^2 + (2\xi\beta)^2]^{1/2}}$$

where $\beta = \omega/\omega_n$.

$$\frac{d[DAR]}{d\beta} = \frac{4\beta^3 + 2(4\xi^2 - 2)\beta}{-2[(1-\beta^2)^2 + (2\xi\beta)^2]^{+3/2}}$$

Letting $\frac{d[DAR]}{d\beta} = 0$ gives

$$4\beta^3 + 2(4\xi^2 - 2)\beta = 0 \quad \text{or} \quad \beta^2 + 2\xi^2 - 1 = 0.$$

Thus $\beta = \frac{\omega}{\omega_n} = \sqrt{1 - 2\xi^2}$ and $\omega = \omega_n \sqrt{1 - 2\xi^2}$ at maximum DAR.

The maximum value of DAR becomes

$$[DAR]_{max} = \frac{1}{\{[1 - (1 - 2\xi^2)]^2 + (2\xi)^2 (1 - 2\xi^2)\}^{1/2}}$$

$$= \frac{1}{2\xi\sqrt{1 - \xi^2}}, \tag{5.21}$$

which occurs at the forcing frequency

$$\omega_p = \omega_n \sqrt{1 - 2\xi^2}. \tag{5.22}$$

In terms of β, $DRA = -\tan^{-1}[2\xi\beta/(1 - \beta^2)]$ so that when $\beta = \omega/\omega_n = 1$ the dynamic response angle is -90 degrees. When $2\xi^2 = 1$ or $\xi = \sqrt{1/2} = 0.706$, $\omega_p = \omega_n \sqrt{0}$. Also, when $\xi = 0.706$, $[DAR]_{max} = 1$.

That is, a second-order system with a damping coefficient of 0.706 or more will show no peak in the DAR.

Table 5.1 gives maximum values of DAR for various values of ξ.

TABLE 5.1 Maximum Values of Dynamic Amplitude Ratio for Various Values of Damping Coefficient for Second-Order Systems

ξ	$[DAR]_{max}$
0.3	1.75
0.4	1.37
0.5	1.16
0.6	1.04
0.7	1.00+

Figures 5.3 and 5.4 show the steady-state sinusoidal behavior of second-order systems with various values of the damping coefficient. For purposes of comparison, the response of a first-order system is also shown.

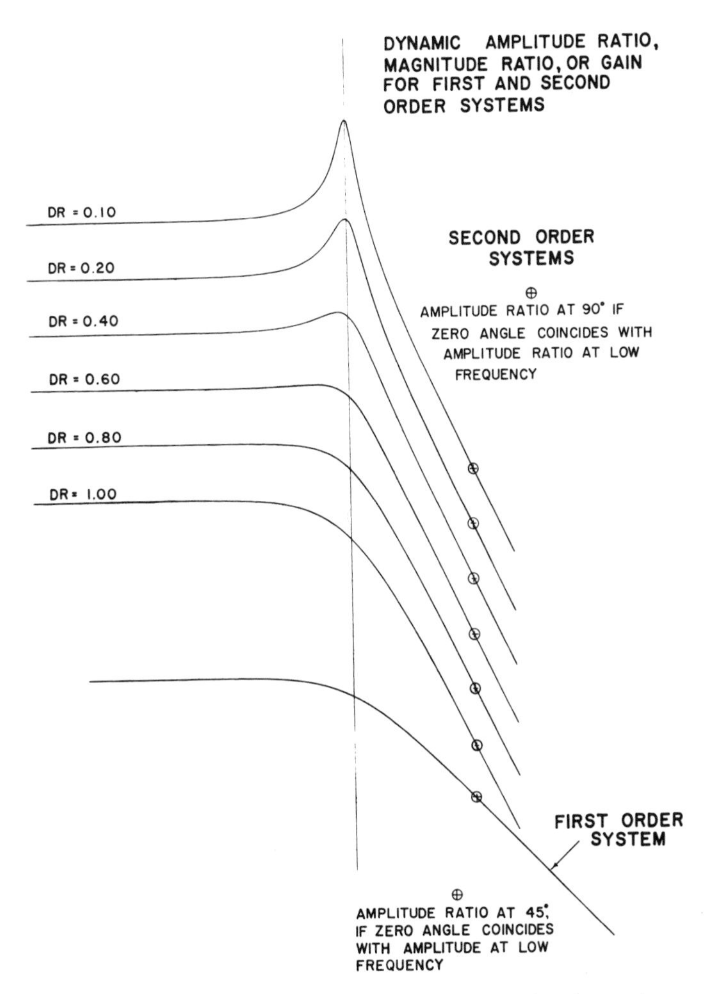

Figure 5.3. Dynamic amplitude ratio for second-order systems.

Step Forcing A standard second-order system forced with a positive step of magnitude B, is shown as

$$\frac{1}{\omega_n{}^2}\frac{d^2x}{dt^2} + \frac{2\xi}{\omega_n}\frac{dx}{dt} + x = B \tag{5.23}$$

The complete solution will be composed of a steady-state component and a transient component

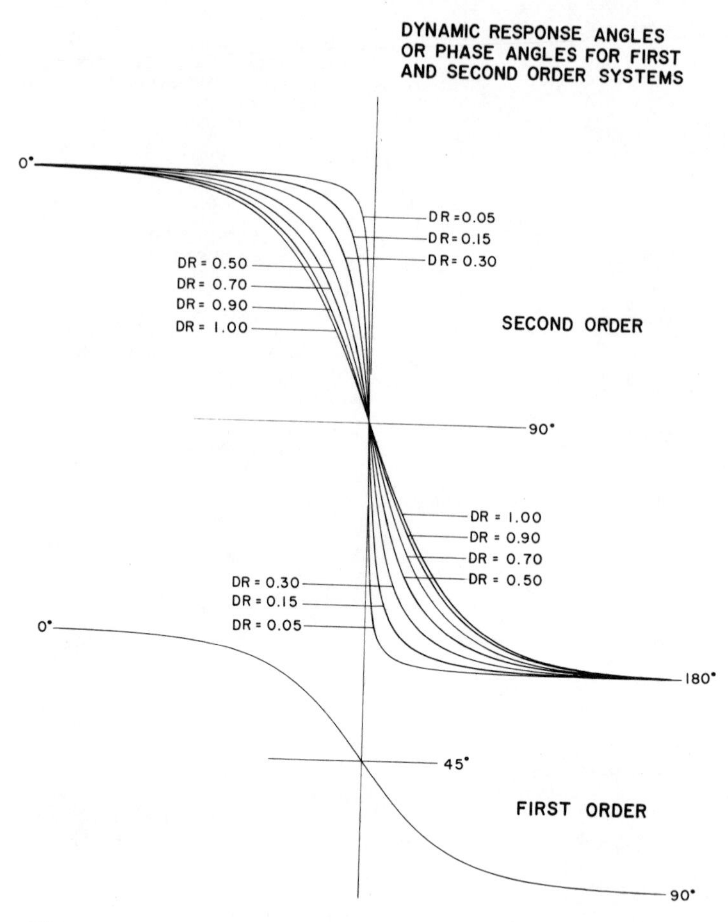

Figure 5.4. Dynamic response angles for second-order systems.

$$x_{ss} = B'.$$

and

$$\begin{aligned} x_{tr} &= C_1 \; e^{p_1 t} + C_2 \; e^{p_2 t} \\ &= C_1 \; e^{(-\xi \omega_n + j \omega_n \sqrt{1-\xi^2})t} + C_2 \; e^{(-\xi \omega_n - j \omega_n \sqrt{1-\xi^2})t}, \end{aligned} \tag{5.24}$$

for the case where $\xi < 1$.

When $t = 0$, let it be assumed that $x = 0$ and $dx/dt = 0$. Note also that, when $t = \infty$ at which time $dx/dt = 0$ and $d^2x/dt^2 = 0$, $x_{ss} = B$ or $B' = B$. The two initial conditions on x are sufficient to determine C_1 and C_2:

(1) $x = 0$, when $t = 0$

$$\text{therefore } 0 = C_1 + C_2 + B \quad \text{or} \quad C_1 = -(B + C_2)$$

(2) $dx/dt = 0$, when $t = 0$

$$\begin{aligned} 0 &= (-\xi\omega_n + j\omega_n\sqrt{1-\xi^2})\,C_1 \\ &\quad + (-\xi\omega - j\omega_n\sqrt{1-\xi^2})\,C_2 \\ &= -(B + C_2)(-\xi\omega_n + j\omega_n\sqrt{1-\xi^2}) \\ &\quad + (-\xi\omega_n - j\omega_n\sqrt{1-\xi^2})\,C_2 = 0 \end{aligned}$$

$$(B + C_2)(-\xi + j\sqrt{1-\xi^2}) + (\xi + j\sqrt{1-\xi^2})\,C_2 = 0$$

$$-B\xi + jB\sqrt{1-\xi^2} - C_2\xi + jC_2\sqrt{1-\xi^2} + C_2\xi + jC_2\sqrt{1-\xi^2} = 0$$

$$2jC_2\sqrt{1-\xi^2} = B\xi - jB\sqrt{1-\xi^2}$$

$$C_2 = \frac{B(\xi - j\sqrt{1-\xi^2})}{2j\sqrt{1-\xi^2}}$$

$$C_2 = \frac{B}{2}\left[\frac{\xi}{j\sqrt{1-\xi^2}} - 1\right] = \frac{B}{2}\left[\frac{j\xi}{-\sqrt{1-\xi^2}} - 1\right]$$

$$C_2 = -\frac{B}{2}\left[1 + j\frac{\xi}{\sqrt{1-\xi^2}}\right] \tag{5.25}$$

$$\begin{aligned} C_1 &= -(B + C_2) = -\left[B - \frac{B}{2}\left(1 + j\frac{\xi}{\sqrt{1-\xi^2}}\right)\right] \\ &= -\left[B - \frac{B}{2} - \frac{jB\xi}{2\sqrt{1-\xi^2}}\right] = -\left[\frac{B}{2} - \frac{jB\xi}{2\sqrt{1-\xi^2}}\right]. \\ &= -\frac{B}{2}\left[1 - \frac{j\xi}{\sqrt{1-\xi^2}}\right]. \end{aligned} \tag{5.26}$$

Thus C_1 and C_2 are complex conjugates.

The total solution then becomes

$$
\begin{aligned}
x &= -\frac{B}{2}\left[1 - \frac{j\xi}{\sqrt{1-\xi^2}}\right] e^{(-\xi\omega_n + j\omega_n\sqrt{1-\xi^2})\,t} \\
&\quad - \frac{B}{2}\left[1 + \frac{j\xi}{\sqrt{1-\xi^2}}\right] e^{(-\xi\omega_n - j\omega_n\sqrt{1-\xi^2})\,t} + B \\
&= -\frac{B}{2}\cdot\sqrt{1 + \left(\frac{\xi}{\sqrt{1-\xi^2}}\right)^2}\; e^{-j\theta}\; e^{(-\xi\omega_n + j\omega_n\sqrt{1-\xi^2})\,t} \\
&\quad - \frac{B}{2}\sqrt{1 + \left(\frac{\xi}{\sqrt{1-\xi^2}}\right)^2}\; e^{j\theta}\; e^{(-\xi\omega_n + j\omega_n\sqrt{1-\xi^2})\,t} + B \\
&= B - \frac{B}{2}\,\frac{1}{\sqrt{1-\xi^2}}\; e^{-\xi\omega_n t}\left[e^{j(\omega\sqrt{1-\xi^2}\,t-\theta)} + e^{-j(\omega_n\sqrt{1-\xi^2}\,t-\theta)}\right] \\
&= B\left\{1 - \frac{e^{-\xi\omega_n t}}{\sqrt{1-\xi^2}}\left[\cos\left(\omega_n\sqrt{1-\xi^2}\,t - \theta\right)\right]\right\}
\end{aligned}
\tag{5.27}
$$

where $\theta = \tan^{-1}\dfrac{\xi}{\sqrt{1-\xi^2}} = \sin^{-1}\xi = \cos^{-1}\sqrt{1-\xi^2}$.

Figure 5.5 shows time histories of the response to a unit step ($B = 1$) for various values of ξ. The frequency of oscillation of this transient response is $\omega_n\sqrt{1-\xi^2}$ and, as ξ approaches zero, the frequency approaches ω_n.

The peaks of the response are bounded by the exponential function, $(e^{-\xi\omega_n t})/\sqrt{1-\xi^2}$; maxima and minima may be found by evaluating the derivative of the response and equating to zero. Crossings of the forcing function, $f(t) = 1$, can be found by equating x to unity. The time to first crossing, t_1, and time to first peak, t_2, are frequently of interest.

The first peak is sometimes called overshoot; the ratio of one peak to the preceding peak, d_2/d_1, is called the decay ratio. The time required for the response to reach a specified deviation from the steady state and be contained therein, t_3, is denoted as the settling time. These characteristics are determined by the damping ratio and are illustrated for $\xi = 0.1$ in Figure 5.5.

A situation commonly encountered in industrial processes can be illustrated by two vessels through which a liquid flows in series under the influence of gravity. Figure 5.6 is illustrative.

The flow rate, F_2, from the second vessel depends on the level, h_2, in that vessel. The flow rate, F_{1-2}, from the first to the second

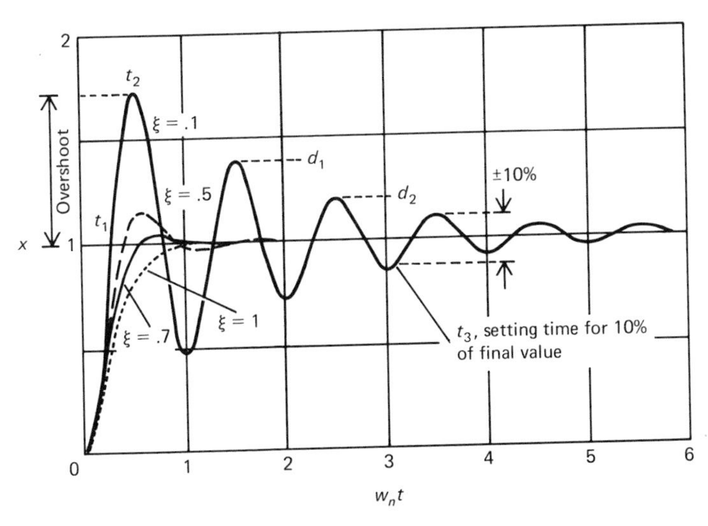

Figure 5.5. Time histories of the response of second-order systems with damping factors to a unit step input.

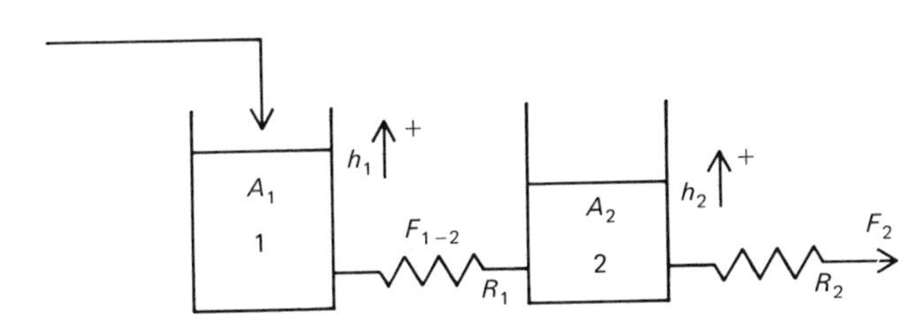

Figure 5.6. Two-tank system illustrating coupling.

vessel depends upon the difference in levels, $h_1 - h_2$. The two vessels are thus coupled through the interconnecting conduit.

Because the influent enters the first vessel, the effluent from that vessel can only proceed in one direction. It is never possible for the level in the second vessel to exceed that in the first.

If inertial effects in the fluid streams are neglected and if constant cross-sectional areas A_1 and A_2 for the vessels are assumed, the following relations may be written:

$$\left.\begin{aligned} F_1 - F_{1-2} &= A_1 \frac{dh_1}{dt}, \\ F_{1-2} - F_2 &= A_2 \frac{dh_2}{dt}. \end{aligned}\right\} \tag{5.28}$$

For convenience, assume flow rates in the conduits to be directly dependent upon the fluid head.

$$\left.\begin{aligned} F_{1-2} &= \frac{h_1 - h_2}{R_1} \quad \text{and} \\ F_2 &= \frac{h_2}{R_2}, \end{aligned}\right\} \tag{5.29}^*$$

where R_1 and R_2 are appropriate fluid resistances.

The variations in h_1 and h_2 in response to changes in F_1 or F_2 may be of interest, or it may be desirable to find the response in F_2 as F_1 changes. Another problem may be to determine how F_1 should be changed in order that levels h_1 and h_2 be retained within specified limits as F_2 is altered.

For convenience, assume that the differential operator notation is valid so that the describing differential equations may be written as follows:

$$\left.\begin{aligned} F_1 - F_{1-2} &= F_1 - \left(\frac{h_1 - h_2}{R_1}\right) = A_1 s h_1 \\ F_{1-2} - F_2 &= \left(\frac{h_1 - h_2}{R_1}\right) - \frac{h_2}{R_2} = A_2 s h_2 \end{aligned}\right\} \tag{5.30}$$

where $s \equiv d/dt$.

The block diagram corresponding to this physical system and set of equations is shown in Figure 5.7. The assumption is made that

*The assumptions of (5.29) linearize the problem. In actual practice, the validity of these relations should be established by experimental data.

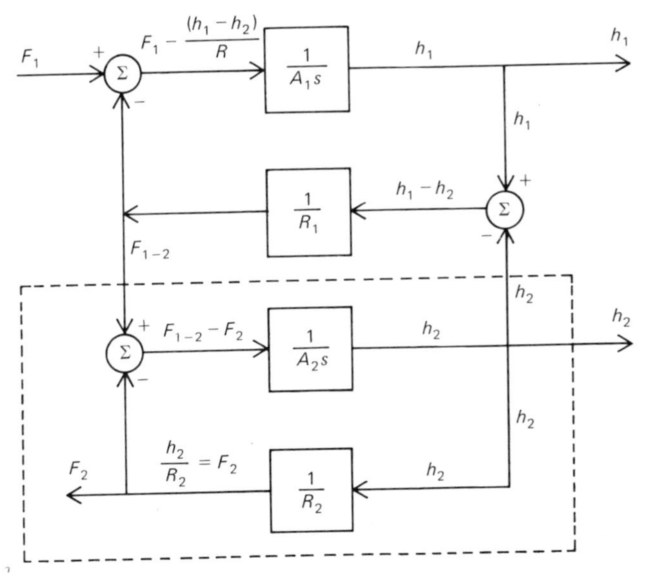

Figure 5.7. Block diagram for a coupled two-tank hydraulic system.

signals h_1 and h_2 are available; the blocks and flow of signals necessary to produce these signals are constructed.

The relation between h_2 and F_{1-2} may be derived by using the section of the diagram enclosed by dotted lines, (the output, F_2, is of no concern).

$$h_2 = \left(\frac{\dfrac{1}{A_2 s}}{1 + \dfrac{1}{A_2 R_2 s}} \right) F_{1-2}$$

$$= \left(\frac{R_2}{1 + A_2 R_2 s} \right) F_{1-2} = \left(\frac{R_2}{1 + \tau_2 s} \right) F_{1-2} \qquad (5.31)$$

where $\tau_2 \equiv A_2 R_2$ in time units, the characteristic time of this portion of the system.

If F_2 is the desired output, the relationship between F_2 and F_{1-2} is

$$F_2 = \left(\frac{\dfrac{1}{A_2 R_2 s}}{1 + \dfrac{1}{A_2 R_2 s}} \right) F_{1-2} = \left(\frac{1}{1 + A_2 R_2 s} \right) F_{1-2} = \left(\frac{1}{1 + \tau_2 s} \right) F_{1-2}. \tag{5.32}$$

If the first-order block representing the relationship between h_2 and F_{1-2} is substituted, the modified block diagram shown in Figure 5.8 is obtained.

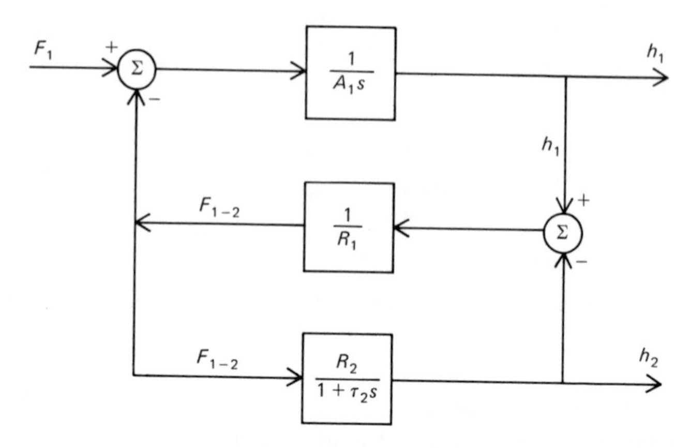

Figure 5.8. Modified block diagram for coupled two-tank hydraulic system.

Next, the relationship between h_2 and h_1 (referring to Figure 5.8) can be written as

$$\begin{aligned} h_2 &= \frac{\dfrac{1}{R_1}\left(\dfrac{R_2}{1+\tau_2 s} \right) h_1}{\left[1 + \dfrac{R_2}{R_1}\left(\dfrac{1}{1+\tau_2 s} \right) \right]} = \left(\frac{R_2}{R_1 + R_2} \right) \frac{h_1}{\left[1 + \left(\dfrac{R_1}{R_1 + R_2} \right) \tau_2 s \right]} \\ &= \left(\frac{R_2}{R_1 + R_2} \right) \frac{h_1}{(1 + \tau_3 s)} \end{aligned} \tag{5.33}$$

where $\tau_3 = \left(\dfrac{R_1}{R_1 + R_2} \right) \tau_2$. Also (referring to Figure 5.8),

$$F_{1-2} = \frac{\left(\frac{1}{R_1}\right) h_1}{1 + \left(\frac{1}{R_1}\right)\left(\frac{R_2}{1+\tau_2 s}\right)} = \left(\frac{1}{R_1+R_2}\right) \frac{(1+\tau_2 s)\, h_1}{\left[1 + \left(\frac{R_1}{R_1+R_2}\right)\tau_2 s\right]}. \tag{5.34}$$

Figure 5.9 may then be constructed so that the relationships between F_1 and either h_1 or h_2 can be readily derived.

$$h_1 = \frac{\left(\frac{1}{A_1 s}\right) F_1}{\left\{1 + \left(\frac{1}{A_1 s}\right)\left(\frac{1}{R_1+R_2}\right)\left[\frac{1+\tau_2 s}{1 + \left(\frac{R_1}{R_1+R_2}\right)\tau_2 s}\right]\right\}}$$

$$= \left[\frac{(R_1+R_2)\left[1 + \left(\frac{R_1}{R_1+R_2}\right)\tau_2 s\right]}{\tau_1 \tau_2{}^2 + (\tau_1 + \tau_2 + \tau_{1-2})\, s + 1}\right] F_1$$

$$= \frac{(R_1+R_2)\left[1 + \frac{\tau_1 \tau_2}{\tau_1 + \tau_{1-2}}\, s\right] F_1}{\tau_1 \tau_2 s^2 + (\tau_1 + \tau_2 + \tau_{1-2})\, s + 1}, \tag{5.35}$$

where

$$\tau_1 = A_1 R_1$$
$$\tau_2 = A_2 R_2$$
$$\tau_{1-2} = A_1 R_2\, .$$

Figure 5.9 shows that

$$h_2 = \left(\frac{R_2}{R_1+R_2}\right)\left[\frac{1}{1 + \left(\frac{R_1}{R_1+R_2}\right)\tau_2 s}\right] h_1$$

$$= \frac{R_2 F_1}{\tau_1 \tau_2 s^2 + (\tau_1 + \tau_{1-2} + \tau_2)\, s + 1}. \tag{5.36}$$

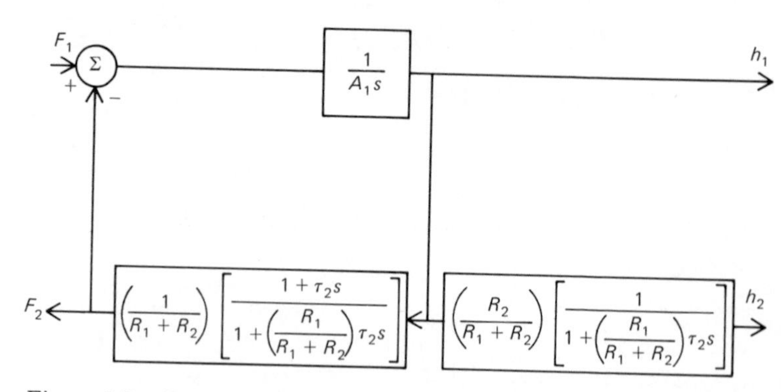

Figure 5.9. Fully modified block diagram for coupled two-tank hydraulic system.

Also

$$F_2 = \frac{\left(\frac{1}{A_1 s}\right)\left(\frac{1}{R_1 + R_2}\right)\left[\frac{1 + \tau_2 s}{1 + \left(\frac{R_1}{R_1 + R_2}\right)\tau_2 s}\right]}{1 + \left(\frac{1}{A_1 s}\right)\left(\frac{1}{R_1 + R_2}\right)\left[\frac{1 + \tau_2 s}{1 + \left(\frac{R_1}{R_1 + R_2}\right)\tau_2 s}\right]} F_1$$

$$= \frac{F_1}{\tau_1 \tau_2 s^2 + (\tau_1 + \tau_{1-2} + \tau_2)\, s + 1}. \tag{5.37}$$

If F_1 is assumed to be a step input at time zero, with the system in equilibrium, the steady-state values of the outputs are found by letting $s = 0$:

$$h_1 = (R_1 + R_2)\, F_1 \text{ from (5.35)},$$
$$h_2 = R_2 F_1 \text{ from (5.36)},$$
$$F_2 = F_1 \text{ from (5.37)}.$$

The denominators of each input-output pair are identical. Except for the relationship for h_1, the numerators are constants. For the h_1 relationship, a first-order component is present in the numerator.

The corresponding differential equations may be written by substituting d/dt for s, where F_1 may be a function of time:

$$\tau_1\tau_2\frac{d^2h_1}{dt^2}+(\tau_1+\tau_{1-2}+\tau_2)\frac{dh_1}{dt}+h_1=(R_1+R_2)F_1+R_1\tau_2\frac{dF_1}{dt}, \tag{5.38}$$

$$\tau_1\tau_2\frac{d^2h_2}{dt^2}+(\tau_1+\tau_{1-2}+\tau_2)\frac{dh_2}{dt}+h_2=R_2F_1 \tag{5.39}$$

and

$$\tau_1\tau_2\frac{d^2F_2}{dt^2}+(\tau_1+\tau_{1-2}+\tau_2)\frac{dF_2}{dt}+F_2=F_1. \tag{5.40}$$

When the coefficients are compared with the standard form of second-order system,

$$\frac{1}{\omega_n{}^2}=\tau_1\tau_2 \quad \text{or} \quad \omega_n=\sqrt{\frac{1}{\tau_1\tau_2}}=\sqrt{\frac{1}{(A_1R_1)(A_2R_2)}} \tag{5.41}$$

$$\frac{2\xi}{\omega_n}=(\tau_1+\tau_{1-2}+\tau_2)$$

and

$$\xi=\frac{A_1R_1+A_1R_2+A_2R_2}{2\sqrt{(A_1R_1)(A_2R_2)}}=\frac{1+\dfrac{R_2}{R_1}+\dfrac{A_2R_2}{A_1R_1}}{2\sqrt{\dfrac{A_2R_2}{A_1R_1}}}. \tag{5.42}$$

If $A_1=A_2$ and $R_1=R_2$, then

$$\xi=\frac{3}{2}.$$

If $A_1 = A_2$ and $R_1 \neq R_2$, then

$$\xi = \frac{1 + 2\dfrac{R_2}{R_1}}{2\sqrt{R_2/R_1}} \tag{5.43}$$

which can never be less than unity, as in the case when $R_1 = R_2$. Thus, as expected, this system never exhibits lightly damped characteristics.

6
Some Mathematical Apparata

6.1 INTRODUCTION

In the previous two chapters, solutions to first- and second-order ordinary linear differential equations were found by what is generally called the *classical* technique. In this method, the complete solution was seen to be the sum of the transient solution and the steady state or forced solution components. The *form* of each was derived separately with suitable fitting constants included.

As the order of the differential equation increases, developing solutions increases in difficulty, due especially to the need to determine the fitting constants with their dependence on boundary conditions. Many mathematicians have concerned themselves with the solution of differential equations. As a result, formal methods exist for coping with some of the classes of equations of interest to engineers. Among these are ordinary linear differential equations with constant coefficients. As a matter of fact, the techniques for handling equations of this kind are so well developed that they pose little challenge to mathematicians.

For the engineer, however, these techniques are of concern because many of the physical systems with which he works can be described reasonably well by differential equations of this kind.

The engineer desires to use mathematics as a tool (one of many) as a means of arriving at satisfactory solutions to problems. If simplification serves to yield an acceptable answer, he is satisfied, and rigor must be sacrificed for expediency on many occasions. For example, if linear behavior can be assumed, at least in restricted ranges in the values of the pertinent variables, the engineer should be willing to accept the assumption in the interest of procuring an estimate of the true solution with minimum investment. Refinements may be made later as the need arises.

6.2 LAPLACE TRANSFORM

In connection with the solution of ordinary, linear, differential equations with constant coefficients, *operational* methods are available which greatly simplify this task. The method discussed herein will be the *Laplace Transform* method.

One purpose which the Laplace transform approach accomplishes is to provide the basis for representing the response of linear systems as the multiplication of the forcing function (input function) by an operator function describing the system being forced; i.e.,

Output Function = Input Function × System Function.

Definition The Laplace transform of a function is defined by

$$f(s) = \int_0^\infty e^{-st} f(t)\, dt = L\,[f(t)]$$

where $s = a + j\omega$ and a, ω and t are real variables. Of course the integral must exist and converge which places certain restrictions on the method. The instances of invalidity in engineering practice appear to be very few.

Note that the function of t (usually time) is *transformed* into a function of s. This is to say that, for every function $f(t)$ which may be transformed, there corresponds a function $f(s)$. This is analogous to the correspondence between a real number and its logarithm or between an angle and its cosine.

The integration operation transforms a function of a real variable, t, into a function of the complex variable, $s = a + j\omega$. The use of the complex exponential kernel, e^{-st}, is a natural outgrowth of function representation by the complex exponential form of the Fourier series.

As normally used, functions in the t (usually time) domain are transformed to the s domain and then manipulated into recognizable forms or forms already existing in a set of tables. The functions in the time domain, corresponding to the s functions, can then be found and combined to yield the desired complete function in the t domain. This is indicated in Table 6-1.

TABLE 6.1

Function of t $f(t)$		Laplace Transform of $f(t)$ $f(s)$
1	$\longleftrightarrow$	$1/s$
A	$\longleftrightarrow$	A/s
$e^{-\alpha t}$	$\longleftrightarrow$	$1/(s+\alpha)$
$1/(\beta) \sin \beta t$	$\longleftrightarrow$	$1/(s^2+\beta^2)$
$\cos \beta t$	$\longleftrightarrow$	$s/(s^2+\beta^2)$
$\cosh \beta t$	$\longleftrightarrow$	$s/(s^2-\beta^2)$

Extensive tabulations of Laplace transforms of functions exist in the references cited as well as in standard handbooks. The derivation of several will be illustrated here and a limited tabulation given in the Appendix for convenience.

Operations In general, the inverse transformation for recovering the function $f(t)$ from the function $f(s)$ may be obtained by evaluating the integral

$$f(t) = \frac{1}{2\pi j} \int_{a-j\infty}^{a+j\infty} f(s) e^{st} ds.$$

Usually more direct methods will be used which will be illustrated later.

Direct transformations will be carried out for some common functions.

(1) $f(t) = A$, a constant.

$$L[A] = \int_0^\infty e^{-st} A dt = \left. \frac{Ae^{-st}}{-s} \right|_0^\infty = \frac{A}{s}.$$

Note that if $A = 1$ then $f(t) = 1$, usually defined as the unit step function, $u(t)$.

(2) $f(t) = e^{-\alpha t}$.

$$L\,[e^{-\alpha t}] = \int_0^\infty e^{-st}\, e^{-\alpha t}\, dt = \int_0^\infty e^{-(s+\alpha)t}$$

$$= \left.\frac{e^{-(s+\alpha)t}}{-\,(s+\alpha)}\right|_0^\infty = \frac{1}{s+\alpha}.$$

Note that if $\alpha = 0$ then $f(t) = 1$, and also note that $L\,[e^{-\alpha t}] = 1/s$ when $\alpha = 0$ in agreement with (1) above.

(3) $$f(t) = Ae^{-\alpha t}$$

$$L\,[Ae^{-\alpha t}] = \int_0^\infty e^{-st}\, Ae^{-\alpha t}\, dt = \frac{A}{s+\alpha}.$$

In general, $L\,[Af(t)] = A\,L\,[f(t)]$.

(4) $$f(t) = Ae^{-\alpha t} + Be^{-\beta t}$$

$$L\,[Ae^{-\alpha t} + Be^{-\beta t}] = \int_0^\infty e^{-st}\,[Ae^{-\alpha t} + Be^{-\beta t}]\, dt$$

$$= \frac{A}{\alpha+s} + \frac{B}{\beta+s}.$$

This is to say that $L\,[f_1(t) + f_2(t)] = f_1(s) + f_2(s)$.

(5) $$f(t) = \sin \beta t = \frac{e^{+j\beta t} - e^{-j\beta t}}{2j}$$

$$L\,[\sin \beta t] = \frac{1}{2j}\left(L\,[e^{j\beta t}] - L\,[e^{-j\beta t}]\right)$$

$$= \frac{1}{2j}\left(\frac{1}{s-j\beta} - \frac{1}{s+j\beta}\right) = \frac{1}{2j}\left[\frac{(s+j\beta)-(s-j\beta)}{s^2+\beta^2}\right]$$

$$= \frac{\beta}{s^2+\beta^2}.$$

(6)
$$f(t) = \cos \omega t = \frac{e^{j\omega t} + e^{-j\omega t}}{2}$$

$$L[\cos \omega t] = \frac{1}{2}[L(e^{j\omega t}) + L(e^{-j\omega t})]$$
$$= \frac{1}{2}\left[\frac{1}{s - j\omega} + \frac{1}{s + j\omega}\right] = \frac{s}{s^2 + \omega^2}.$$

Note that, if $t = 0$, $L[\cos \omega t] = 1/s$, the same as for a unit step, $u(t) = 1$.

(7)
Let $f(t) = t$
$$L[f(t)] = \int_0^\infty e^{-st}\, t\, dt.$$

Integrate by parts, making use of the fact that
$$\int u dv = uv - \int v du.$$

Let $u = t$ and $dv = e^{-st}\, dt$.
Then $du = dt$ and $v = e^{-st}/-s$.
Therefore,

$$\int e^{-st}\, t\, dt = \int u dv = \frac{t\, e^{-st}}{-s}\Bigg|_0^\infty - \int_0^\infty \left(\frac{e^{-st}}{-s}\right) dt$$
$$= 0 - \frac{e^{-st}}{s^2}\Bigg|_0^\infty = \frac{1}{s^2}.$$

(8)
$$f(t) = t^2.$$
$$L[f(t)] = \int_0^\infty e^{-st}\, t^2\, dt.$$

Again, integrate by parts letting $u = t^2$ and $dv = e^{-st}\, dt$. Therefore, $du = 2t\, dt$ and $v = \int e^{-st}\, dt$ and

$$L[t^2] = t^2 \int_0^\infty e^{-st}\,dt \Big|_0^\infty - \int_0^\infty \left[\int e^{-st}\,dt\right] 2t\,dt$$

$$= \frac{t^2 e^{-st}}{-s}\Big|_0^\infty - \int_0^\infty \left(\frac{e^{-st}}{-s}\right) 2t\,dt,$$

$$= 0 + \frac{2}{s}\int_0^\infty e^{-st}\,t\,dt = \frac{2}{s^3}. \quad \text{[See (7) above.]}$$

By repeating the procedure, it will be observed that

$$L[t^n] = \frac{n!}{s^{n+1}}.$$

(9) First derivative.

Evaluate $\int_0^\infty e^{-st}\left[\frac{d\,f(t)}{dt}\right] dt.$

Let $u = e^{-st}$ and $dv = [d\,f(t)]/[dt]\;dt$; therefore, $du = -se^{-st}\,dt$ and $v = f(t)$.

Thus,

$$\int_0^\infty e^{-st}\left[\frac{d\,f(t)}{dt}\right] dt = e^{-st} f(t)\Big|_0^\infty + s\int_0^\infty e^{-st} f(t)\,dt$$

$$= -f(0^+) + s\,f(s)$$

where $f(0^+)$ indicates the value of the function itself as zero is approached from the positive direction.

(10) Second derivative.

Evaluate

$$\int_0^\infty e^{-st}\left[\frac{d^2 f(t)}{dt^2}\right] dt.$$

Let $u = e^{-st}$ so that $du = -s\,e^{-st}\,dt$ and

$$dv = \left(\frac{d^2 f}{dt^2}\right) dt \text{ and } v = \frac{df}{dt};$$

therefore,

$$L\left[\frac{d^2 f(t)}{dt^2}\right] = e^{-st}\frac{df}{dt}\Bigg|_0^\infty + s\int_0^\infty e^{-st}\left(\frac{df}{dt}\right)dt$$

$$= -f'(0^+) + s\,[sf(s) - f(0^+)]\,, \text{ [see (9)]}$$

$$= s^2 f(s) - sf(0^+) - f'(0^+)$$

where $f'(0^+)$ is the value of the first derivative of $f(t)$ evaluated at $t = 0$ approaching zero from the positive direction.

General Form The pattern which emerges can be generalized;

$$L\left[\frac{d^n f(t)}{dt^n}\right] = s^n f(s) - \sum_{k=0}^{k=n-1} s^{(n-1-k)} f^k(0^+)$$

where $f^k(0^+)$ indicates the derivative of the kth order of $f(t)$ evaluated at $t = 0^+$. The polynomial indicated by the summation depends upon the initial conditions of the function and its derivatives up to order $n - 1$. It is sometimes called the initial condition polynomial of the nth order derivative of $f(t)$. (See Reference 4.)

The above results may be used to find the Laplace transforms of functions as shown in the following examples.

To find $L\,[\sin kt]$, use the relation

$$L\left[\frac{d^2 f(t)}{dt^2}\right] = s^2 f(s) - sf(0) - f'(0)$$

and

$$f(t) = \sin kt.$$

Therefore

$$f'(t) = k\cos kt$$

and

$$f''(t) = -k^2 \sin kt.$$

Then, since

$$f(0^+) = 0 \text{ and } f'(0^+) = k,$$

$$L[-k^2 \sin kt] = s^2 f(s) - s(0) - k,$$

and

$$-k^2 L[\sin kt] = s^2 L[\sin kt] - k.$$

Therefore

$$(s^2 + k^2) L[\sin kt] = k,$$

or

$$L[\sin kt] = \frac{k}{s^2 + k^2}.$$

As another example to find $L[\cos kt]$, begin with

$$L[f''(t)] = s^2 f(s) - sf(0) - f'(0),$$

and let

$$f(t) = \cos kt,$$

so that

$$f'(t) = -k \sin kt,$$

and

$$f''(t) = -k^2 \cos kt.$$

Therefore,

$$L[-k^2 \cos kt] = s^2 L[\cos kt] - s(1) - 0$$

since

$$f(0^+) = 1$$

and

$$f'(0^+) = 0.$$

Hence,

$$-k^2 L[\cos kt] - s^2 L[\cos kt] = -s$$

or

$$L[\cos kt] = \frac{s}{k^2 + s^2}.$$

(11) First integrals.
Evaluate

$$\int_0^\infty e^{-st} \int_0^t f(t)\,dt \quad dt.$$

Let

$$\int_0^t f(t)\,dt = g(t).$$

Therefore,

$$f(t) = \frac{dg(t)}{dt}.$$

Now $\int_0^\infty e^{-st}\left[\frac{dg(t)}{dt}\right] dt = sg(s) - g(0^+) = sg(s)$ if the value of the integral at $t = 0$ is zero.

It follows that

$$g(s) = \frac{1}{s}\int_0^\infty e^{-st} f(t)\,dt = \frac{f(s)}{s},$$

but

$$g(s) = \int_0^\infty e^{-st} g(t)\,dt = \int_0^\infty e^{-st}\left[\int_0^t f(t)\,dt\right] dt$$

$$= L\left[\int_0^t f(t)\,dt\right].$$

Thus,

$$L\left[\int_0^t f(t)\,dt\right] = \frac{f(s)}{s}.$$

An alternate procedure is to begin with the definition of the Laplace transform $f(s) = \int_0^\infty e^{-st} f(t)\,dt$ and integrate by parts letting $u = e^{-st}$ and $dv = f(t)\,dt$. Then $du = -se^{-st}\,dt$ and $v = \int f(t)\,dt$. Therefore,

$$f(s) = \int_0^\infty e^{-st} f(t)\,dt = uv\Big|_0^\infty - \int_0^\infty v\,du$$

$$= e^{-st}\int f(t)\,dt\Big|_0^\infty - \int_0^\infty (-se^{-st})\,[\int f(t)\,dt]\,dt.$$

After rearranging,

$$s\int_0^\infty e^{-st}\left[\int f(t)\,dt\right] dt = \int_0^\infty e^{-st} f(t)\,dt - e^{-st}\int f(t)\,dt\Big|_0^\infty$$

or

$$\int_0^\infty e^{-st}\left[\int f(t)\,dt\right] dt = \frac{1}{s}\int_0^\infty e^{-st} f(t)\,dt - \frac{e^{-st}}{s}\int f(t)\,dt \,\Bigg|_0^\infty .$$

The left-hand term is recognized as the transformation desired while the first term on the right is thè Laplace transform of the function divided by s. Thus,

$$L\left[\int f(t)\,dt\right] = \frac{f(s)}{s} - \left[\frac{e^{-st}}{s}\int f(t)\,dt\right]_0^\infty = \frac{f(s)}{s} + \frac{f^{-1}(0^+)}{s}$$

where $f^{-1}(0^+)$ is the initial value of the integral.

For higher integrals, a repetition of the above procedure results in

$$L\left[f^{(-n)}(t)\right] = \frac{1}{s^n} F(s) + \sum_{k=1}^{k=n} s^{(-n-1+k)} f^{(-k)}(0^+)$$

where $f^{(-n)}(t)$ indicates the nth integral of $f(t)$ and $f^{(-k)}(0^+)$ indicates the initial value of the kth integral of $f(t)$. The summation is, once again, a polynomial dependent upon the initial values of integrals of $f(t)$ and is referred to as the initial condition polynomial for the nth integral of $f(t)$. (See Reference 4).

The use of the Laplace transform to obtain solutions to differential equations will be illustrated by application to the simple examples previously considered.

Example. A first-order differential equation being forced with a positive unit step, $u(t) = 1$, may be written

$$\tau \frac{dv}{dt} + v = 1.$$

For convenience, assume $v = v_0$ when $t = 0$.

Solution. The transformation of each term is formally shown below:

$$\tau L\left[\frac{dv}{dt}\right] + L[v] = L[(1)].$$

Substitution of the appropriate transforms gives

$$\tau\,[sv(s) - v(0^+)] + v(s) = \frac{1}{s}$$

or

$$\tau\, sv(s) - \tau v(0^+) + v(s) = \frac{1}{s}$$

$$v(s)\,(1 + \tau s) = \frac{1}{s} + \tau v_0, \text{ since } v(0^+) = v_0.$$

$$v(s) = \frac{1}{s(1 + \tau s)} + \frac{\tau v_0}{1 + \tau s} = \frac{1}{s\tau\left(\frac{1}{\tau} + s\right)} + \frac{v_0}{\left(\frac{1}{\tau} + s\right)}.$$

The solution in terms of variable t will be the inverse Laplace transform indicated below:

$$v(t) = L^{-1}\left[\frac{1}{s\tau\left(\frac{1}{\tau} + s\right)}\right] + L^{-1}\left[\frac{v_0}{\frac{1}{\tau} + s}\right].$$

The inverse of the last term has been derived as shown in 2, above and in Table 6-1.

$$L^{-1}\left[\frac{v_0}{\frac{1}{\tau} + s}\right] = v_0\, e^{-t/\tau}.$$

The inverse of the remaining term may be obtained by partial fraction expansion and finding the inverse of each fraction:

$$\frac{1}{s\tau\left(\frac{1}{\tau} + s\right)} = \frac{A}{s} + \frac{B}{\left(\frac{1}{\tau} + s\right)},$$

from which

$$\frac{1}{s\tau\left(\frac{1}{\tau}+s\right)}=\frac{A\left(\frac{1}{\tau}+s\right)+Bs}{s\left(\frac{1}{\tau}+s\right)};$$

equating numerators and comparing coefficients gives

$$\tau A\left(\frac{1}{\tau}+s\right)+\tau Bs=1,$$

or

$$A+\tau As+\tau Bs=1.$$

from which $A = 1$

$$A=1$$

and

$$\tau Bs+\tau As=0$$

or

$$B=-A=-1.$$

Therefore,

$$L^{-1}\left[\frac{1}{s\tau\left(\frac{1}{\tau}+s\right)}\right]=L^{-1}\left[\frac{1}{s}\right]+L^{-1}\left[\frac{-1}{\frac{1}{\tau}+s}\right]=1-e^{-t/\tau}.$$

The complete solution is $v(t) = 1 + (v_0 - 1)\,e^{-t/\tau}$.

Example. As another example, assume $f(t) = \cos\omega t$. The transformed equation then yields

$$\tau sv(s)-\tau v(0^{+})+v(s)=\frac{s}{s^{2}+\omega^{2}}$$

or

$$v(s) = \frac{s}{(s^2 + \omega^2)(1 + \tau s)} + \frac{\tau v(0^+)}{(1 + \tau s)}$$

$$= \frac{s}{\tau(s^2 + \omega^2)\left(\frac{1}{\tau} + s\right)} + \frac{v(0^+)}{\left(\frac{1}{\tau} + s\right)}.$$

Solution. The inverse of the last term is recognized as $v_0 \, e^{-t/\tau}$. The first term on the right-hand side requires manipulation unless a table having an appropriate inverse is available.

The method of partial fractions can again be applied along with the identity $s^2 + \omega^2 = (s + j\omega)(s - j\omega)$.

The rational fraction is expanded in partial fractions:

$$\frac{s}{\tau(s + j\omega)(s - j\omega)\left(\frac{1}{\tau} + s\right)} = \frac{A}{s + j\omega} + \frac{B}{s - j\omega} + \frac{C}{\left(\frac{1}{\tau} + s\right)}.$$

To find C, multiply by $\left(\frac{1}{\tau} + s\right)$ and let $s = -1/\tau$:

$$C = \frac{-\frac{1}{\tau}}{\tau\left(\frac{1}{\tau^2} + \omega^2\right)} = -\left(\frac{1}{1 + \omega^2\tau^2}\right).$$

To find A, multiply by $(s + j\omega)$ and let $s = -j\omega$:

$$A = \frac{-j\omega}{\tau(-j\omega - j\omega)\left(\frac{1}{\tau} - j\omega\right)} = \frac{1}{2(1 - j\omega\tau)}$$

$$= \frac{1}{2\sqrt{1 + \omega^2\tau^2}} e^{j\theta}, \theta = \tan^{-1} \omega\tau.$$

To find B, multiply by $(s - j\omega)$ and let $s = j\omega$:

$$B = \frac{j\omega}{\tau(j\omega + j\omega)\left(\dfrac{1}{\tau} + j\omega\right)} = \frac{1}{2(1 + j\omega\tau)}$$

$$= \frac{1}{2\sqrt{1 + \omega^2\tau^2}}\, e^{-j\theta}, \quad \theta = \tan^{-1} \omega\tau.$$

The constants, A and B, will be recognized as complex conjugates. The Laplace transform of the original differential equation is therefore.

$$v(s) = \frac{e^{j\theta}}{2\sqrt{1 + \omega^2\tau^2}\,(s + j\omega)} + \frac{e^{-j\theta}}{2\sqrt{1 + \omega^2\tau^2}\,(s - j\omega)} - \left(\frac{1}{1 + \omega^2\tau^2}\right)\left(\frac{1}{\dfrac{1}{\tau} + s}\right) + \frac{v(0^+)}{\left(\dfrac{1}{\tau} + s\right)}.$$

The inverse can then be written as follows:

$$v(t) = \frac{1}{\sqrt{1 + \omega^2\tau^2}}\left[\frac{e^{j\theta}\, e^{-j\omega t} + e^{-j\theta}\, e^{j\omega t}}{2}\right] - \frac{e^{-t/\tau}}{1 + \omega^2\tau^2} + v(0^+)\, e^{-t/\tau},$$

or

$$v(t) = \frac{1}{\sqrt{1 + \omega^2\tau^2}}\left[\frac{e^{j(\omega t - \theta)} + e^{-j(\omega t - \theta)}}{2}\right] - \left[\frac{1}{1 + \omega^2\tau^2} - v(0^+)\right] e^{-t/\tau}$$

$$= \frac{1}{\sqrt{1 + \omega^2\tau^2}} \cos(\omega t - \theta) - \left[\frac{1}{1 + \omega^2\tau^2} - v(0^+)\right] e^{-t/\tau}$$

$$= \frac{1}{\sqrt{1 + \omega^2\tau^2}} \cos(\omega t - \theta) + \left[v(0^+) - \frac{1}{1 + \omega^2\tau^2}\right] e^{-t/\tau}.$$

To verify the initial condition when $t = 0$,

$$v_0 = \frac{1}{\sqrt{1 + \omega^2\tau^2}} \cos(-\theta) + v(0^+) - \frac{1}{1 + \omega^2\tau^2}\,.$$

Since $\cos(-\theta) = \cos\theta = \dfrac{1}{\sqrt{1+\omega^2\tau^2}}$,

$$v_0 = v(0^+).$$

The complete solution then becomes

$$v(t) = \frac{\cos(\omega t - \theta)}{\sqrt{1+\omega^2\tau^2}} + \left[v(0) - \frac{1}{1+\omega^2\tau^2}\right] e^{-t/\tau}.$$

This is the solution obtained by the classical method described previously,

$$v(t) = \frac{\cos(\omega t - \theta)}{\sqrt{1+\omega^2\tau^2}} + Ce^{-t/\tau},$$

where

$$C = \left(v(0) - \frac{\cos\theta}{\sqrt{1+\omega^2\tau^2}}\right).$$

Example. As another example, consider a second-order system being forced with a unit step:

$$\frac{1}{\omega_n^2}\frac{d^2v}{dt^2} + \frac{2\xi}{\omega_n}\frac{dv}{dt} + v = 1.$$

Solution. When the Laplace transformation is performed,

$$\frac{1}{\omega_n^2}[s^2 v(s) - sv(0^+) - v'(0^+)] + \frac{2\xi}{\omega_n}[sv(s) - v(0^+)] + v(s) = \frac{1}{s}$$

$$\frac{1}{\omega_n^2} s^2 v(s) + \frac{2\xi}{\omega_n} sv(s) + v(s) = \frac{1}{s} + \frac{sv(0^+)}{\omega_n^2} + \frac{2\xi}{\omega_n} v(0^+) + \frac{v'(0^+)}{\omega_n^2}$$

$$v(s) = \frac{1}{s\left[\dfrac{s^2}{\omega_n^2} + \dfrac{2\xi s}{\omega_n} + 1\right]} + \frac{\left(\dfrac{s}{\omega_n^2} + \dfrac{2\xi}{\omega_n}\right)v(0^+)}{\left(\dfrac{s^2}{\omega_n^2} + \dfrac{2\xi s}{\omega_n} + 1\right)} + \frac{v'(0^+)}{\omega_n^2\left(\dfrac{s^2}{\omega_n^2} + \dfrac{2\xi}{\omega_n}s + 1\right)}.$$

If initial conditions are such that $v(0^+) = 0$ and $v'(0^+) = 0$

$$v(s) = \frac{\omega_n^2}{s(s - s_1)(s - s_2)} = \frac{\omega_n^2}{s[s - (-a + jb)]\,[s - (-a - jb)]}.$$

The expression may then be expanded in partial fractions:

$$v(s) = \frac{\omega_n^2}{s(s - s_1)(s - s_2)} = \frac{A}{s} + \frac{B}{s - s_1} + \frac{C}{s - s_2}.$$

To find A, multiply by s and let $s = 0$:

$$A = \frac{\omega_n^2}{(-s_1)(-s_2)} = \frac{\omega_n^2}{(a - jb)(a + jb)} = \frac{\omega_n^2}{a^2 + b^2}$$

$$= \frac{\omega_n^2}{(\omega_n \xi)^2 + (\omega_n \sqrt{1 - \xi^2})^2} = \frac{\omega_n^2}{(\omega_n \xi)^2 + \omega_n^2 - (\omega_n \xi)^2} = 1.$$

To find B, multiply by $(s - s_1)$ and let $s = s_1$:

$$B = \left.\frac{\omega_n^2}{s(s - s_2)}\right|_{s=s_1} = \frac{\omega_n^2}{s_1(s_1 - s_2)} = \frac{\omega_n^2}{(-a + jb)(-a + jb + a + jb)}$$

$$B = \frac{\omega_n^2}{(-a + jb)\,2jb} = \frac{\omega_n^2}{-(2b^2 + j2ab)} = -\frac{\omega_n^2}{2\sqrt{b^4 + (ab)^2}}\, e^{-j\psi}.$$

To find C, multiply by $(s - s_2)$ and let $s = s_2$:

$$C = \left.\frac{\omega_n^2}{s(s - s_1)}\right|_{s=s_2} = \frac{\omega_n^2}{-(2b^2 - j2ab)} = \frac{-\omega_n^2\, e^{+j\psi}}{2\sqrt{b^4 + (ab)^2}}$$

where

$$\psi = \tan^{-1} \frac{2ab}{2b^2} = \tan^{-1} \frac{a}{b} = \tan^{-1} \frac{+\xi}{\sqrt{1 - \xi^2}}.$$

Since

$$b = \omega_n \sqrt{1 - \xi^2}, \qquad b^4 = \omega_n^4 (1 - \xi^2)^2$$

and

$$ab = \xi\omega_n^2 \sqrt{1 - \xi^2}, \qquad (ab)^2 = \xi^2 \omega_n^4 (1 - \xi^2)$$

$$b^4 + (ab)^2 = \omega_n^4 (1 - 2\xi^2 + \xi^4) + \xi\omega_n^4 - \omega_n^4 \xi^4 = \omega_n^4 (1 - \xi^2)$$

$$B = \frac{-1}{2\sqrt{1 - \xi^2}} e^{-j\psi}$$

and

$$C = \frac{-1}{2\sqrt{1 - \xi^2}} e^{j\psi}.$$

Thus,

$$v(s) = \frac{1}{s} - \frac{e^{-j\psi}}{2\sqrt{1 - \xi^2}\,(s - s1)} - \frac{e^{j\psi}}{2\sqrt{1 - \xi^2}\,(s - s_2)}.$$

The inverse, term by term, gives

$$v(t) = 1 - \frac{e^{-j\psi}\, e_1^{jst}}{2\sqrt{1 - \xi^2}} - \frac{e^{j\psi}\, e_2^{jst}}{2\sqrt{1 - \xi^2}}$$

$$= 1 - \frac{1}{2\sqrt{1 - \xi^2}} [e^{-j\psi}\, e^{(-\xi\omega_n - j\omega_n\sqrt{1-\xi^2})t}]$$

$$+ e^{j\psi}\, e^{(-\xi\omega_n - j\omega_n\sqrt{1-\xi^2})t}]$$

$$= 1 - \frac{e^{-\xi\omega_n t}}{\sqrt{1 - \xi^2}} \left[\frac{e^{j(\omega_n\sqrt{1-\xi^2}t - \psi)} + e^{-j(\omega_n\sqrt{1-\xi^2}t - \psi)}}{2}\right]$$

$$v(t) = 1 - \frac{e^{-\xi\omega_n t}}{\sqrt{1 - \xi^2}} [\cos(\omega_n\sqrt{1 - \xi^2}\, t - \psi)].$$

For the case where $\xi > 1$, a similar process will yield

$$v(t) = 1 - e^{-\xi\omega_n t}\left[\cosh \omega_n\sqrt{\xi^2 - 1}\, t + \frac{\xi}{\sqrt{\xi^2 - 1}} \sinh \omega\sqrt{\xi^2 - 1}\, t\right].$$

The time histories for various values of ξ are shown in Figure 5.5. As ξ decreases from a value in excess of unity, the time to approach the final value of unity decreases but no overshoot occurs until ξ becomes less than unity.

As ξ decreases below unity, the response becomes increasingly oscillatory, the frequency being $\omega_n\sqrt{1-\xi^2}$.

When $\xi = 0$, the system oscillates continuously at the frequency, ω_n, which is therefore called the undamped natural angular frequency. $\xi = 0$ corresponds to the condition where the coefficient of the first-order derivative is zero.

6.3 SUMMARY OF USEFUL THEOREMS

(1) Final Value Theorem

If $f(s) = L[f(t)]$, then $\lim_{t\to\infty} [f(t)] = \lim_{s\to 0} [sf(s)]$ provided $sf(s)$ does not become infinite for any value of s such that $Re(s) \geqslant 0$.

This theorem is useful for determining if the function of t becomes bounded as t approaches infinity.

Example. A first-order system forced with a step of magnitude B.

$$\tau \frac{dv}{dt} + v = B \text{ (a constant).}$$

$$\tau s v(s) - \tau v(0) + v(s) = \frac{B}{s}$$

$$v(s)\,[\tau s + 1] = \frac{B}{s} + \tau v(0)$$

$$v(s) = \frac{B}{s\,[\tau s + 1]} + \frac{\tau v(0)}{[\tau s + 1]}.$$

To find the final value of t, apply the following formula:

$$\lim_{t\to\infty} v(t) = \lim_{s\to 0} s v(s) = \lim_{s\to 0}\left[\frac{Bs}{s\,[1+\tau s]} + \frac{s\,\tau v(0)}{1+\tau s}\right]$$

$= B$, which is the steady-state solution to a step forcing of magnitude B.

(2) Initial Value Theorem

If $f(s)$ is $L[f(t)]$, then $\lim_{t\to 0} [f(t)] = \lim_{s\to\infty} [sf(s)]$.

This states that the value of $f(t)$ just after $t = 0$ can be found from the Laplace transform of the function. This theorem can be used to verify initial conditions used in obtaining the Laplace transforms of $f(t)$.

Example. A first-order system forced with a step.

$$\tau \frac{dv}{dt} + v = B \text{ (a constant).}$$

$$\tau\, sv(s) - \tau v(0) + v(s) = \frac{B}{s}$$

$$v(s) = \frac{B}{s\,(1+\tau s)} + \frac{v(0)}{(1+\tau s)}$$

$$\lim_{t\to 0} f(t) = \lim_{s\to\infty} sv(s) = \lim_{s\to\infty}\left[\frac{sB}{s\,(1+\tau s)} + \frac{s\,\tau v(0)}{1+\tau s}\right]$$

$= v(0)$. This is the value of $f(t)$ at $t = 0^+$.

(3) Translation Theorem

Suppose a function is translated t_1 units to the right as indicated in the graph below:

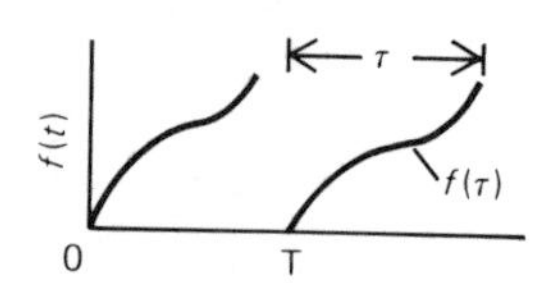

Let $f(\tau)$ be the translated function so that by definition $L[f(\tau)] =$

$$\int_0^\infty e^{-st} f(\tau)\, d\tau.$$

If $f(\tau)$ is $f(t)$ translated T units to the right, then $\tau = t - T$ and

$$\int_0^\infty e^{-s\tau} f(\tau)\, d\tau = \int_T^\infty e^{-s(t-T)} f(t-T)\, dt = e^{+sT} \int_T^\infty e^{-st} f(t-T)\, dt.$$

Thus,

$$\int_T^\infty e^{-st} f(t-T)\, dt = e^{-sT} \int_0^\infty e^{-s\tau} f(\tau)\, d\tau.$$

If during the interval 0 to T the function $f(t - T) = 0$, then the lower limit of T on the integral may be taken as zero, so that

$$\int_0^\infty e^{-st} f(t - T)\, dt = e^{-sT} \int_0^\infty e^{-s\tau} f(\tau)\, d\tau = e^{-sT} f(s).$$

This is to say that the Laplace transform of a translated function is found by multiplying the Laplace transform of the function by the exponential, e^{-sT}, where T is the magnitude of translation.

This theorem shows how to handle pure time delays or transportation lags which are commonly encountered in process dynamic response. It is also useful in deriving transforms of functions which can be considered as composed of translated functions.

Example. Translated step function of magnitude A.

$$f(t) = 0,\ 0 < t < T$$

$$f(t) = A,\ t > T$$

$$L[f(t)] = e^{-Ts} \frac{A}{s}.$$

Example. As another example of the use of the translation theorem, consider a rectangular pulse of height A and duration T. This may be denoted as $[RPF(t)]$.

$$L[RPF(t)] = \int_0^\infty e^{-st} A\, dt = \int_T^\infty e^{-st} A\, dt = \frac{A}{s} + \frac{Ae^{st}}{s}\Bigg|_T^\infty$$

$$= \frac{A}{s} - \frac{e^{-sT}A}{s} = \frac{A}{s}[1 - e^{-sT}].$$

A special rectangular pulse function is the unit rectangular pulse function for which $A = 1/T$. The area of this pulse is unity. The function is denoted as $[URPF(t)]$.

$$L[URPF(t)] = \frac{1}{T}\left[\frac{1 - e^{-sT}}{s}\right].$$

A new function is defined as T approaches zero. This function is called the unit impulse function $[UIF(t)]$, the Dirac or Delta function

$$\delta(t) = \lim_{T \to 0} [URPF(t)] = \lim_{T \to 0} \left[\frac{1}{T} \left(\frac{1 - e^{-sT}}{s} \right) \right].$$

Applying L' Hospital's Rule, useful in evaluating functions which become 0/0 as a variable goes to zero,

$$\lim \left[\frac{1 - e^{-sT}}{Ts} \right] = \lim_{T \to 0} \left[\frac{\frac{d(\text{num})}{dT}}{\frac{d(\text{denom})}{dT}} \right]$$

$$= \lim_{T \to 0} \frac{\frac{d[1 - e^{-sT}]}{dT}}{\frac{d[Ts]}{dt}}$$

$$= \lim_{T \to 0} \frac{se^{-sT}}{s} = 1.$$

Therefore, $L[\delta(t)] = 1$.

The Delta function or unit impulse function, $[UIF(t)]$, is a very useful concept. As a forcing function, $\delta(t)$ is particularly convenient since its Laplace transform is unity. The time response of a system forced with the Delta function is called the *weighting function*.

Occasionally, physical systems are encountered, the performance of which is described by the form

$$y(s) = \left(\frac{1 + As}{1 + Bs} \right) x(s).$$

The corresponding differential equation is

$$B \frac{dy}{dt} + y = x + A \frac{dx}{dt}.$$

Here the forcing function is $x + A \dfrac{dx}{dt}$.

Suppose that the forcing variable, x, is changed in a step fashion from zero to C, for example. A question arises about the nature of the forcing function. It is clear that the forcing function includes the term C/s as a direct consequence of the step change. The Laplace transform of $A\ (dx)/(dt)$, when the change in x is a step, must be considered. Intuitively, it appears that some kind of impulse function should result due to the abruptness in the change of x as the step is inserted.

By definition, $L[f(t)] = f(s)$ and, for initial conditions of zero,

$$L\left[\frac{df(t)}{dt}\right] = sf(s).$$

If $f(t)$ is taken to be the unit step function, $u(t)$, then

$$L\left[\frac{du(t)}{dt}\right] = sL[u(t)] = s\left(\frac{1}{s}\right) = 1 = L[\delta(t)].$$

It follows that, where $x(t) = C \cdot u(t)$,

$$L\left[A\,\frac{dx}{dt}\right] = ACL[\delta(t)].$$

Apparently, at the point where $x(t)$ makes a step-like change of C units, $(dx/dt) = C\,\delta(t)$.

In this illustration, therefore, the Laplace transform of the forcing function becomes, where $x(t) = C$,

$$L\left[x + A\,\frac{dx}{dt}\right] = \frac{C}{s} + AC.$$

so that, for the above situation,

$$y(s) = \frac{C}{s(1 + Bs)} + \frac{AC}{(1 + Bs)}$$

and

$$y(t) = C - C\,e^{-t/B} + \frac{ACe^{-t/B}}{B}$$

$$= C\left[1 + \left(\frac{A}{B} - 1\right) e^{-t/B}\right].$$

The transient component, $C\left(\frac{A}{B} - 1\right) e^{-t/B}$, will contribute a positive response if $A > B$, negative if $A < B$, and nothing if $A = B$.

Owing to the limitations of imposing an impulse forcing as well as limitations of a physical system to respond to such a forcing, the initial time history obtained from a forcing of this kind will generally be unreliable. As a practical test signal, the impulse is generally not useful despite its attractiveness from a purely mathematical point of view.

If such a forcing function is introduced into a real system, it usually results in exciting components the dynamics of which may be of no interest or in driving components into nonlinear regions of operation or to their limits of performance (saturation).

As a mathematical concept and as an ideal forcing function, the impulse is indeed extremely useful.

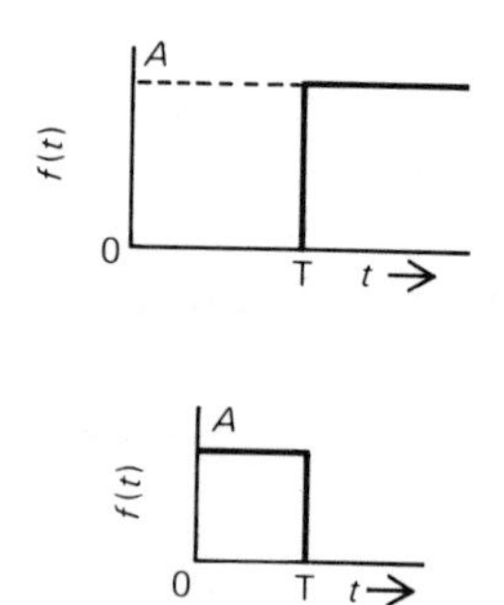

(4) Change of scale theorem

$$L[f(at)] = \int_0^\infty e^{-st} f(at)\, at.$$

Let $\tau = at$, $d\tau = adt$

$$L[f(at)] = L[f(\tau)] = \int_0^\infty e^{-st} f(\tau)\, dt = \int_0^\infty e^{-st/\tau} f(\tau) \frac{d\tau}{a}$$

$$= \frac{1}{a} f\left(\frac{s}{a}\right).$$

This theorem is useful if a change in the time scale is made and the effect on the Laplace transform is desired.

(5) Complex Differentiation Theorem

Differentiation of a transform of a function corresponds to the multiplication of the function by $-t$.

Thus $f^{(n)}(s) = L[(-t)^n f(t)]$, $n = 1, 2, 3 \ldots$ and $\lim_{s \to 0} f^{(n)}(s) = 0$.

Example. Consider $L[\sin kt] = \dfrac{k}{s^2 + k^2}$

$$\frac{d\left[\dfrac{k}{s^2 + k^2}\right]}{ds} = \frac{-2\,ks}{(s^2 + k^2)^2} = L[-t \sin kt].$$

Example. $f(t) = B, f(s) = \dfrac{B}{s}$

$$\frac{d}{ds}\left(\frac{B}{s}\right) = \frac{-B}{s^2}$$

$$L[-t\, f(t)] = L[-Bt] = -\frac{B}{s^2}.$$

Thus, in order to find the Laplace transform of any function multiplied by t, differentiate the Laplace transform of that function and multiply by $(-1)^1$. Where the function is multiplied by t^2, differentiate twice and multiply by $(-1)^2$.

Example. $f(t) = B \quad f(s) = \dfrac{B}{s}$

What is $L[t^2 B]$?

$$\frac{d}{ds}[f(s)] = \frac{d\left(\dfrac{B}{s}\right)}{ds} = -\frac{B}{s^2};$$

therefore,

$$L[tB] = (-1)^1\left(\frac{-B}{s^2}\right) = \frac{B}{s^2}.$$

Then,

$$\frac{d}{ds}\left[\frac{B}{s^2}\right] = -\frac{2B}{s^3};$$

therefore,

$$L[t^2 B] = (-1)^2 \left(\frac{2B}{s^3}\right) = \frac{2B}{s^3}.$$

(6) Theorems relative to multiplication or division of the Laplace transform of a function by s.

Division of the transform of a function by s corresponds to integrating the function between the limits of 0 and t.

$$L^{-1}\left[\frac{1}{s} f(s)\right] = \int_0^t F(\tau)\, d\tau$$

Let

$$f(s) = L[f(t)]$$

or

$$L^{-1}\ [f(s)] = f(t);$$

therefore,

$$L^{-1}\left[\frac{f(s)}{s}\right] = \int_0^t f(t)\, dt.$$

Example.

$$L^{-1}\left[\frac{k}{s(s^2 + k^2)}\right] = \int_0^t \sin k\tau d\tau$$

$$= -\left.\frac{\cos k\,\tau}{k}\right|_0^t$$

$$= \frac{1}{k}\,[1 - \cos kt].$$

Note: Displaced cosine form.

Example. Let $f(t) = A$

$$L[f(t)] = L[A] = \frac{A}{s}.$$

Now

$$\int_0^t f(t)\,dt = \int_0^t A\,dt = At$$

$$L[At] = \frac{A}{s^2};$$

therefore,

$$\frac{L[f(t)]}{s} = L\left[\int_0^t f(t)\,dt\right].$$

Example. Suppose one wishes to obtain the Laplace transform of

$$\int_0^t (a + bt)\,dt$$

where

$$f(t) = a + bt$$

$$L[f(t)] = L[a] + bL[t] = \frac{a}{a} + \frac{b}{s^2};$$

therefore,

$$\frac{L[f(t)]}{s} = \frac{a}{s^2} + \frac{b}{s^3} = L\left[\int_0^t (a + bt)\,dt\right].$$

If the rules involving integrals are used,

$$L\left[\int_0^t f(t)\,dt\right] = \frac{f(s)}{s} + \frac{f'(0^+)}{s},$$

$$L\left[\int_0^t bt\,dt\right] = \frac{b}{s^3} + \frac{f'(0^+)}{s^2}$$

$$L\left[\int_0^t a\,dt\right] = \frac{a}{s^2} + \frac{f'(0^+)}{s^2},$$

and if $f'(0^+) = 0$

$$L[(a + bt)] = \frac{a}{s^2} + \frac{b}{s^3}.$$

References

1. Gardner, Murray F. and John L. Barnes. *Transients in Linear Systems.* John Wiley & Sons, Inc., New York 1942.

   This book is one of the earliest but also one of the best because of the many applications to real problems. It contains a résumé of the historical development of the Laplace method.

2. Kaplan, Wilfred. *Operational Methods for Linear Systems.* Addison-Wesley Publishing Co. Inc., Reading, Massachusetts, 1962.

   Directed more toward the mathematical aspects. Excellent for background, proofs, etc.

3. Grabbe, E. M., S. Ramo, and D. E. Wooldridge, eds. *Handbook of Automation and Computation and Control*, vol. 1. John Wiley and Sons, Inc., New York 1958.

   A convenient compilation of useful information by experts of the time. Treats a wide range of areas of interest to control engineers.

4. Draper, C. S., Walter McKay, and Sidney Lees. *Instrument Engineering*, vol. 2. McGraw-Hill Book Co., New York, 1953.

   The 3-volume set under this title constitutes a definitive work on the theory of instrumentation, analysis and synthesis. Volume 2 is devoted to mathematical techniques. Thorough and detailed solutions are given to first- and second-order ordinary linear differential equations with a large variety of forcings. Charts are large enough to be directly useful. In an attempt to generalize, a rather formidable nomenclature emerges, but, with proper care and some patience the book can be used with great advantage.

Both classical and Laplace transform methods are used to develop solutions to ordinary linear differential equations with constant coefficients. Many useful and practical techniques and mathematical tools are described. An excellent reference.

5. Churchill, R. V. *Operational Mathematics.* McGraw-Hill Book Co., New York, 1958.

The theory and applications of Laplace transforms and other integral transforms is presented. A chapter is devoted to Fourier transforms. The numerous examples of applications of both Laplace and Fourier transforms are pertinent and of engineering interest. An excellent reference.

7
Measuring Systems for Plant Studies

7.1 INTRODUCTION

In the previous chapters, reference has been made to some of the problems of process control and to the means of organizing these problems. Some situations have been described with differential equations, and the expected behavior of these systems to various disturbances have been derived.

The systems for which mathematical descriptions have been presented have been relatively simple. For most real processes, it is easy to visualize far more complexity than the systems mentioned heretofore. The theoretical dynamic descriptions of a heat exchanger, a distillation column, a reactor, or a crystallizer are certainly considerably more complicated than a mass-spring-dashpot system or a perfectly mixed vessel.

An engineer viewing the vast ensemble of a petroleum refinery, for example, is likely to despair of ever discovering relations between dependent and independent variables, even of an empirical nature. The hope of formulating exact theoretical relations seems even more remote.

Much has been published concerning theoretical descriptions of processes, this endeavor being called 'model building.' Some mathematical 'models' are devoted to describing static performance (as contrasted to dynamic). They are developed in a variety of ways based on theory, empiricism or a combination of both. Sometimes a 'model' is derived from the statistical analysis of a mass of data, the basic form of the model having a very tenuous basis on realistic theory. However, within specified limits, the relation may predict performance satisfactorily even though the parameters bear only a casual relation to the real system properties. Modeling of chemical processes is treated at length in References 1 and 2 listed at the end of this chapter.

Traditionally, engineers have been forced to build systems without having knowledge of all pertinent facts. Theoretical knowledge is generally incomplete and may never be sufficient to enable an industrial system to be constructed which will perform exactly as desired. In view of the difficulty of developing completely sufficient theoretical descriptions, the need for some experimental information is generally acknowledged.

When it is the task of an engineer to improve an existing process, he has a choice of methods. He may choose to seek a solution through a completely theoretical analysis, through an entirely empirical study, or a judicious combination of both approaches. Engineers logically select the latter method since it is generally recognized that, whereas it may be possible to write formal expressions for the physical and chemical processes taking place, it is so extremely difficult to make satisfactory theoretical predictions that accurate determinations of performance of actual processing systems must usually be found by experimentation.

The question which requires an answer is this: how much or, perhaps better, how little information is needed to achieve a satisfactory result? Associated questions are "what should be measured and with what precision," and "what accuracy and resolution should measuring systems possess?"

Without prior knowledge of the problem, it is impossible to answer these questions quantitatively. Perhaps the wisest decision is to perform the measurements in the best manner reasonably attainable.

The example of the reactor study described in chapter 1, the process diagram of which was shown in Figure 1-8, is typical. Here it was desired to control the pressure in a reactor within 1/2 inch of water at some fixed level. A pressure sensor (transducer) having almost infinite resolution and a measuring system capable of accurately recognizing changes of as little as 1/10 inch of water were necessary. In another study, it was found that a temperature had to be controlled within 1°F (at a level of about 300°F) in order to assure stable operation of a large and ponderous process. If an iron-constantan thermocouple were used as a sensor, the data system would be required to accurately measure 0.03 millivolts at a level of about 8 millivolts and to detect, meaningfully, changes of about 3 microvolts (0.1°F). It was not possible, a priori, to know that such exacting temperature control and measurement precision were necessary. A considerable amount of testing was necessary before these requirements were made evident.

In another study, a heat balance around a tube and shell heat exchanger was desired. The temperature change produced in one stream was about 5°F. To achieve an accuracy of 2 percent required the temperature difference to be measured within 0.1°F. Instead of being unusual, these requirements of static performance appear to be commonplace.

Dynamic performance characteristics of process measurement systerms must also be considered, these being generally even more stringent. The dynamic error which a temperature sensor can possess has been illustrated in Table 4.1.

Inferior performance of industrial control systems can be very frequently attributed to excessive dynamic error in some vital component. Sensors and final control elements, such as valve actuators, are common offenders.

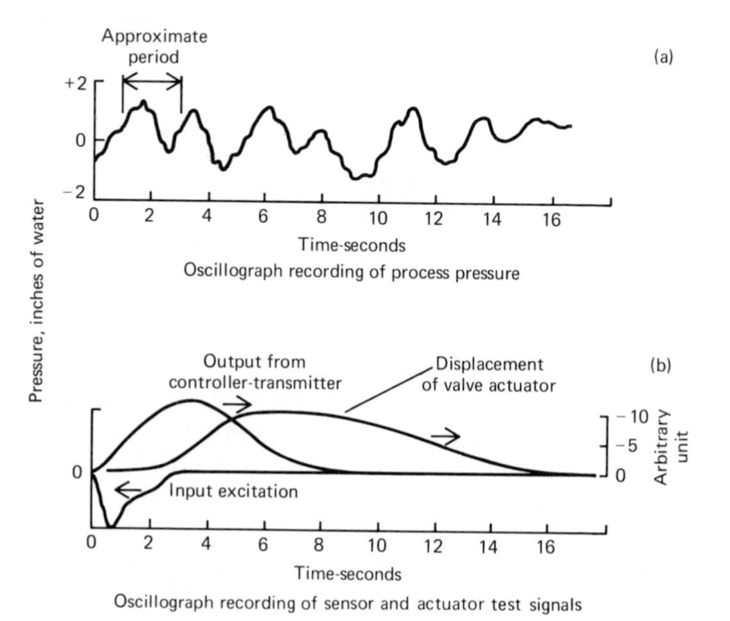

Figure 7.1. Comparison of uncontrolled process variable with the response of sensor and actuator to a test signal. (a) oscillograph recording of process pressure, (b) oscillograph recordings of sensor and actuator test signals.

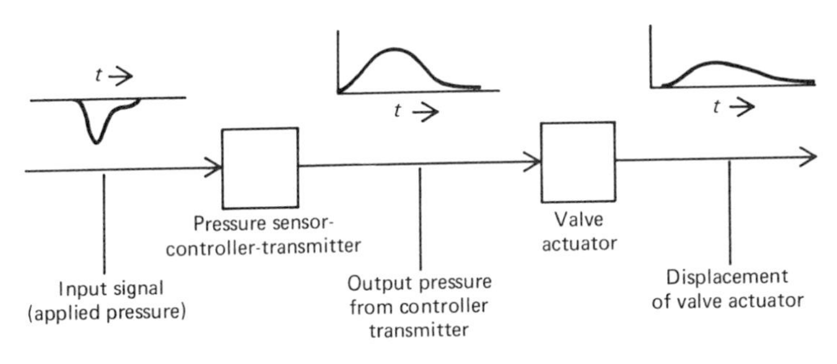

Figure 7.2. Arrangement of components and origin of signals for testing of pressure sensor-transmitter and control valve.

Examples taken from an actual case study illustrate the serious nature of dynamic error. Figure 7.1(a) shows records of the pressure in a reactor under controlled conditions. Very approximately, the process pressure is capable of changing as rapidly as 1 cycle every 2 seconds with evidence of oscillations of a higher frequency. Figure 7.1(b) shows the time histories of the response of the transmitted pressure from an existing controller and the response of the valve actuator to a smooth, pulse-like change in pressure to the primary sensing element, the change having approximately the same duration as the 'period' of the typical disturbance. Figure 7.2 shows the physical arrangement of the components and the nature of signals along the system.

A cursory examination of the time histories in Figure 7.1 confirms that this pressure sensor-transmitter component is incapable of accurately measuring the transient input signal, (excitation). The actuator device is obviously many-fold less capable of following the excitation and hence entirely inadequate as a component in a control system designed to attenuate the rapid pressure changes in this process.

Examples of gross incapability of control components for the function assigned are present in most industrial control systems existing today.

7.2 DATA SYSTEMS

The data acquisition systems currently installed on today's processes have a very limited capability for retrieving useful information even of a static nature. Dynamic error in the sensor is only one deficiency. Another shortcoming is the lack of provision to bias out (suppress) accurately the majority of the steady-state signal and to amplify deviations from that level.

In addition to static (sometimes called steady-state) data, dynamic characteristics of processes and components must be known if systems for the control of processes are to be *designed.* Experimental characteristics of process dynamics may be recovered from measurements of the transient relations between independent and dependent variables. A common technique is to introduce a measureable change in an independent variable and measure the time history of changes in the dependent variables. Suppression and amplification capability enables the experimenter to measure very small perturbations and thus minimize disturbances to normal plant operations.

Additionally, it is highly desirable to have the records of these changes continuously displayed so that the experimenter can quickly observe test results. Since the speed of response depends upon the process studied, it is mandatory that a versatile recorder have a variable chart speed. Industrial data recording systems are usually not provided with variable speed recording mechanisms. Moreover, the recorders are generally distributed over an extensive panel so that pertinent input and output records are not closely associated, physically, with each other. There is thus little opportunity to develop intuition concerning the relations between independent and dependent variables.

Engineers who intend to obtain data from existing plants are well-advised to scrutinize existing or proposed data acquisition systems with extreme care. The conclusion will generally be that a data system almost completely unrelated to the existing system will be required, beginning with the basic sensors and terminating with the read-out components.

A data system consists of the following basic elements or subsystems: (1) a detecting or sensing element, (2) signal conditioning components, (3) an indicating, and usually (4) a recording system.

Components and subsystems which have been found particularly useful for defining processing problems will be discussed. All of the items described will be of the analog (as contrasted to digital) type.

Although there is increasing interest in digital systems, to date these are more expensive and in some ways more difficult to use, especially for the task of procuring the basic information needed for problem definition.

The intention here is to point out the salient features of components and subsystems which are particularly useful and convenient for experimental investigations of pilot and full-scale plant processes.

The scientific literature devoted to measurement is vast indeed owing to the need for measurements in every facet of engineering and scientific endeavor. Some 40,000 journals contain information relevant to measurements, and some of the journals are devoted to instruments and measurement exclusively. Thousands of companies exist whose sole output is instruments of various kinds. Perhaps a hundred new products appear each month.

Many books have been published dealing with measurements and instrumentation practice. Some of these are listed in the bibliography (particularly References 3-13 listed at the end of this chapter).

Engineers interested in plant test work should become familiar with the basic theory and techniques of measurement and be alert to new methods which may be particularly useful.

The engineer will feel relieved to know that the knowledge of a few basic principles, standard configurations of instruments, and electric circuits will serve most of his needs. Applied with ingenuity, the principles can be used to improvise measuring systems which will satisfy most of the requirements demanded in a specific situation. Some of the most popular measuring systems will be described here.

Sensors The most common process measurements encountered in conducting plant studies are (1) temperature and temperature difference, (2) pressure and pressure difference, (3) flow, (4) level, (5) force, (6) angular velocity (rotational speed), (7) linear velocity, (8) displacement, and (9) power.

In addition, signals which depend on the properties of the materials processed are sometimes conveniently available from analytical instruments. Among these are viscosity, density, refractive index and composition. Information relevant to analysis instrumentation is not included here because of its highly specialized nature and the numerous excellent reference sources currently available. However, many of the principles described herein apply to the measuring and signal conditioning problems which will be encountered in procuring useful information from such instruments in an industrial environment.

Most analysis instruments are extremely sensitive (e.g. chromatographs), and high amplification and sophisticated electronic circuits are needed to yield useful signals. This invites the speculation that similar treatment of the signals from the measurement of the more common variables would add considerably to their usefulness. The incredible sensitivity and reproducibility of most plants would become better appreciated, and the increased understanding of process performance obtained via superior measurements, would most certainly lead to improved processes, better control systems, and perhaps to new processing techniques.

The most popular detectors for sensing temperatures of industrial processes make use of the effect of temperature upon the resistance of material or the electromotive force developed at a junction of unlike materials. Resistance elements are most commonly metallic (resistance thermometers) or oxides (thermistors). Those sensors employing junctions of unlike materials (usually metallic) are called thermocouples.

Because of their low cost, thermocouples are by far the most popular industrial temperature sensor. In addition to low cost, other advantages are the very small sizes which can be fabricated, their simplicity, and ruggedness. Their low electrical impedance is another advantage. The disadvantages of a thermocouple are principally the following. (1) A reference junction is needed, (2) the signal produced is small, (3) lead wires of matching composition, or equivalent, are required, and (4) material composition must be maintained. The upper temperature range for metallic thermocouples is about 3000°F (1650°C). Ceramic 'thermocouples,' a relatively recent development, may be used to about 5000°F. Above 1000°F, radiation pyrometers are frequently used.

Several thermocouple pairs arranged in series (called a thermopile) are sometimes used to increase the output signal. Such multiple junctions are commonly used in radiant energy sensors–bolometers. Average temperatures of areas or volumes may be obtained from the signal produced by a number of thermocouples arranged in parallel, *provided the resistances of all circuits are equal.*

Thermocouple systems may be either grounded or floating. Figures 7.3(a) and 7.3(b) illustrate the two arrangements. This distinction is important because the choice of signal conditioning depends upon the arrangement.

Resistance elements for temperature sensing are almost always used in a Wheatstone bridge circuit shown in Figure 7.4. They are useful in the range from −100°F to 600°F.

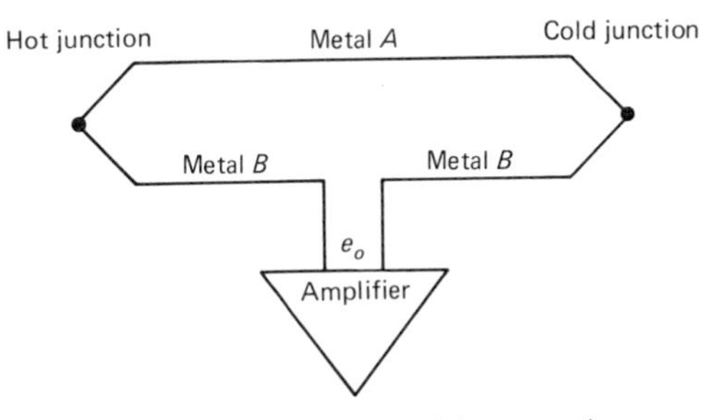

(a) Floating or ungrounded thermocouple

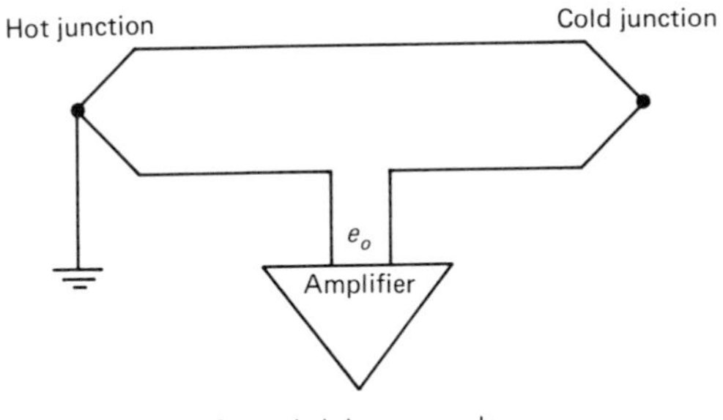

(b) Grounded thermocouple

Figure 7.3. Two thermocouple configurations (a) ungrounded thermocouple, (b) grounded thermocouple.

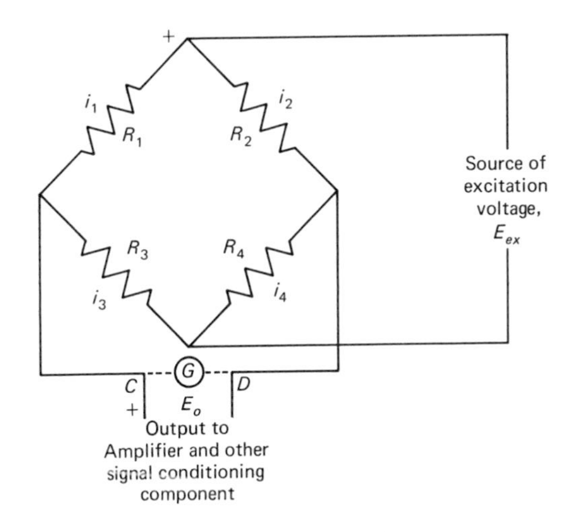

Figure 7.4. Basic Wheatstone bridge circuit.

Used in the classical way, a current sensor, G, is inserted between C and D (Figure 7.4) and the resistances adjusted until no current flows. R_4 may be the unknown resistance, the others adjustable in a known way. Assume that resistance R_4 is the sensing element, that the resistances of R_1 and R_3 may be selected, and that resistance R_2 is adjustable. R_1 and R_3 will be chosen equal to some suitable value–e.g., 350 ohms. The bridge is balanced by exposing the active element to a standard or known condition and adjusting R_2 until the output voltage is zero. Under these conditions,

$$i_1 R_1 = i_2 R_2 \quad \text{and} \quad i_3 R_3 = i_4 R_4 .$$

Since $R_1 = R_3$, $R_4 = R_2$ when balanced. Thus, the unknown resistance is measured by adjusting R_2.

Instead of using the resistance, R_2, to compensate for changes in R_4, it is possible to use the voltage developed at E_0 as a measure of the bridge unbalance which, in turn, is a measure of the change in the desired variable.

When used as a temperature sensor, the circuit shown in Figure 7-5

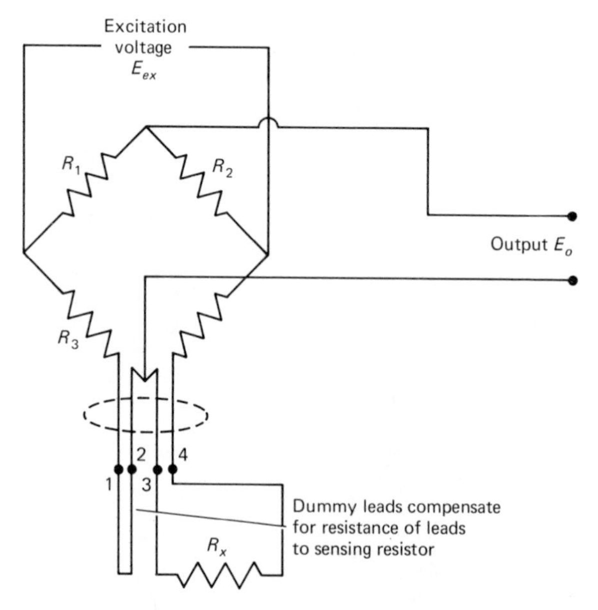

Figure 7.5. Typical four-wire Wheatstone bridge circuit for temperature measurement.

may be used. Here the resistance of wires 3 and 4, leading to the remotely located sensing element R_x, is compensated by an identical set of conductors 1 and 2, the resistance of which is added to R_3.

To make the output linear with temperature, special circuitry has been devised to compensate for the nonlinear variation of resistance with temperature. One such circuit is shown in Figure 7.6. In

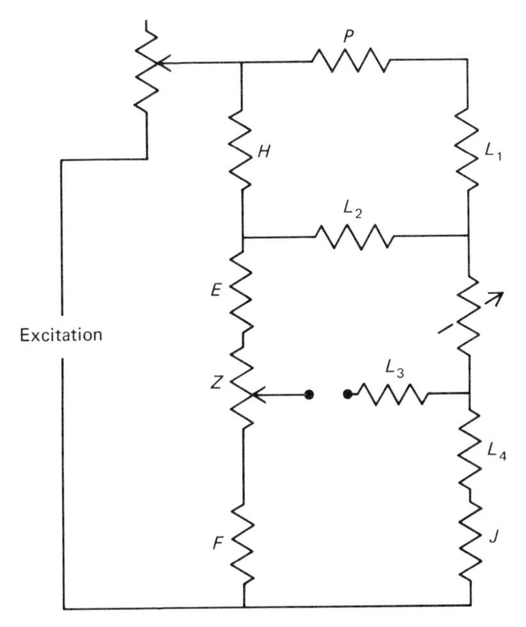

Figure 7.6. Rosemount Engineering Model 400-A resistance bridge.

this bridge, resistances P and J have large values compared to the resistances of the leads, L_1 and L_4; changes in lead resistance will thus have only a very slight effect on the total resistance, $P + L_1$ and $J + L_4$.

L_3 is in series with the output, the readout device normally having a very high impedance so no error is created. L_2 is a low resistance; thus, the voltage at H is nearly that at P. The result is to virtually remove the effect of one lead and reduce errors associated with the other. When used with an industrial data system, a high impedance voltmeter replaces the galvanometer, G (Figure 7.4); the voltage unbalance, E_0, is used as a measure of the temperature change from a reference.

Assuming that terminal C (Figure 7.4) is positive with respect to terminal D and that no current flows through the high gain amplifier associated with the readout device, $i_1 = i_2$, $i_3 = i_4$, and $E_0 = i_4 R_4 - i_2 R_2$. But $i_4 = E_{ex}/(R_3 + R_4)$ and $i_2 = E_{ex}/(R_1 + R_2)$; therefore,

$$E_0 = \left[\frac{R_4}{R_3 + R_4} - \frac{R_2}{R_1 + R_2}\right] E_{ex}.$$

If R_4 is the temperature sensitive element and all other resistances are constant, at some reference value, R_4°,

$$E_0^\circ = \left[\frac{R_4^\circ}{R_3 + R_4^\circ} - \frac{R_2}{R_1 + R_2}\right] E_{ex}. \qquad (7.1)$$

The difference $E_0 - E_0^\circ$ will be a measure of the temperature change; i.e.,

$$E_0 - E_0^\circ = \left[\left(\frac{R_4}{R_3 + R_4} - \frac{R_2}{R_1 + R_4}\right) - \left(\frac{R_4^\circ}{R_3 + R_4^\circ} - \frac{R_2}{R_1 + R_2}\right)\right] E_{ex},$$

$$= \left[\frac{R_4}{R_3 + R_4} - \frac{R_4^\circ}{R_3 + R_4^\circ}\right] E_{ex}.$$

If $R_4 = R_4^\circ + \Delta R$

$$\Delta E = E_0 - E_0^\circ = \frac{R_3 \, \Delta R \, E_{ex}}{(R_3 + R_4^\circ)^2 + (R_3 + R_4^\circ)\, \Delta R}.$$

Since ΔR_4 is very small compared with R_4° or R_3 and usually $R_3 \cong R_4^\circ$, it follows that terms involving ΔR_4 may be neglected in the denominator. That is,

$$\frac{\Delta E_0}{\Delta R_4} = \frac{R_3 \, E_{ex}}{(R_3 + R_4^\circ)^2}$$

or

$$\frac{dE_0}{dR} = \frac{R_3 \, E_{ex}}{(R_3 + R_4^\circ)^2},$$

which can be obtained directly by differentiating (7.1).

Depending upon whether the power supply furnishing the excitation is floating or grounded, the sensing circuit is either balanced-floating or balanced-grounded.

Pressure, pressure differential, level, force and displacement may be very conveniently measured with a variety of strain-gage configurations. The strain gage consists of a wire of small diameter or thin film, bonded to or associated with a force summing member, the deflection of which changes the cross-sectional area of the wire or film by virtue of the strain induced. Reference 14 contains circuit diagrams and technical information, and Reference 15 discusses applications of differential pressure sensors. The strain gages are usually arranged in a bridge circuit as in Figure 7.7, one or more of the elements being active.

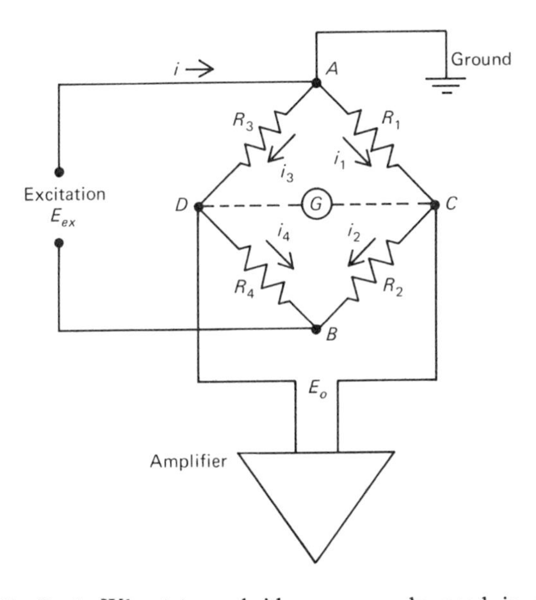

Figure 7.7. Basic Wheatstone bridge commonly used in pressure transducers.

Differential pressure strain-gage transducers are available for measuring a wide range of values, from ±0.05 psi to ±2,500 psi. Overload capacities can range from ±0.10 psi to ±5,000 psi, respectively. The bridges respond to the difference in forces on the diaphragm system.

Excitation may be a constant a-c, or d-c voltage usually between 5 and 15 volts. The impedance of the bridge is nominally about 350 ohms.

Recently, systems complete with resistance elements or strain-gage elements and solid-state integrated circuit power supplies and amplifiers have become available. These transducers can have a full range output of several volts. Since the system can be protected from disturbances by excellent shielding, the noise to signal ratio of the signal received at a remote data system can be sharply reduced as compared with the case where low-level signals are transmitted.

Force is measured indirectly by measuring the strain developed in an elastic member, the stress-strain relationship for which is known. The mass contained in a vessel can sometimes be measured by the deflection in the supporting members. Alternately, the vessel may be mounted on 'load' cells which have been calibrated.

The rate of flow into or out of a vessel can sometimes be measured by differentiating the output of a load cell or other device. High-quality instrumentation and signal conditioning must be used.

The above measurements may also be made utilizing other electri-

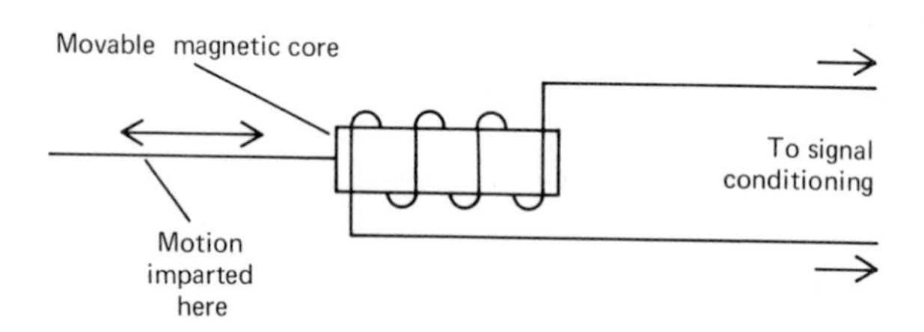

Figure 7.8. Signal-producing element of a magnetic type transducer.

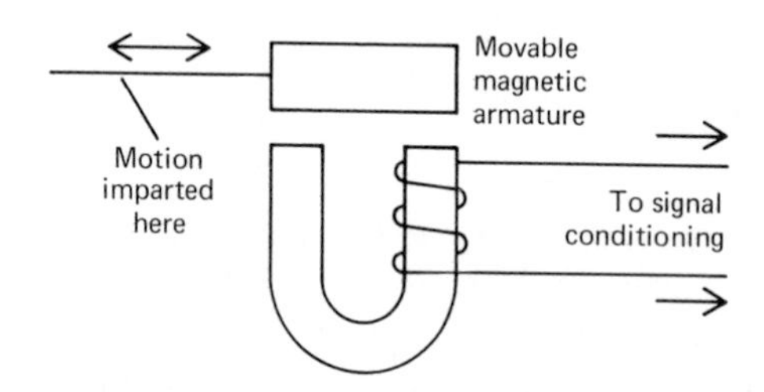

Figure 7.9. Signal-producing element of a variable reluctance transducer.

cal phenomena. These are illustrated in Figures 7.8 and 7.9. In all cases a motion or force is developed by the signal to be measured.

The linear variable differential transformer (LVDT) is an exceptionally fine transducer for displacement measurements. Figure 7.10 shows one basic circuit. The primary coil is excited with a constant a-c signal of 5-10 volts with a constant frequency from about 400-2400 cycles per second. The output signal is demodulated (to re-

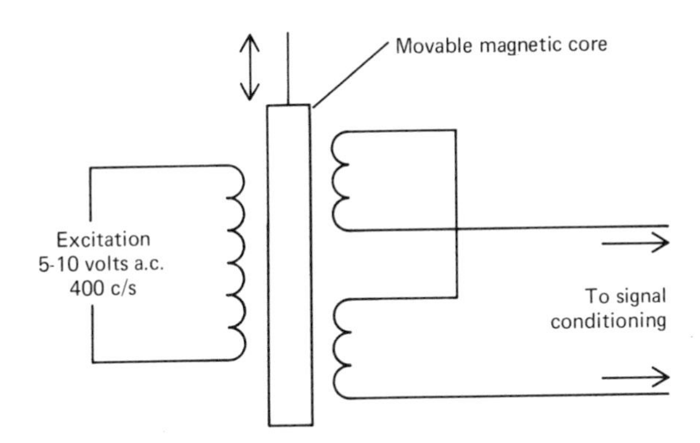

Figure 7.10. Schematic of signal-producing element of a linear variable differential transformer.

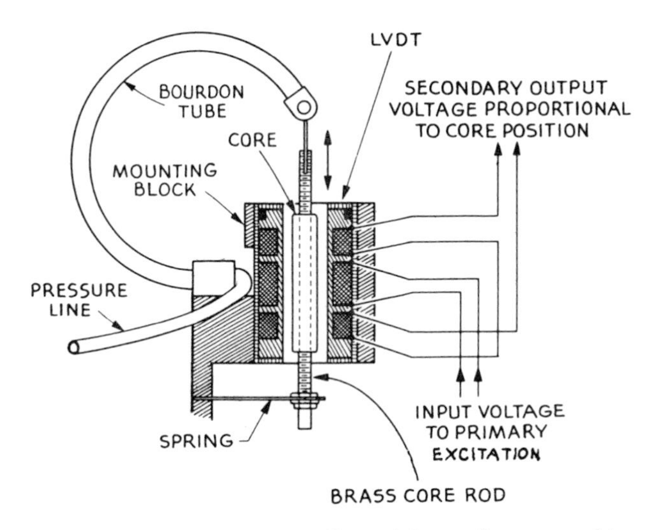

Figure 7.11. A linear variable differential transformer used to measure pressure via a bourdon tube (Courtesy of Schaevitz Engineering).

move the excitation signal), amplified and filtered to give a useable d-c output. The output bears an unusually linear relation to the displacement, and extremely small changes can be detected. This device has been used extensively in plant test work with excellent results. Figure 7.11 shows how the LVDT can be used to measure pressure, and Figure 7.12 illustrates an extremely sensitive dif-

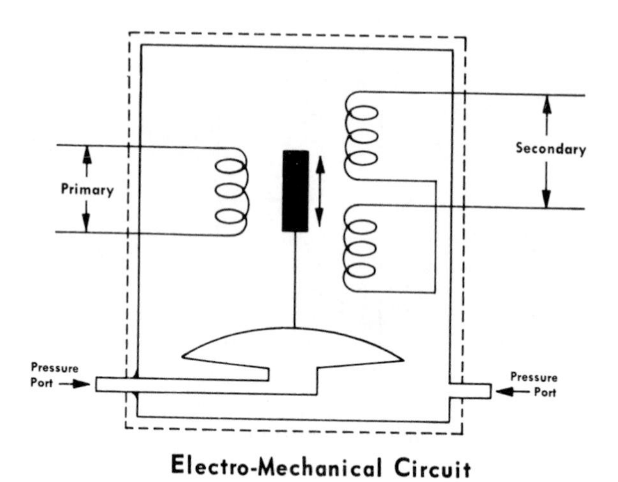

Figure 7.12. Electro-mechanical circuit of a differential pressure sensor utilizing the linear variable differential transformer (Courtesy of Hewlett-Packard, Sanborn Div.).

ferential pressure sensor using the same principles. The ability to measure pressure differentials as low as 0.000035 psi is claimed.

Displacements can frequently be measured with a battery-powered circuit involving a 10-turn precision wire wound potentiometer. Figure 7.13a shows a circuit, and Figure 7.13b shows an arrangement successfully used to measure valve-stem displacement.

The signal from the d-c potentiometric device shown in Figure 7.13 is called single ended-floating if point A is ungrounded. If grounded at A, it is called single ended-grounded. The nature of the signals from a-c excited transducers depends upon the circuits used to convert the primary transducer signal to a useable d-c signal. The ultimate output will usually be single-ended-floating or grounded.

Very recently, a differential pressure measuring device utilizing a variable electrical capacitance has become available. This is shown in

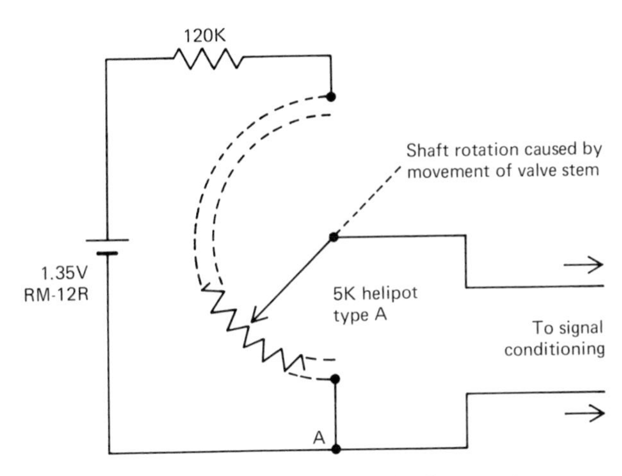

Figure 7.13a. Potentiometric circuit for displacement measurement.

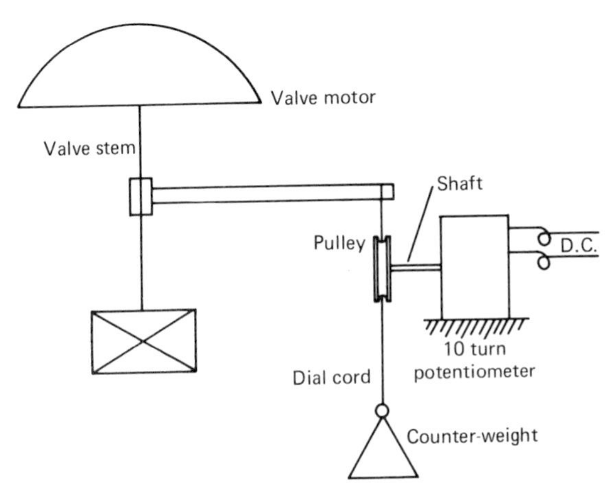

Figure 7.13b. Valve stem displacement measuring system.

Figure 7.14. Small displacements of the diaphragm-capacitance plate are caused by differential pressures transmitted through the silicone oil and isolating diaphragms. The output from the integrated circuit associated with the system is a linear d-c voltage, a function of differential pressure.

Exceptional overload capability, a feature of this component, is ac-

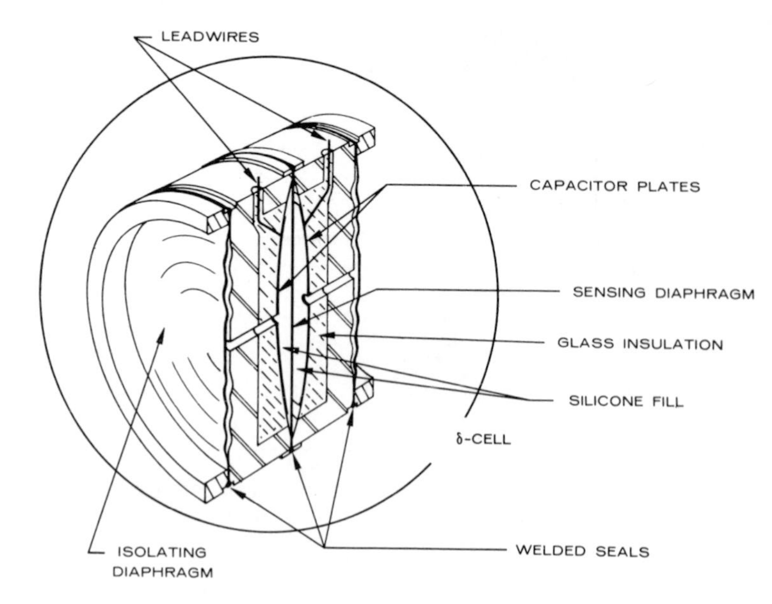

Figure 7.14. Variable capacitance type differential pressure transducer.

complished by fully supporting the measuring diaphragm against a back surface.

The turbine flow meter, Figure 7.15a may be used to measure the flow rate of liquids very accurately, easily within one percent. (See Reference 16) It is essentially a volumetric meter and is not affected appreciably by moderate changes in viscosity. Owing to the precision required in the manufacture of this instrument, the cost is relatively high. Figure 7.15b, an exploded view, clearly shows the construction. Read-out depends on counting the rate of electrical pulses developed when the magnetic turbine rotor blades pass the pole-piece of the magnetic pulse pick-up. (See insert, Figure 7.15a) The pulses are amplified, shaped and integrated, and a d-c signal is produced which is a function of the turbine angular velocity and hence volumetric flow rate.

Pulse conversion components (supplied by such firms as Airpax Electronics, Controls Div., Ft. Lauderdale, Florida and Bell & Howell Controls Div., Bridgeport, Conn.) which produce d.c. outputs are simple and inexpensive, the outputs being entirely acceptable to a millivoltmeter, digital voltmeter or recording oscillograph.

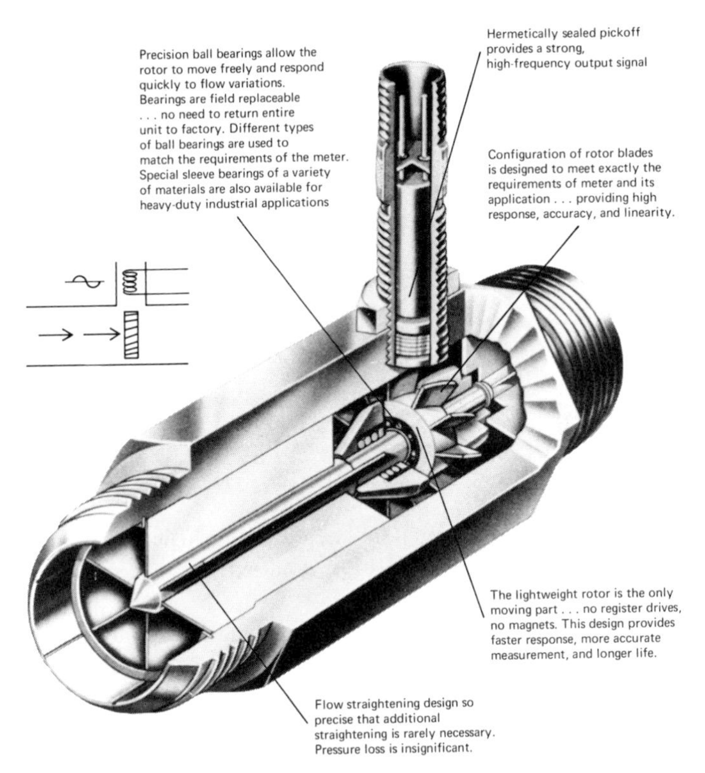

Figure 7.15a. Turbine flow meter.

Recently, a liquid flow meter has been developed the output from which depends on changes in magnetic reluctance developed in an electromagnetic circuit. The elements of the scheme are shown in Figure 7.16a, and a cut-away view is shown in Figure 7.16b. The spring-loaded magnetic spool piece is displaced in the tapered throat as a result of the flow of liquid. The a-c output is demodulated, rectified and amplified. Two percent accuracy is claimed. The meter is bidirectional.

The use of the above turbine and variable reluctance type of flow sensor is limited to liquid streams free from solid particles and to applications where corrosion is not a problem.

Both the turbine and variable reluctance meter produce signals

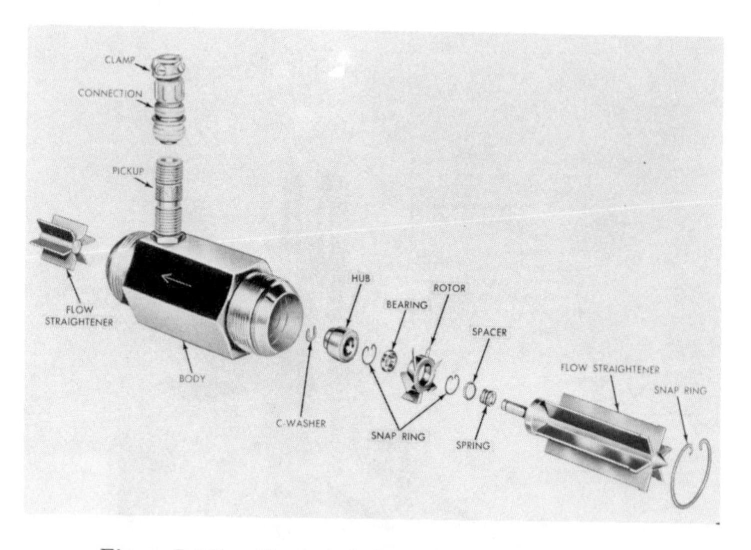

Figure 7.15b. Exploded view of turbine flow meter.

which are linear with flow rate. The output is single-ended floating in both instances. They have been used extensively for plant test work with very satisfactory results.

Flow sensors which measure the pressure gradient developed across a constriction are the most commonly used in industrial practice. They are useful for both gases and liquids. The orifice plate, because of its low cost, is the most popular (Figure 7.17a).

When installed in strict accordance with specifications, the flow of a fluid with known physical properties can be measured quite accurately with an orifice plate, perhaps within one percent of full scale. In practice, it is frequently very difficult to satisfy all specifications, and more frequently the properties of the fluid are somewhat uncertain. These conditions limit the accuracy practically attainable to about five percent. A very large literature is extant relevant to flow measurements with orifici, some of which are included in the list of publications given at the end of this chapter. A study of orifici for measuring flow in pipes less than one inch is reported in Reference 17.

Other differential pressure flow sensors are the Venturi tube (Figures 7.17b and 7.17c), the Dall tube (Figure 7.17d), and nozzles of various configurations (Figures 7.17e and 7.17f).

The use of the throat tapped nozzle (Figure 7.17e) for measuring

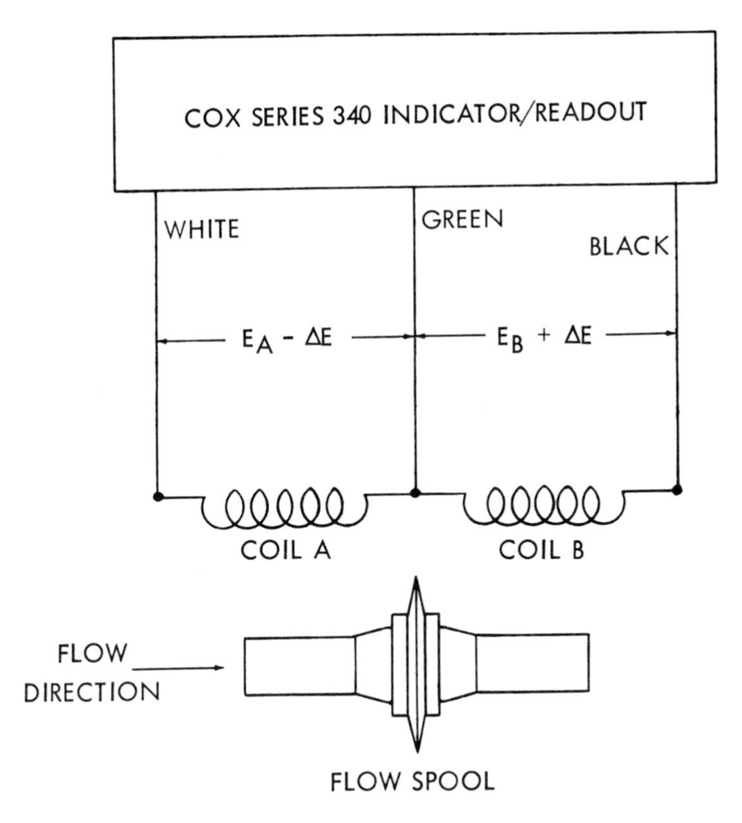

Figure 7.16a. Schematic diagram of electrical circuit for variable reluctance flow sensor (Courtesy of Cox Instrument, Div. of Lynch Corp.).

steam to turbines is described by Cotton and Wescott in Reference 18. Very high accuracy is claimed at sufficiently high Reynolds numbers.

A novel flow meter, called the Flowloop, (see Reference 19) has several advantages. The permanent pressure loss is low, the ratio of signal corruption (noise) to useful signal is low (about one-third that of an orifice), and the signal is virtually independent of viscosity. An arrangement used to measure the flow of molten heat transfer salt is shown in Figure 7.18. Air or gas must be excluded from the sealing oil connecting the transducer to the seals, and these lines should be

Figure 7.16b. Cutaway view of spring-mounted flow detector, variable area flow path and twin coils (Courtesy of Cox Instrument, Div. of Lynch Corp.).

small and kept in the same temperature environment. The meter is bidirectional.

The strain gage and variable capacitance differential pressure transducers are well suited as primary sensors of the output differential pressure signal generated by orifici, Venturi or Dall tubes, nozzles and Flowloops.

Among other flow meters are those which meter mass directly (supplied by such firms as Technology, Incorporated, Dayton, Ohio and General Electric Co., Lynn, Mass.), and magnetic flow meters (Foxboro Co., Foxboro, Mass., and Fischer & Porter Co., Warminster, Pa.). The latter operate well with fluids which have some electrical conductivity and have the advantage of being able to handle liquids containing solids. Cost is a principal disadvantage of both mass meters and magnetic flow meters.

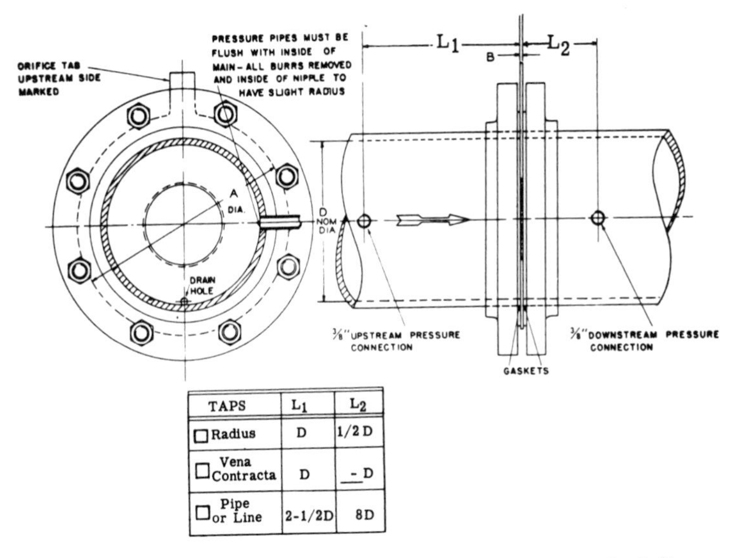

TAPS	L1	L2
☐ Radius	D	1/2 D
☐ Vena Contracta	D	- D
☐ Pipe or Line	2-1/2D	8D

Figure 7.17a. Orifice plate for installation between standard flanges (Courtesy of BIF, a unit of General Signal Corp.).

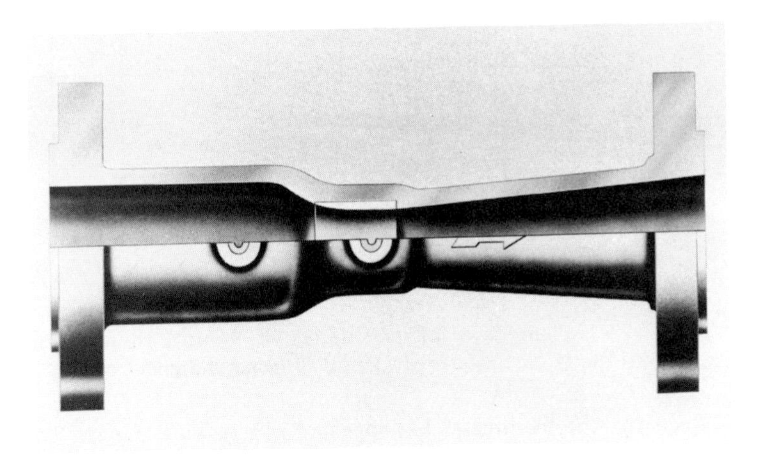

Figure 7.17b. Venturi flow nozzle sectional elevation view (Courtesy of BIF, a unit of General Signal Corp.).

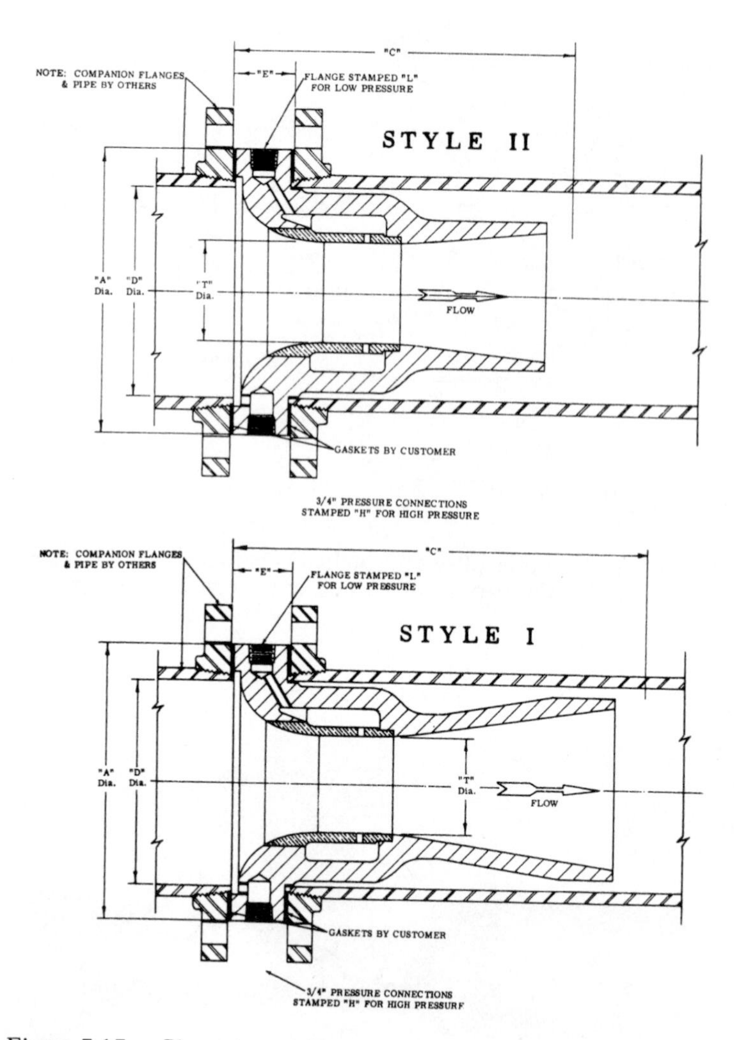

Figure 7.17c. Plan views of two styles of Venturi flow nozzles (Courtesy of BIF, a unit of General Signal Corp.).

Recently, the Swirlmeter has appeared as a gas-flow meter. This operates on the principle that the frequency of rotation of the eccentric vortex in a stream downstream from a properly designed restriction is proportional to the fluid flow. The rate of variation in resistance of a heated thermistor is the output signal. Figure 7.19 illustrates this meter.

Where sufficient pressure is available, the critical orifice is an ex-

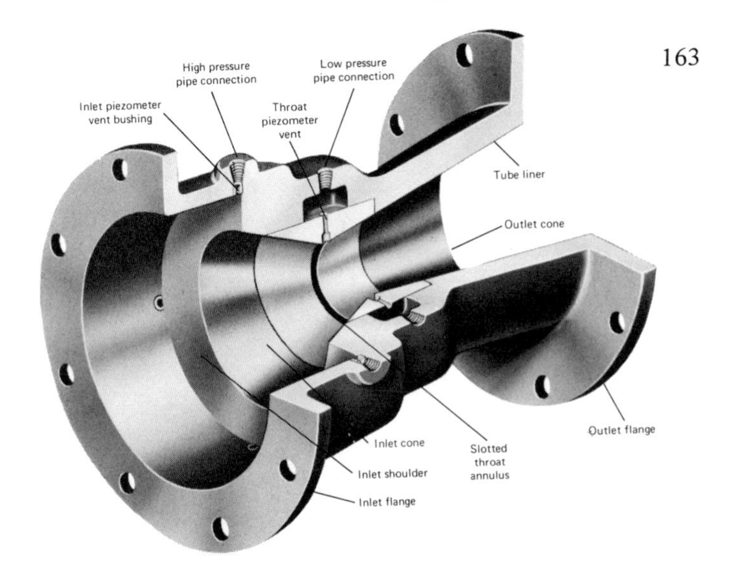

Figure 7.17d. Sectional view of typical Dall flow tube (Courtesy of BIF, a unit of General Signal Corp.).

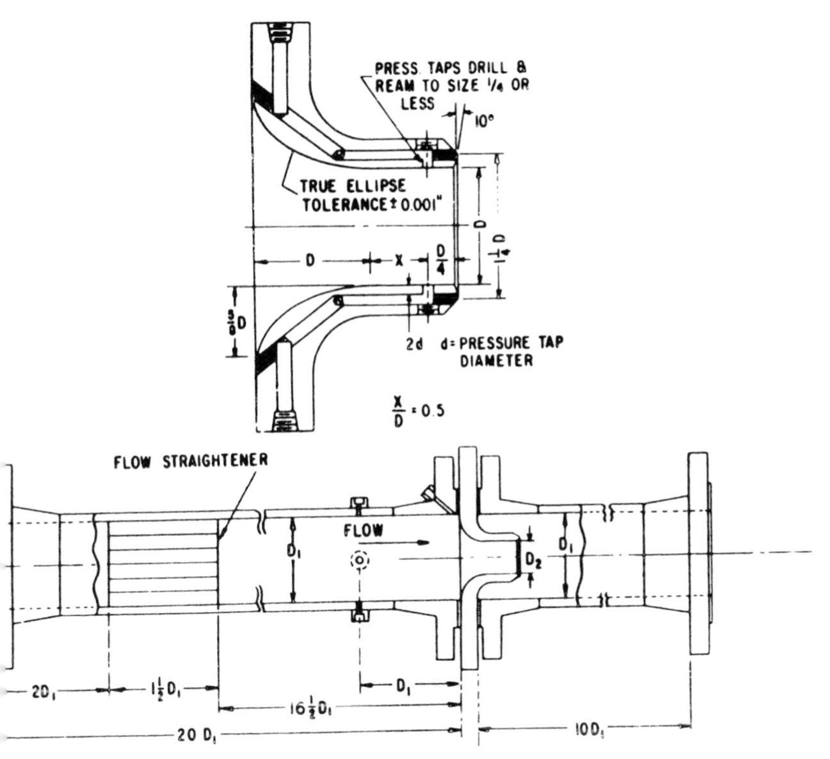

Figure 7.17e. Throat tapped flow nozzle and recommended method of installation.

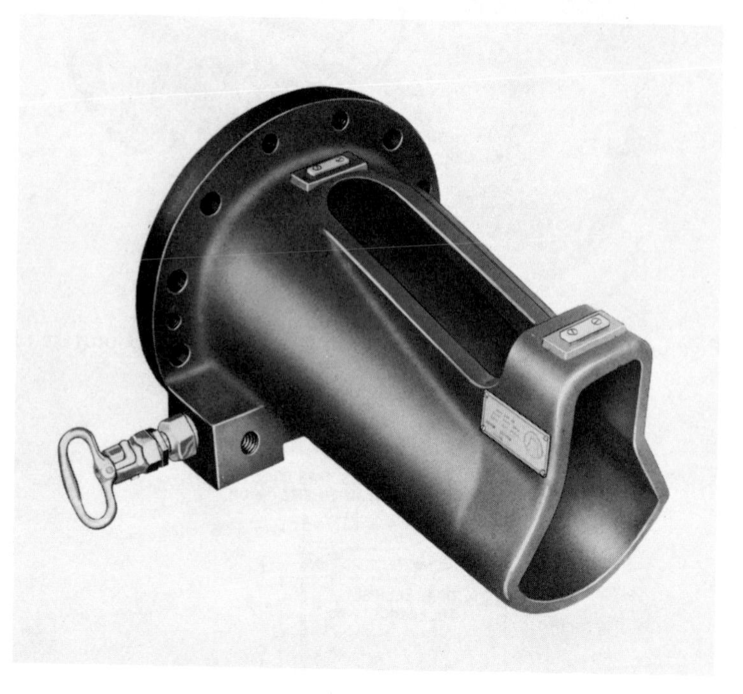

Figure 7.17f. Kennison flow nozzle (Courtesy of BIF, a unit of General Signal Corp.).

ceptionally excellent flow meter for gases, especially for measuring small flow rates. This device uses the fact that, if the absolute upstream pressure is about 2.5 times the absolute pressure on the downstream side of a sharp-edged orifice, the velocity of flow depends only upon the upstream pressure. The theory is developed in *Chemical Engineering Thermodynamics*, B. F. Dodge, McGraw-Hill (Reference 20).

For low-molecular weight gases,

$$W = CpA\sqrt{\frac{MW}{T}}$$

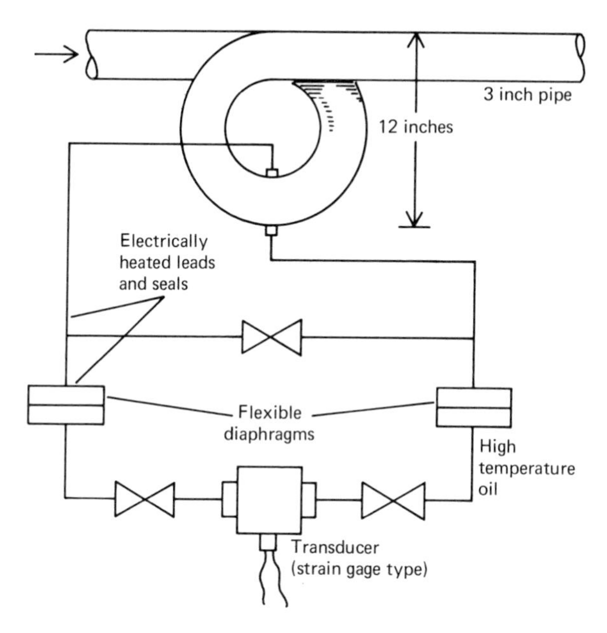

Figure 7.18. A Flowloop used to meter the flow of molten salt.

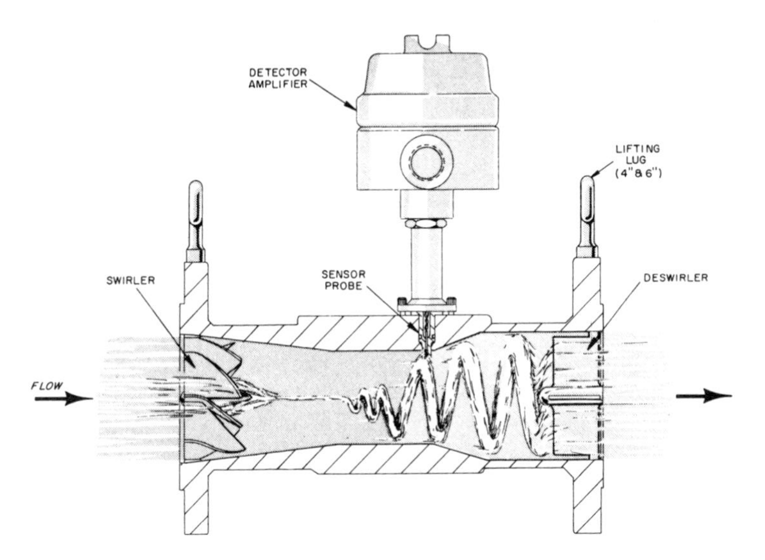

Figure 7.19. Cutaway of a Swirlmeter (Courtesy of Fischer & Porter Co.).

where

W = mass rate of flow
C = discharge coefficient
A = cross-sectional area of orifice
p = fore pressure, absolute
MW = molecular weight of gas
T = absolute temperature.

Calibration is convenient since only two or three points are required for a given gas to establish the straight-line relation which exists for values of p in excess of 2.5 times the downstream absolute pressure. Also the calibrating gas need not be the gas to be metered. Calibrated critical flow nozzles are commercially available (supplied by such firms as Flow-Dyne Engineering, Inc., Fort Worth, Texas) in all sizes.

Where sufficient upstream pressure is available and a high pressure drop can be tolerated, the critical flow device should not be overlooked. For very small gas flows, it is particularly attractive. In Reference 21, Carter describes techniques for making such orifici for very low flow rates. Other critical flow meters used to measure gas flow rate are described in References 22 and 23.

Electrical signals from flow meters depend upon the transducer used to measure the sensor output. Where strain gage bridges are involved, the signal is balanced–off ground. The usual output from a pulse converter used in connection with a turbine flow meter is floating and single-ended.

Angular and linear velocity may be measured by pulse-counting techniques. The rotating or moving member must be provided with magnetic proturbances in such a manner that they pass close to the magnetic pulse pick-up sensor. A nominal clearance of about 0.005 inches is recommended. The measurement of angular velocity is illustrated in Figure 7.20. Linear velocity can sometimes be measured by applying the above technique.

Figure 7.21 shows how the linear velocity of, or the differential velocity between points on, a moving surface can be measured. Technical data and recommended practices are available from the manufacturers of the pulse-detection and read-out devices.

For plant test work, liquid level measurements can be measured by differential pressure transducers of the strain-gage type. Appropriate

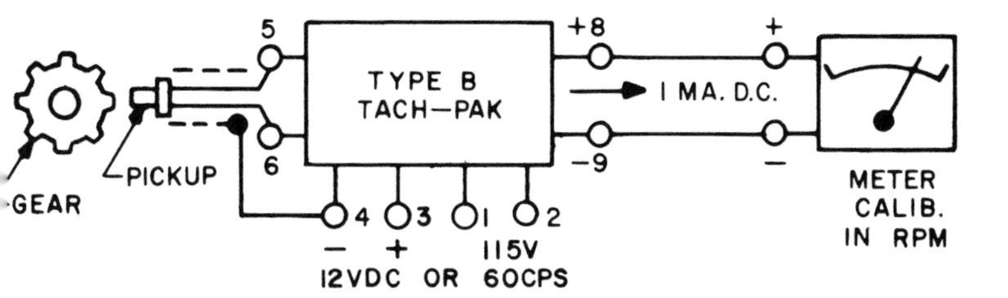

RPM TO FREQUENCY CONVERSION

$$\text{FREQ.} = \frac{\text{RPM X NO. OF GEAR TEETH}}{60}$$

BLOCK DIAGRAM

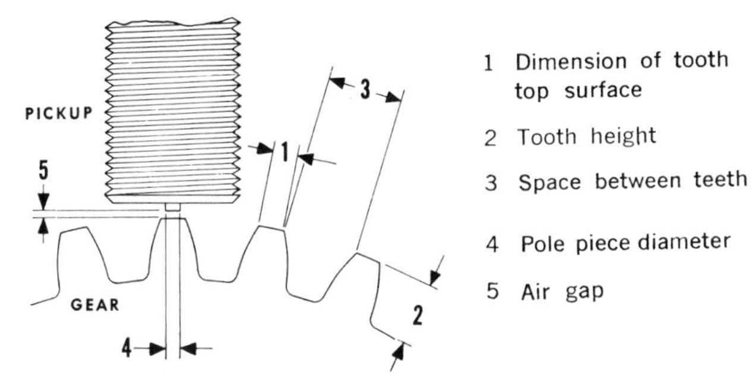

Figure 7.20. Pulse counting ensemble, components and method of installation for measuring angular velocity (Courtesy of Airpax Electronics, Controls Div.).

sealing techniques must be used if the sensor is to be protected from the process fluids.

Electrical power can be measured very conveniently by using Hall effect watt meters. Voltage and current are usually transformed, and the attenuated signals are presented to the watt meter. At least one manufacturer (Beckman Instrument, Inc., Schiller Park, Illinois) has a special plug-in module to be used with their recording oscillograph (Dynagraph II) designed to produce a linear output as a function of electrical power.

Mechanical power usually requires a measure of torque and shaft speed. The latter can be measured via pulse counting or with a tachometer. Torque requires a measure of the angular deflection of a

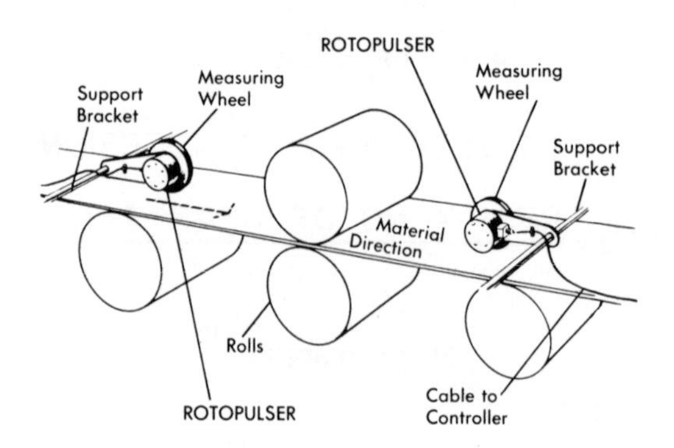

Figure 7.21. Pulse generating devices used for measuring velocity and velocity differential of a moving surface (Courtesy of Louis Allis Co.).

shaft with a known stress-strain relationship. Special torque sensors are available from a number of sources (supplied by such firms as B-L-H Electronics). Transmission of the signal from the torque sensor usually (although not always) requires a connection to the moving shaft. Slip rings can be purchased (supplied by such firms as Lebow Associates, Inc., Oak Park, Michigan) or shop-fabricated. One assembly is illustrated in Figure 7.22. (Courtesy Professor J. Bollinger, The University of Wisconsin.) As the shaft rotates, the continuous helix travels in the grooved retainer ring, rolling in the same direction as the shaft.

Multibristled copper brushes contacting a broad copper rail insulated from the kiln shell are used to transmit signals from thermocouples measuring the temperature of cement kilns. Provision is made to maintain alignment of the contact as the kiln length changes with temperature. Figure 7.23 shows one arrangement.

Slip rings may be eliminated by transformer coupling of a special shaft section provided with a torque strain gage bridge with a set of pickup windings mounted on a stationary member. The basic circuit is shown in Figure 7.24. (Available from C-E Electronics, Inc.,

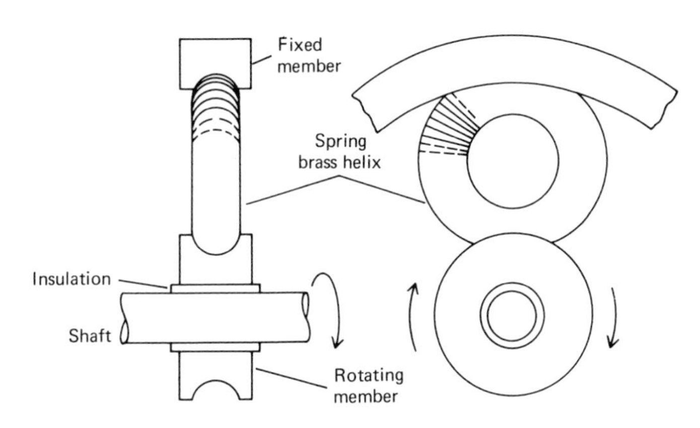

Figure 7.22. Slip rings for transmitting signals from rotating members.

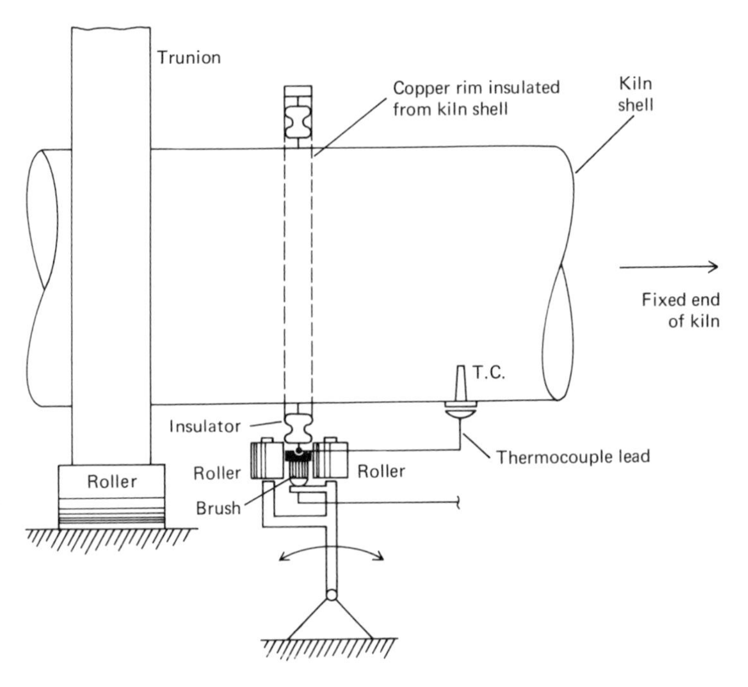

Figure 7.23. Brush contacts for transmitting signals from moving members.

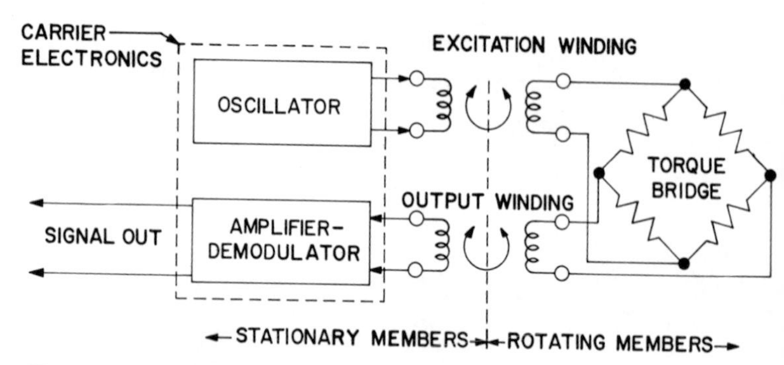

Figure 7.24. Shaft type torque sensing circuit for rotary transformer signal transmission (Courtesy of S. Himmelstein).

Glenside, Pennsylvania and S. Himmelstein and Co., Elk Grove Village, Illinois.)

Telemetering of signals from inaccessible and moving parts is described in References 24 and 25. In the future, telemetering and 2-wire systems will find increased application in the process industry.

The foregoing descriptive material merely indicates the nature of some of the basic electrical circuits, components and techniques for measuring the most commonly encountered industrial variables. Journals and books, some of which are listed in references at the end of this chapter, should be consulted for information concerning sources, theory and performance data. The books cited are replete with excellent information helpful to the engineer interested in plant measurements. Specialized information on component performance and methods of application can be obtained from vendors. The many documents available from the Instrument Society of America contain a wealth of useful information.

Signal Conditioning The conversion and processing of signals from the basic sensing device or transducer is called signal conditioning. Signal conditioning of analog signals consists of the following:

(1) filtering to attenuate signal corruption,

(2) amplifying to produce a signal strength sufficient to activate an indicating or recording device, and

(3) Suppressing to remove all or part of the steady-state value of a

complex signal. A complex signal consists, in this sense, of a dynamic or transient component and a steady-state d-c component. Although suppression can be applied after a complex signal has been amplified, more frequently the d-c component is biased out ahead of the amplifier leaving only the transient portion to be amplified.

A data system with a high degree of versatility and capability in respect to signal conditioning is essential if meaningful data are to be acquired from a plant testing program. It is precisely because conventional industrial data systems of the kind being currently installed are remiss in signal conditioning capabilities that they are also ill-suited for procuring useful information.

Knowledge of the nature of signal sources, amplifier characteristics, basic circuitry and recommended wiring practices is necessary if acceptable measurement accuracy is to be achieved. It is important to retrieve reliable data having a fairly well-defined and narrow margin of uncertainty; otherwise, the data are worse than none at all. A major source of uncertainty is the signal corruption (noise) which accompanies the desired signal. The ratio of noise to signal may be as high as 10^6 to 1.

Signal corruption may appear overemphasized because recording of low-level d-c voltages from thermocouples or other sources using existing plant instrumentation does not appear to exhibit difficulties. The reason thermocouple outputs (or other low-level d-c voltages) as measured by present plant instrumentation appear noise-free is because the measuring instruments are excellent low-pass filters—only the very low frequency signal is indicated, higher frequency signals being almost completely rejected. Such instruments cannot be used to measure signals which vary rapidly with time.

Two basic amplifier configurations are commonly used for handling signals from transducers producing low-level signals: (1) chopper input d-c amplifiers which can be used with transducers producing a d-c output, and (2) carrier amplifiers which are used with transducers externally excited with a constant voltage—constant frequency a-c supply.

In order to create floating internal signals which are at a low level with respect to ground, high-performance chopper-and carrier-type amplifiers are usually transformer coupled. Thus, while the input signals may be considerably off ground, subsequent signals are not and hence can be handled easier with less danger of breakdown of insulation, leakage, etc. Schematic diagrams of the two types of amplifiers are shown in Figures 7.25 and 7.27. More complete descriptions are available from manufacturers, such as Beckman Instruments, Inc., Electronic Instruments Division, 3900 River Road, Schiller Park, Illinois and Hewlett-Packard Co., Sanborn Division, 175 Wyman Street, Waltham, Massachusetts).

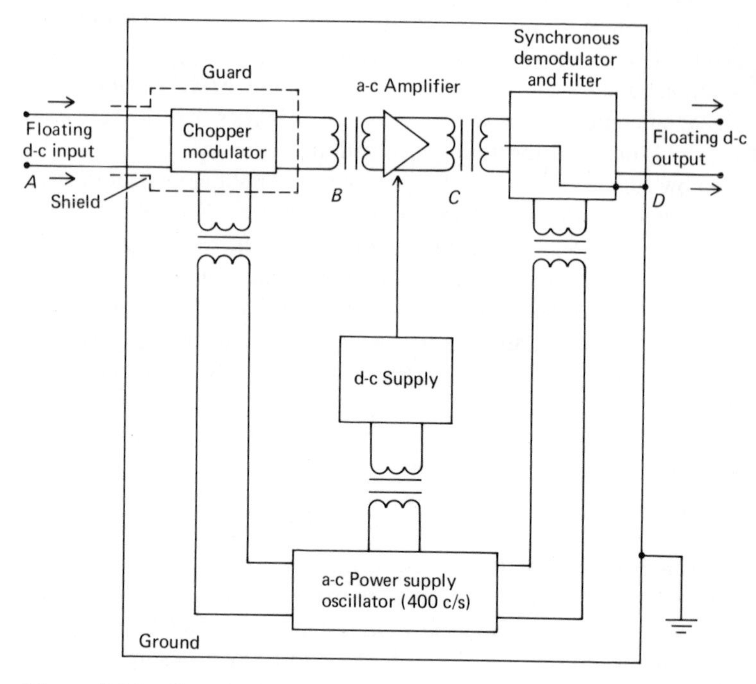

Figure 7.25. Standard configuration of a chopper input d-c amplifier.

The chopper input d-c amplifier converts a floating d-c input into an 'a-c' signal, the amplitude of which is determined by the value of the d-c input. The chopped signal is coupled through a transformer to a high sensitivity a-c amplifier. By means of the synchronous demodulator, the amplified a-c signal is converted back to a d-c signal. The demodulation is kept synchronous by driving all transformers from a common source. The time history of a transient input signal at various points in the amplifier system is shown in Figure 7.26. Whereas signals at *A* and *B* may be considerably off ground, the signals at *C* and *D* are usually only very slightly off ground.

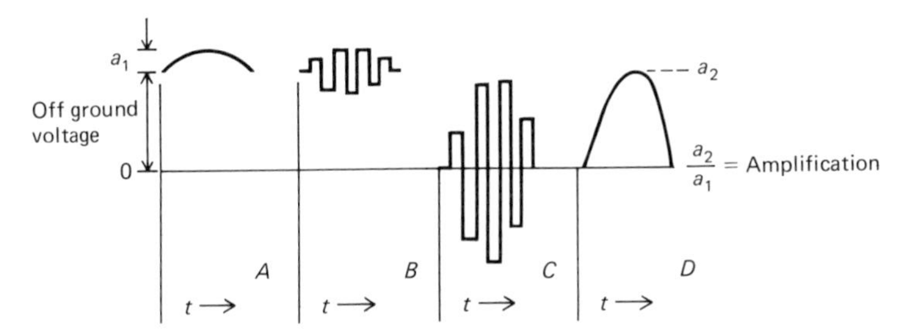

Figure 7.26. Appearance of a transient d-c signal at various points in a chopper input amplifier.

It should be noted that the chopper modulator, Figure 7.25 which may be considerably off ground, is protected by a guard shield to which is connected the shield or drain wire enclosed in the signal cable. The final transformer is center-tapped to ground along with the chassis of the amplifier ensemble.

Chopper input d-c amplifiers can measure voltages oscillating up to about 50 percent of the chopper frequency—i.e., 200 cps. This is usually 5-6 times the frequency at which a mechanical ink or hot stylus recording mechanism can follow faithfully an oscillatory input. Thus, this amplifier is classified as d-c. It's simplified schematic diagram is given in Figure 7.27.

Carrier amplifiers are used in connection with a-c excited transducers. In a sense, this technique eliminates the need for a chopper because a modulated a-c signal is generated by the transducer. The low-level modulated a-c signal is amplified in an a-c amplifier and then demodulated in a manner similar to that described above. A

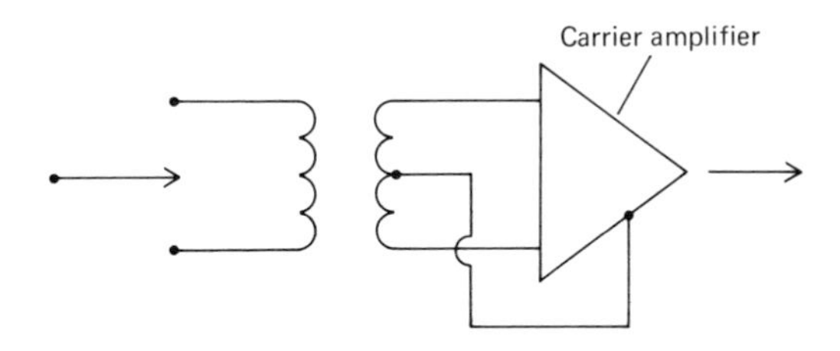

Figure 7.27. Diagrammatic representation of a chopper stabilized d-c amplifier system.

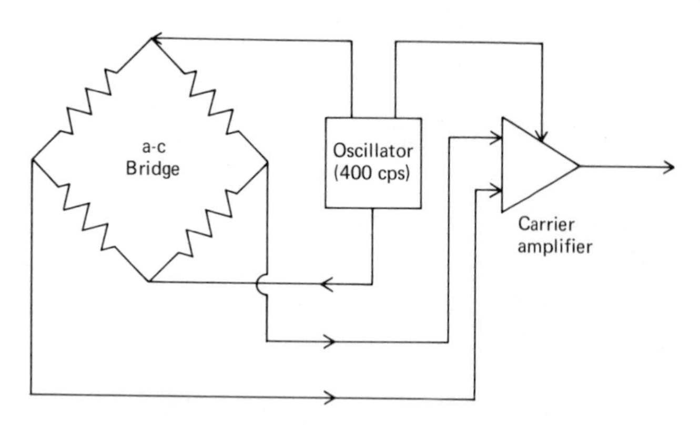

Figure 7.28. Diagrammatic representation of a carrier amplifier and a-c excited transducer.

schematic diagram of an a-c excited bridge oscillator and amplifier is shown in Figure 7.28.

Signal conditioning systems for use with low-level inputs should possess the following properties.

(1) The equipment should have good stability including both zero-line stability and gain stability. The gain, for example, should remain constant at a given setting, and the output should not deviate for a constant input. Deviations should not exceed 0.1 percent. Stability should be maintained in spite of environmental changes such as rapid temperature fluctuations.

(2) The input impedance should be high with respect to the source output impedance and should remain constant at all attenuator and gain settings. If line resistance is neglected, a ratio of source output to amplifier input impedance as low as 10:1 can be tolerated if the resulting error is known and compensated via an adjustment to the amplifier gain setting. Similarly, compensation for insertion loss, due to filters or very long signal cable runs, should be taken into account. However, an amplifier input impedance of at least 100,000 ohms is commonly recommended. Extremely high impedance transducers can be the cause of noise at the amplifier input.

When measuring outputs from electrometers, pH sensors, or quartz crystal transducers, an extremely high input impedance is required, 10^{10} ohms, for example.

(3) Preferably the input should be floating with respect to ground.

(4) A guard should be provided around the chopper modulator to protect this section from disturbances, and the cable shield or drain wire should be connected to this guard. The guard may be floating in respect to the chassis ground.

(5) A wide range of sensitivity selections should be available to enable both amplification of signals in the microvolt level and attenuation of high level signals.

For process studies, sensitivity adjustments which provide a range from 1 microvolt to 100 volts per millimeter chart readout are recommended if multichannel oscillograph recorders are used.

(6) When the information of interest consists of very small deviations from a steady-state condition, suppression sufficient to bias-out all of the d-c (steady-state) level must be provided. This is important because it is from such observations that much useful static and dynamic information is retrieved.

This feature is especially convenient for obtaining static data, for the signal may be nulled with the high quality potentiometer using a high amplification. The steady-state value can then be read directly from the position of the calibrated potentiometer with great precision.

(7) Linearity of the measuring system output should be preserved within at least 0.2 percent of the input signal.

(8) The frequency response of the amplifiers should be 4–5 times that of the recording system. For direct writing oscillographs, the pen mechanism is usually flat to about 30–40 cps. The amplifier should be flat to about 200 cps.

While response of this quality seldom is needed for process studies, it is not uncommon that signals varying at 10 cycles per second are encountered.

(9) Adjustable filtering capability sufficient to virtually eliminate signals from 400 to 10 cps. Especially important is the capability to attenuate effectively very sharply peaked low level noise and the ever-present 60 cycle "hum."

It is important to know the characteristics of the filters used so that an evaluation of the information rejected can be made.

Noise Sources. Sources of signal corruption or noise and possible remedies are listed below. (Also, see References 26, 27, and 28.)

Inductive Pickup From Power Sources. This noise usually appears as 60-cps "hum" from power transmission lines, 120-cps noise from fluorescent lamps, and high frequency disturbances from switching, commutator and pulse transmitting devices. To minimize unwanted signals from these sources, obey the following rules.

(a) Select transducers giving high fidelity outputs.
(b) Protect the transducer from spurious inputs by proper shielding.
(c) Use high quality cables in which the signal-conducting pair is twisted and shielded and with a ground or drain wire included inside the outer insulation of the cable. (See Figure 7.29.) Belden 8723 has served very well in extensive plant work using analog recording. (Belden 8728 provides maximum protection from signal corruption.)
(d) Never ground the drain wire or shield at more than one point.
(e) Keep cable lengths short and the shielding continuous.
(f) Separate signal cables from power cables as much as possible, and minimize parallel runs.
(g) Never splice low-level signal cables.
(h) At terminals, keep the separation between the signal wires as small as possible to minimize inductive pickup.

Common-impedance Coupling Via Ground Loops. If more than one connection to ground exists on a signal circuit, the difference in ground potentials, which may be large, will cause a current flow. Sixty-cycle voltage will usually appear in these cases which will couple with the signal, completely obscuring it.

The remedy is to assiduously avoid multiple grounds. Select transducers giving a floating output, if possible, and amplifiers with a floating guard. Ground the signal source and cable shield (and guard) only at the source or at the data system. Electronic racks and chasses are grounded at the data system, isolated from the guard.

Electrostatic Coupling to a-c Signals. This is caused by distributed capacitance between signal conductors and between signal conductors and ground. This kind of interference is sometimes referred to as cross-talk.

Corruption of this kind is reduced by using signal conductors in twisted pairs, each pair wrapped with a lapped foil shield and with a low-resistance drain wire making contact with the outside of the foil at all points. (The drain wire is superior to the more conventional braided wire shield.) The drain wire is well-grounded at some fixed potential and is carried through connectors and connected to any extra pins in the connectors. Unused shielded conductors within the

STRAIN GAUGE QUAD CABLES

Description	Trade Number	No. of Cond.	AWG & (Stranding)	Insulation Thickness (Inch)	Jacket Thickness (Inch)	Nom. O.D. (Inch)	Cond. Color Coding	Percent Shield Coverage	Nom. *Cap. (mmf/ft)	Nom. **Cap. (mmf/ft)	Suggested Working Voltage	Standard Spool Lengths in ft
 BELDFOIL®	**8434·**	4	25 (7x33) 3 copper 4 copper-weld	.013	.020	.179	Red, Blk, Grn, Clear	100	25	40	400	100, 500, 1000
	Tinned copper, polyethylene insulated, black and red conductors under BELDFOIL aluminum-polyester shield, stranded ground wire, green and clear conductors under over-all BELDFOIL aluminum-polyester shield, chrome vinyl jacket. Pairs cabled on common axis to reduce diameter. ⊖											
 BELDFOIL®	**8723·**	4	22 (7x30) copper	.008	.019	.165	Red, Blk, Grn, Wht	100	35	62	400	100, 500, 1000
	Tinned copper, polypropylene insulated, black and red under a BELDFOIL aluminum-polyester shield. Green and white under a BELDFOIL aluminum-polyester shield, stranded tinned copper drain wire, chrome vinyl jacket. Pairs cabled on common axis to reduce diameter. ⊖											
 BELDFOIL®	**★8728**	4	22 (7x30)	.008	.021	.188	Red, Blk, Grn, Wht	100	35	62	400	500, 1000
	Tinned copper, polypropylene insulated, cabled in pairs each pair BELDFOIL aluminum-polyester shielded with stranded copper drain wire, polyester film over each shield, overall BELDFOIL aluminum-polyester shield and stranded tinned copper drain wire, chrome vinyl jacket. Pairs cabled on common axis to reduce diameter. ⊖											

Figure 7.29. Shielded instrumentation, strain gauge and communication cables (Courtesy Belden Corp.).

cable should be single-end grounded with their shields grounded at the other end.

Ineffective Temperature Compensation. Zero drift in the recording system may be caused by temperature changes which are not properly compensated either within the transducer or in the lead wire, amplifier or recorder. Strain-gage bridges, such as used in pressure transducers, resistance type temperature sensing bridges and other balanced bridge devices, are particularly sensitive to temperature effects.

To combat this source of uncertainty, select components (transducers, power supplies, amplifiers, etc.) with temperature compensation or which are stable in this respect. (Strain-gage bridges are usually temperature compensated.) Use circuits which compensate for temperature change in the lead wires to the bridges. In some cases, it may be necessary to use an extra pair of conductors in order to measure (and maintain) the excitation voltage at the bridge instead of at the power supply output. (Sometimes constant current excitation may be required) Cold junction compensators for thermocouples must also be stable. These should be verified as adequate prior to use.

Inadequate Common-mode Rejection. The accurate transmission of low level signals in the environment of electrical disturbances or between points at different ground potentials requires exacting wiring practices and attention to small details. The difficulty basically centers on the fact that an amplifier cannot distinguish between the the signal from the transducer and that produced by disturbances.

For example, suppose the voltage from a grounded thermocouple is to be measured–i.e., amplified sufficiently to drive a galvanometer which in turn causes the deflection of a writing pen. Let the resistance of the lead wires be R_1 and R_2 so that the circuit appears as shown in Figure 7.30a.

Between ground A and B, assume the existance of a voltage difference e_{cm}, referred to as the "common mode" voltage. This is usually an a-c voltage and very frequently is 60 cps.

Ideally, e_{cm} should not be permitted to drive current through R_1 or R_2 nor should it drive current through the amplifier in the absence of R_1 or R_2.

The ability of an amplifier to not respond to or reject e_{cm} is measured by its common mode rejection ratio (CMR). This is a measure of the ratio of e_{cm} to the equivalent input voltage that it produces.

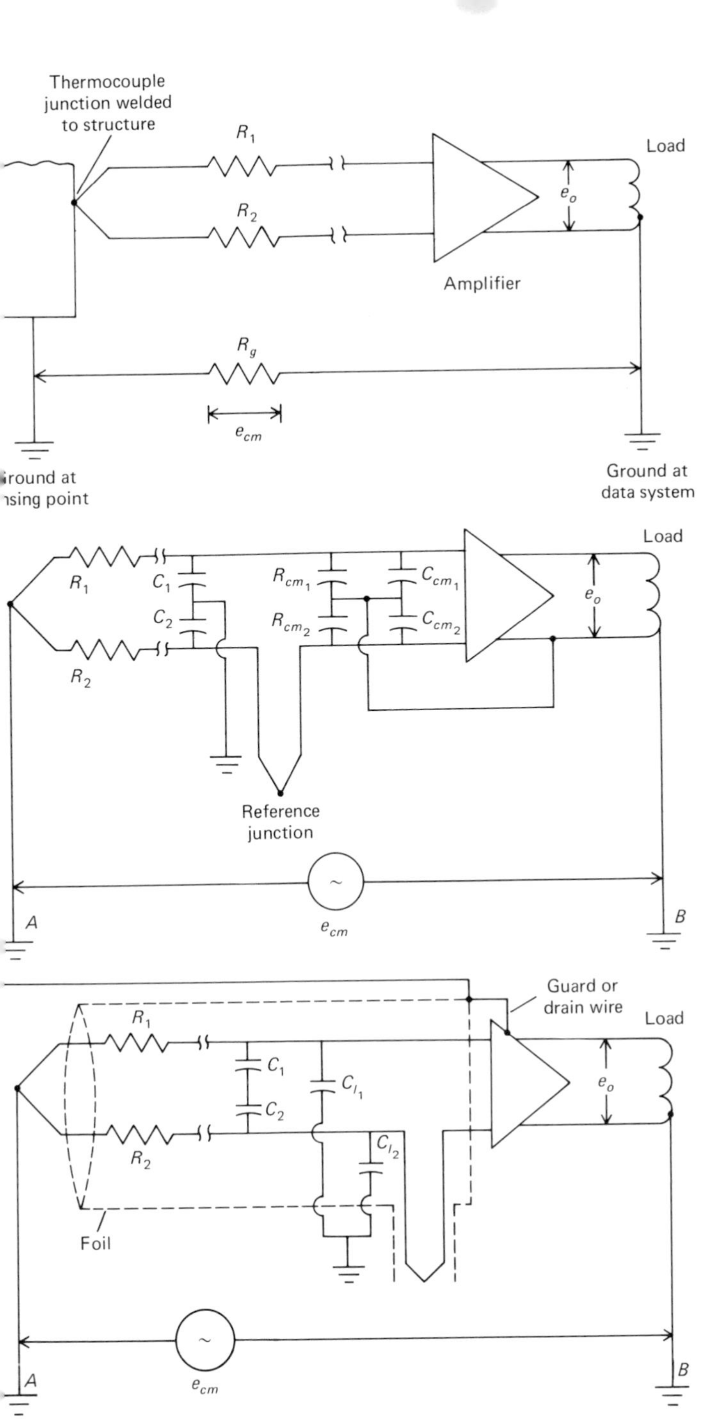

Figure 7.30. Origin of common mode signals.

In decibels, it is written

$$(CMR)_{db} = 20 \log_{10} \left[\frac{e_{cm}}{\left(\frac{e_o}{K} \right)} \right]$$

where,

e_{cm} = common mode voltage,
e_o = output voltage produced by e_{cm}
K = amplifier gain, and

$\frac{e_o}{K}$ is the ideal input which would produce e_o in the output. It is desired to have *CMR* as large as possible.

A more realistic situation is shown in Figure 7.30b. R_1 and R_2 are resistive impedances; C_1 and C_2 represent distributed capacitances. R_{cm_1}, R_{cm_2}, C_{cm_1} and C_{cm_2} are the input-output coupling of the amplifier by virtue of which a common mode voltage on the input appears in the output of the amplifier. It is clear that R_1 and R_2 could be quite different depending upon the type and length of the thermocouple wires and the length of copper leads used. C_1 and C_2 could also be different, but in any event the *impedance* of the two branches could be appreciable and could produce a phase shift in the a-c signals appearing at the amplifier input.

High quality amplifiers have R_{cm} values from 10^9 to 10^{13} ohms, and C_m usually varies from about 0.3 to 3 picofarads; the *CMR* may be as high as 120 db at 60 cps.

To reduce the errors associated with common mode voltages, it is necessary to surround as much of the source and signal conductors as possible with a shield or guard shield. Thus, the input signal pair is twisted and wrapped with metallized foil, and an uninsulated guard wire, making contact with the foil along its length, is included within the outer insulation of the cable. This is shown in Figure 7.30c. With this arrangement, the voltage surrounding the conductors and guard around the amplifier corresponds very closely to the common mode voltage. Phase shift is minimized in the distributed system, and the capacitance between conductors to ground, shown as C_{1_1} and C_{1_2}, is diminished. Coupling through the amplifier is also minimized.

Signal Source Loading. If the impedance of the amplifier is too low, an appreciable flow of current may occur in the lead-wires. The *IR* drop thus developed is deducted from the potential at the source. If the extent of loading is unpredictable, it is not possible to calibrate the system.

The best solution is to use amplifiers with such a high impedance that errors of this kind are negligible. The impedance of the amplifier should be at least 1000 times that of the output impedance of the signal source.

Variable Contact Resistances. Resistances which occur in switches and connections of any kind must remain constant. The measuring system cannot distinguish the source of voltage differences. Balanced circuits, of which bridges are typical, are particularly susceptible.

This difficulty is reduced by using high-quality compression-type connectors, expert soldering or fusing and cleaned, tinned copper binding posts.

Banana-type plugs are not recommended in low level signal circuits.

Conducted a-c Line Transients. These enter through the source of power to the amplifiers and power supplies, being generated by large transients in the main supply line voltage. They are removed by power line filters, isolation transformers or by eliminating the cause at its source. Many high quality power supplies have a remarkable ability to handle power line transients.

Thermo-electric Drift. This develops at junctions of dissimilar metals and is temperature dependent (like a thermocouple). By minimizing the number of junctions and keeping susceptible junctions at the same temperature, uncertainties from this cause can be reduced. The voltage produced from a resistive transducer depends upon the transducer impedance and the current flow. Any interference which changes the current flow will produce a spurious output or noise. For this reason, low-impedance transducers are desired. Low-impedance transducers together with high-impedance amplifiers are the best combination. References listed at the end of this chapter discuss common noise sources and offer remedies.

Figure 7.31 serves to show the effect of transducer loading on the voltage at the amplifier. If the amplifier impedance is R_a ohms, the ratio of voltage produced at a transducer of resistance R_t to that measured at the amplifier is given as $R_a/(R_a + R_t)$. The percentage

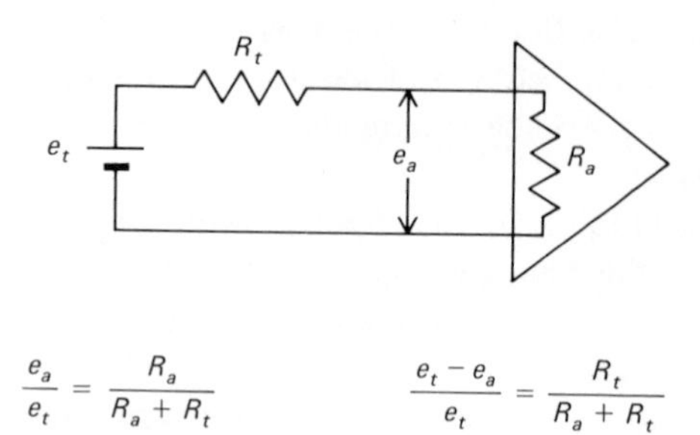

Figure 7.31. Error incurred by loading transducers.

error is

$$\left(\frac{e_t - e_a}{e_t}\right) \times 100 = \left(\frac{R_t}{R_a + R_t}\right) \times 100.$$

Table 7.1 shows the errors caused by transducer loading for various transducer or line resistances and an amplifier impedance of 100,000 ohms

TABLE 7.1 Errors caused by transducer loading

Transducer impedance, in ohms	% Error
0.1	0
10.0	-0.01
100.0	-0.1
1000.0	-0.99
5000.0	-4.75
10000.0	-9.11

Loading produces a negative error while noise, manifesting itself as induced current through a transducer, contributes both positive and negative errors. That is, the current-induced noise is $\pm i_i Z_t$, where i_i is the induced current and Z_t is the transducer impedance.

Signal corruption, or noise, can be removed or attenuated by various filter circuits. Where the signals arise from d-c transducers (as contracted to a-c driven transducers), a capacitor connected across the input terminals of the amplifier is usually sufficient. It is important to know the cut-off frequency of the filter in order to approximate the frequency of the discarded signal. Table 7.2 gives some approximate time constants of the equivalent first-order system composed of 300 feet of Belden No. 8723, 4-conductor shielded cable, with various sizes of capacitors. The capacitors were 10 percent quality.

Suppression. Calibrated suppression sufficient to null out all the d-c level of a complex signal is extremely important. With this capability, it is possible to amplify small deviations around some static level which enables detecting very small changes in the measured variable.

Some recording systems do not have sufficient suppression so that it may be necessary to improvise circuitry for this purpose. Low level d-c signals, such as from thermocouples, may be suppressed by

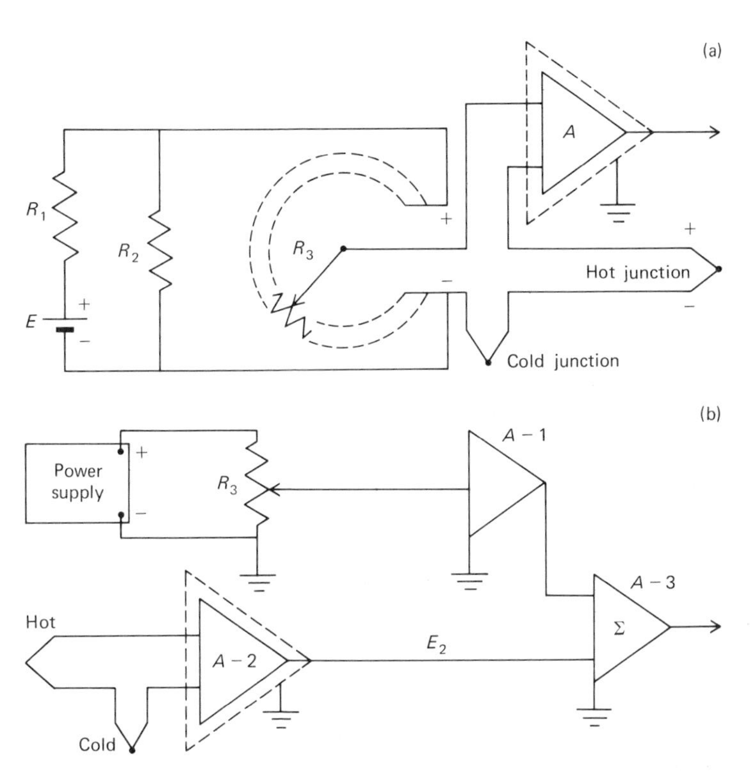

Figure 7.32. (a) Passive suppression circuit for d-c signals (b) Active suppression circuit for d-c signals.

a battery-powered arrangement as shown in Figure 7.32a. R_1 is chosen sufficiently large to limit the current flow from the battery E (Mercury cells with about one and one-half volts output are satisfactory for thermocouple suppression). R_2 is selected to give the desired suppression range for the multiturn, wire-wound precision potentiometer, R_3. The net signal may be amplified in a high-gain, high impedance, d-c amplifier, shown as A.

If the thermocouple is grounded in the field, the suppression circuit must be floating–i.e., have no ground. The amplifier, A, must also float and should be guarded. The output of the amplifier is usually referred to a ground at that point. The shielding (preferably a drain wire) should be continuous from the guarded amplifier to the signal source and the voltage supply carefully protected from disturbances. The entire ensemble must be calibrated and critical potentials periodically measured to insure constant performance.

If a high-quality regulated power supply is available along with suitable amplifiers, a suppression circuit as shown in Figure 7.32b may be constructed. Again the output is amplified in a guarded amplifier, A-2, the output of which is in reference to ground. R_3 is adjusted to give the desired suppression. Amplifier A-1 gives isolation, and the signals E_1 and E_2 are subtracted in the active summer A-3, to give the desired difference signal. Preferably the thermocouple should be floating with the drain wire grounded at the guarded amplifier. Signals beyond that point are with respect to a common ground, usually the amplifier chassis.

Great care is required if high accuracy is to be achieved. Potentiometers must be calibrated, junctions carefully prepared, thermal disturbances minimized and crucial voltages monitored. With reasonable attention, an overall accuracy of about 0.2 microvolt can be achieved. For an iron-constantan thermocouple, this is equivalent to an uncertainty of 7°F in the temperature measurement. The precision attainable depends upon the extent to which noise (60-cycle hum is the chief offender) and thermal drift are eliminated. Since departure from a static level is frequently the most important observation, an uncertainty of the above amount can usually be tolerated in experimental plant studies. Extreme precautions and very high quality components are required if measurements of temperature with thermocouples are to be accurate to within 0.1°F, for example. (See References at end of this chapter.)

The cold junction of a thermocouple pair can be eliminated by compensatory circuits. Convenient components are available from several vendors (for example Consolidated Ohmic Devices, Long Island, N. Y.).

Resistance thermometry is preferred because the primary output can be made larger for precision temperature measurements in the range for which they are acceptable. Present-day components and technique enable a precision of 0.1°F to be attained almost with impunity. The output of d-c excited resistance bridges used to measure temperature may be suppressed in the manner described above.

Strain gage bridges require balancing and suppression circuits. Commonly, these are part of the amplifying and signal conditioning apparatus furnished by the vendor. The a-c excited versions usually possess sufficient capability in this regard. Two functions are desirable: zero suppression and sensitivity adjustment. A circuit which gives a calibrated zero suppression is shown in Figure 7.33. If additional circuitry for balancing the gage is provided (at a reference value of the variable to be measured—e.g., zero gage pressure for a pressure sensor) then the potentiometer, R_7, is placed in its midpoint and the transducer balanced. Suppression, either plus or minus, is achieved by adjustments of R_7 from the midpoint. The *sensitivity of the suppression* is altered by adjusting resistor R_5 to obtain a convenient value—for example, 10 inches of water per turn of R_7.

By introducing a variable resistance in series with the excitation, the *sensitivity of the transducer* can be adjusted. Such a circuit is

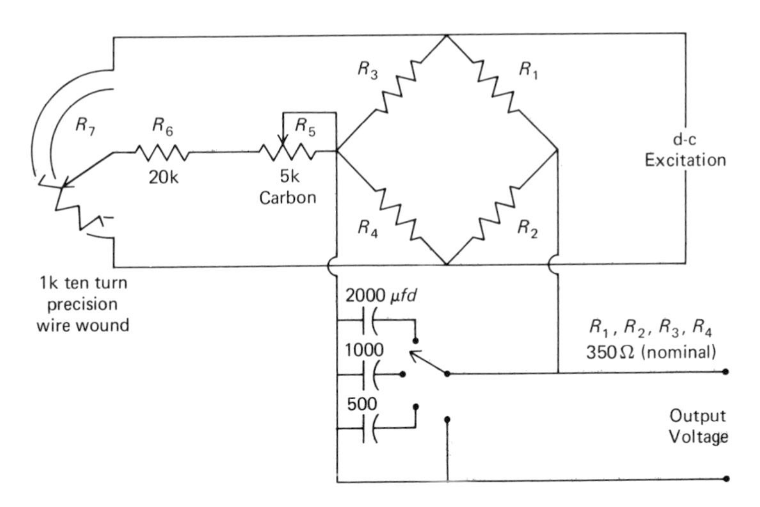

Figure 7.33. Signal conditioning circuit for strain gage transducers.

shown in Figure 7.34 and described in the sources indicated in the end of this chapter. With both overall sensitivity and suppression sensitivity adjustments, a very flexible bridge network is obtained. The sensitivity adjust is very useful for obtaining equal sensitivities for a number of similar transducers excited from either common or individual power supplies.

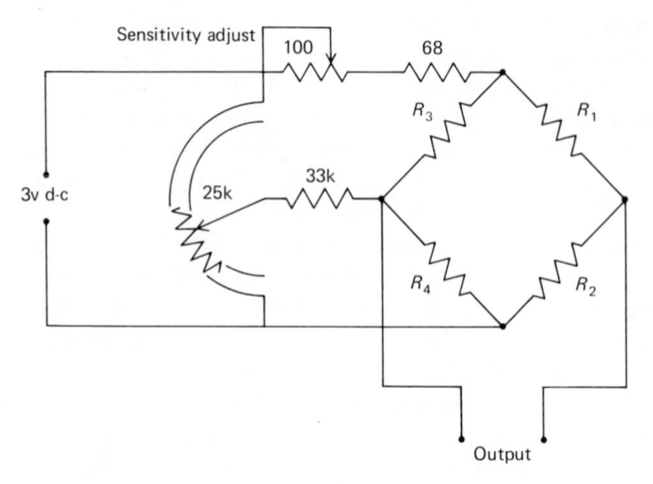

Figure 7.34. Circuit for balancing and sensitivity adjustments of d-c excited bridge systems.

TABLE 7.2 Response characteristics of cable with capacitance shunt at amplifier

Cable: 300 feet Belden No. 8723 (about 8 ohms)
Data System: Beckman Type S II Dynagraph with Type 481B Preamplifier and Type 486A Power Amplifier

Capacitor microfarads, (± 10%)	Time constant, seconds	Break point frequency, radians/sec
3000	0.12	8.3
2000	0.072	14
1000	0.046	22
500	0.024	42
350	0.016	62
250	0.012	83
100	0.006	167

Filtering. Filtering for the attenuation of spurious a-c signals can usually be accomplished by merely inserting a capacitor across the output of the *d-c* bridge at the amplifier. It is also convenient to be able to short out the bridge (for zeroing purposes). The arrangement shown in Figure 7.33 has been found to be satisfactory. The smallest capacitor is chosen which will just attenuate enough noise to enable a fairly clean record to be obtained. Table 7.2 shows experimental values of cut-off frequencies of this simple filter in a typical plant testing situation.

The recommended wiring practice for minimizing noise depends upon the nature of the signal generating source.

Types of Signal Six classes of signal sources are of interest. These are described below and illustrated in Figure 7.35a-f.

Single Ended-grounded (Fig. 7.35a). This is a signal source with a two-terminal output, with one terminal connected to ground.

With the source turned on, a high impedance voltmeter will show no voltage above ground when connected to terminal 1 but will indicate a usable signal from terminal 2 to ground. With the source turned off, an ohmmeter will measure the transducer resistance, R_t.

Single ended-floating (7.35b). This is an unbalanced two-terminal source which is isolated from ground.

With the source turned on, a voltmeter with high frequency response (such as a recording oscillograph) will show 60-cycle noise between each terminal and ground. A usable signal will appear between terminals. An ohmmeter across the *de-energized* transducer will read the source resistance, R_t. A high resistance between each terminal and ground will verify that the source is floating. A floating output may be grounded or reversed without disturbing the circuit.

Single Ended-driven Off Ground (Fig. 7.35c). An example of this kind of signal is the voltage across a shunt of known resistance used to measure the current in a high-voltage conductor. The voltage level can be very high and may be constant or oscillating.

To identify such a source, the voltage to ground from each terminal is measured. A zero voltage to ground identifies a ground connection (3). The voltage between an output terminal to ground is the common-mode voltage.

With the source turned off, an ohmmeter will measure the transducer resistance. A driven off ground signal source can *never* be grounded.

Source	Description	Examples
Single ended—grounded (a) 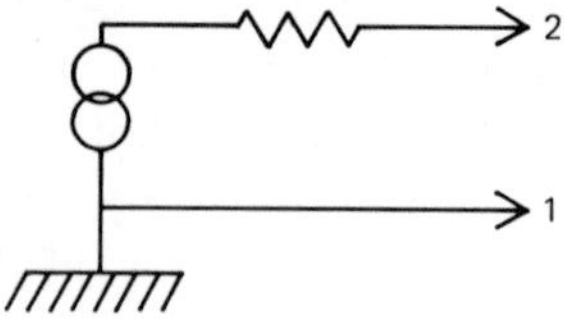 2, 1	Two output terminals one of which is connected to ground	AC line powered signal generator.
Single ended—floating (b) 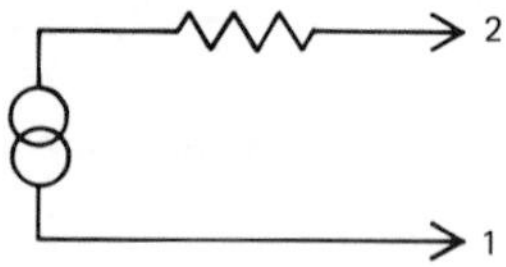 2, 1	Unbalanced output, isolated from ground. Can be grounded without disturbing circuit.	Dry cell battery. Magnetic tape head. Battery-powered signal generator.
Single ended—driven off ground (c) 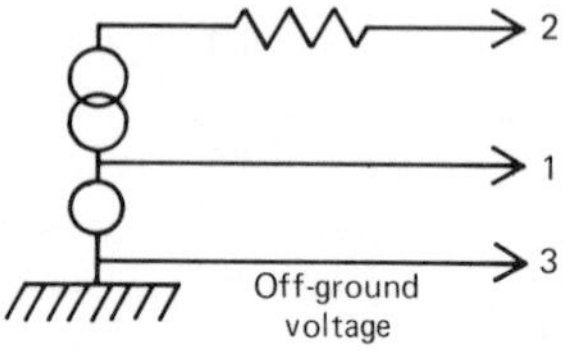 2, 1, 3 Off-ground voltage	Unbalanced output, driven off ground by second voltage source. Cannot be grounded.	Resistive shunt in hot side of line or bus—for measuring current.
Balanced—grounded (d) 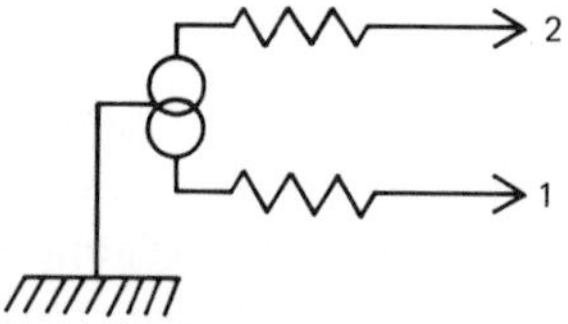 2, 1	Terminals have equal impedance to common ground.	Four arm Wheatstone bridge, excited from grounded DC supply.
Balanced—floating (e) 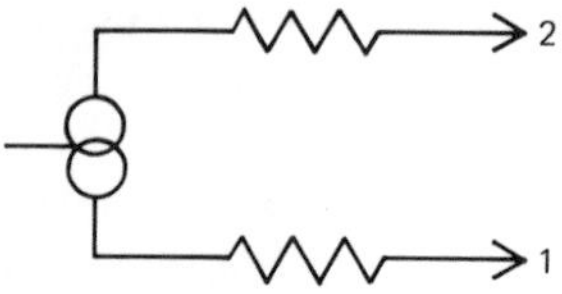 2, 1	Terminals have equal impedance to floating common point. Common point can be grounded without disturbing circuit.	Four arm Wheatstone bridge excited from floating DC supply. Center-tapped transformer.
Balanced—driven off ground (f) 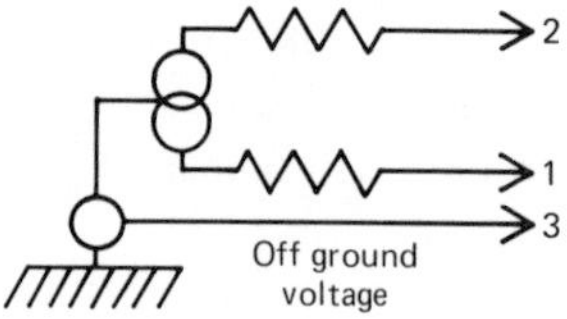 2, 1, 3 Off ground voltage	Terminals have equal impedance to common point, driven off ground by a second voltage source. Cannot be grounded.	Differential output recorder amplifier (e.g., device with ±30 v output, operates in 0–60 v range).

Figure 7.35. Six classes of signal sources.

In the above cases, the resistive signal sources are called unbalanced if the resistance between the output terminals and ground are different.

Balanced-grounded (Figure 7.35d). The two output terminals of a balanced-grounded source have equal impedance to ground. A Wheatstone bridge which is excited with a grounded d-c power supply is typical.

Such a source is identified by measuring the resistance to ground from the two active terminals with the excitation absent. The output terminals can be reversed without disturbing the circuit.

Balanced floating (Figure 7.35e). This signal source is typified by a Wheatstone bridge excited with a floating power supply. This source will have essentially equal resistance between all active terminals when it is not energized. The resistance to ground from any active terminal will be very high, indicating the source is floating. Between any active terminal and ground, 60-cycle noise will appear with excitation off. The output terminals can be reversed, or the common terminal can be be grounded without disturbing the circuit.

Balanced-driven off ground (Figure 7.35f). This is similar to *d* configuration except that a voltage source is imposed between the "center tap" of the transducer and ground.

The resistance between terminals will be essentially equal (excitation off). Signals between terminals and ground will reveal the common point since this will be minimum or different. The active output terminals can be reversed to invert signal polarity, but the circuit can *never* be grounded without disturbing or destroying the signal source.

The recommended wiring arrangement for these various sources will be indicated.

Types of Amplifiers In order to extract the maximum amount of information from test signals, it is necessary to suppress as much of the static signal as possible and amplify only the deviations about the static level.

Where the signals are small in magnitude (millivolts), the differences usually become very small indeed, generally in the microvolt level. Amplifiers for this service must not only be able to provide very high amplification but must also have high common-mode rejection, stability, low drift, etc.

An amplifier of this class is the *balanced, floating, and guarded am-*

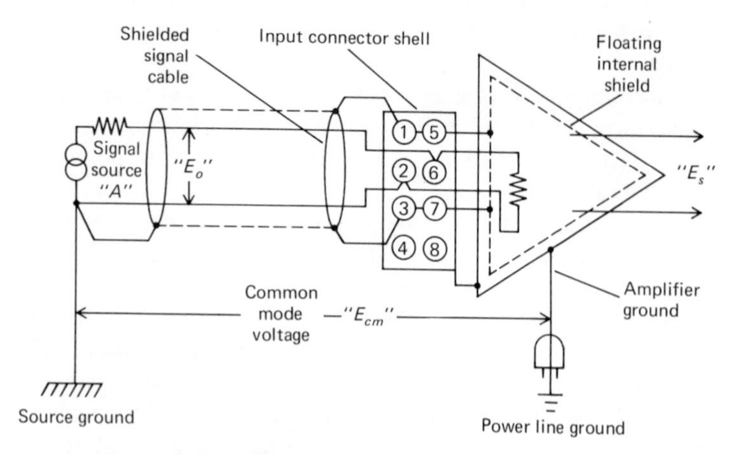

Figure 7.36. Balanced-floating and guarded amplifier with single-ended grounded source (Courtesy of Brush Instruments Div., Gould Inc.).

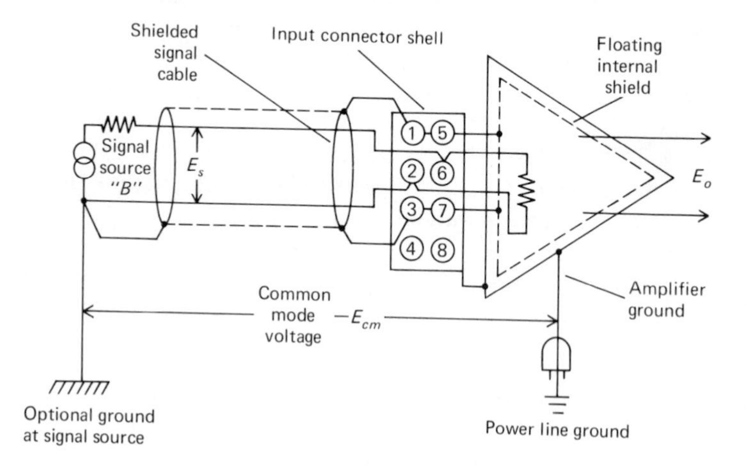

Figure 7.37. Balanced-floating and guarded amplifier with single-ended floating source (Courtesy of Brush Instruments Div., Gould Inc.).

plifier. It is called *balanced* because the impedance to ground from either input terminal is the same. Both inputs are free to *float* in accordance with the signal imposed. The entire amplifier is protected by a *guard* which is isolated from the chassis and the outputs, and

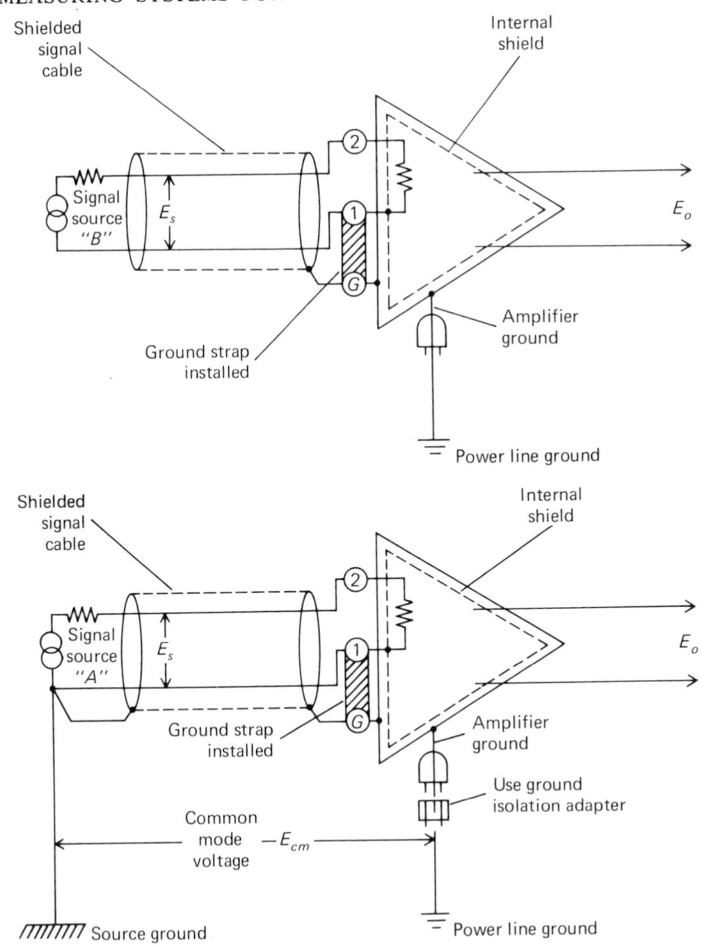

Figure 7.38. Balanced-floating and guarded amplifier used in single ended-floating mode for grounded or floating single-ended sources.

the impedance from either isolated input to this guard is equal. The guard reduces internal capacitance between the input terminals and the chassis. This amplifier accepts signals from almost all transducers either grounded, ungrounded, or floating, center-tapped, balanced or unbalanced.

Recommended arrangements are discussed and illustrated by Figures 7.36, 7.37, 7.38, and 7.39.

The arrangement used with a *single ended-grounded source* is shown in Figure 7.36. The grounded side of the transducer is con-

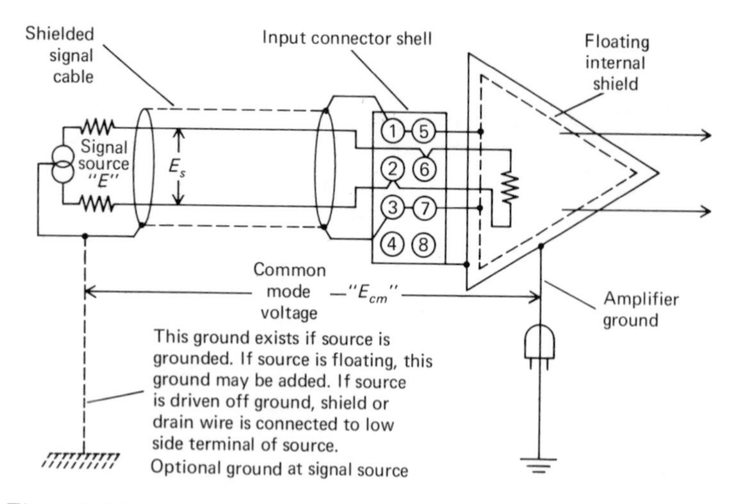

Figure 7.39. Balanced-floating and grounded amplifier configurations for various balanced signal sources (Courtesy of Brush Instruments Div., Gould Inc.).

nected to the low side amplifier input; the other transducer terminal is connected to the high side. The drain wire (cable shield) is connected to the grounded terminal of the transducer, the other end to the amplifier guard. The chassis (and connector shell) is grounded, usually through the third wire of the power plug. When used with a *single ended-floating source,* the arrangement is as shown in Figure 7.37. The low side terminals of the transducer and amplifiers are connected. Corresponding high side terminals are similarly connected. The drain wire (shield) is connected between the low side of the transducer and the amplifier guard.

The source can float or be grounded, preferably at the transducer end. (If grounded, it appears identical to Figure 7.36.) Other connections are as previously described.

If the transducer is *floating,* the amplifier may be operated in a *single ended-floating* mode by removing any ground at the transducer and connecting the low side of the amplifier input, the cable shield, the guard, the chassis to ground at the amplifier end (through the power cord ground lead). Alternately, the transducer can be grounded, but the ground at the amplifier should be lifted by inserting a ground isolation adapter on the power plug. Figures 7.38 (a) and (b) illustrate these arrangements.

When used to measure *single-ended-driven off ground* signals, the balanced-floating amplifier is connected just as in Figure 7.36, being sure that the drain wire or cable shield is connected at the low signal side of the source, between source and driver.

This means that the common-mode voltage appears at the floating amplifier inputs and guard. Since the driving voltage may be high, great care must be taken to maintain insulation along the cable and within connectors.

For measuring signals from *balanced-floating, balanced-grounded and balanced-driven off ground* sources, the balanced-floating and guarded amplifier is connected as shown in Figure 7.39.

There are several other basic amplifier designs available, but generally they are not well suited for measuring low-level signals. Two such types are illustrated in Figures 7.40 and 7.41.

The *single ended-grounded amplifier* (Figure 7.40) has one output terminal grounded at the amplifier. It has *no common-mode rejection* and cannot be used with sources which are grounded or driven off ground. It is unsuited for amplifying microvolt signals.

The *balanced to ground* amplifier (Figure 7.41) has equal impedance to ground from either input terminal. One output is connected to ground at the amplifier. When the signal source is floating, the common-mode rejection is usually satisfactory. This amplifier should not be used with single ended-grounded or single ended-driven off ground sources. When used with balanced-driven off

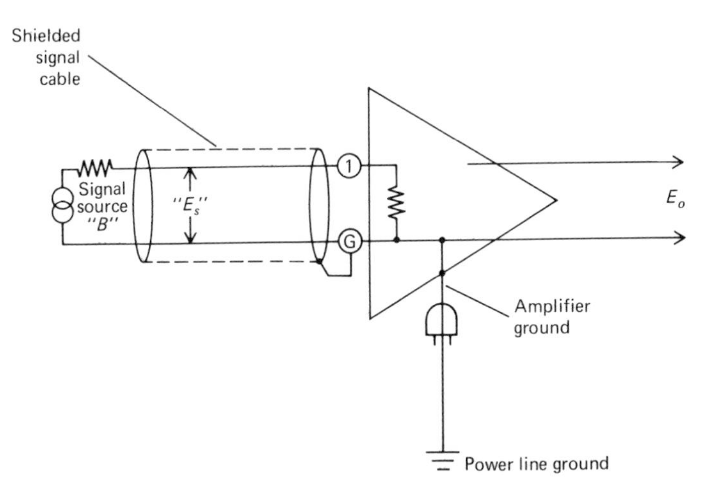

Figure 7.40. Single ended-grounded amplifier with floating source (Courtesy of Brush Instruments Div., Gould Inc.).

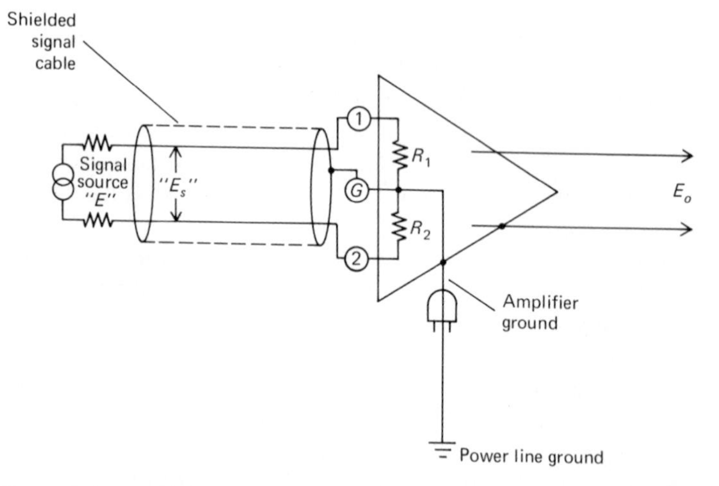

Figure 7.41. Balanced to ground amplifier with balanced floating source (Courtesy of Brush Instruments Div., Gould Inc.).

ground sources, the maximum tolerable amplifier sensitivity or gain decreases as the off ground voltage increases.

Because the balanced, floating and guarded amplifier can be used with any signal source (Figures 7.36, 7.37, 7.38, and 7.39), it is highly recommended for experimental plant studies where the maximum potential for improvisation is desired and where the environment is generally severe and unpredictable.

Extreme care and attention to details are mandatory in preparing a data system for in-plant tests. The test engineer should supervise each step of the operation and not relinquish any responsibilities to technicians unless it is assured that specifications are rigidly followed. The greatest attention must be given to wiring and soldering techniques and practices, with only the highest quality materials used. It is far better to invest time in assembling the system correctly initially than to diagnose, locate and correct faults after completion.

7.3 GLOSSARY

⟨(Courtesy of Gould Inc., Brush Division)⟩

Accuracy The capability of an instrument to follow the true value of a given phenomenon. Often confused with "inaccuracy," which is the departure from the true value into which all causes of error attributable to the instrument are lumped: repeatability, hysteresis, linearity, drift, gain stability, temperature effect and many others.

Balanced input A symmetrical input circuit having equal impedance from both input terminals to ground.

Balanced line A transmission line consisting of two identical signal conductors having equal resistance and equal capacitance with respect to the cable shield or to ground. The **signal** currents in the two conductors are equal in magnitude and opposite in direction.

Bandwidth The range of frequencies over which a given device is designed to operate within specified limits.

Common mode rejection (or in-phase rejection). A measure of how well a differential amplifier ignores a signal which appears simultaneously at both input terminals.

Common mode signal A signal that appears simultaneously at both amplifier input terminals with respect to a common point.

Chopper An electromechanical or electronic device used to interrupt a d-c or low-frequency a-c signal at regular intervals to permit amplification of the signal by an a-c amplifier.

DC amplifier One which has a frequency response band that goes down to d-c. This definition includes direct-coupled amplifiers but is not restricted to direct-coupled amplifiers.

Differential input A symmetrical input circuit that rejects voltages which are the same at both input terminals and amplifies the voltage difference between the two input terminals. May be either balanced or floating and may also be guarded.

Distributed capacity Capacitance evenly distributed over the entire length of a signal cable. Includes capacitance between signal conductors and from each conductor to ground.

Drain wire A metallic conductor frequently used with foil-type signal-cable shielding that provides a low resistance path to ground at any point along the signal-cable shield.

Electromagnetic Pertaining to the mutually perpendicular electric and magnetic fields associated with the movement of electrons through conductors—as in an electromagnet.

Electrostatic coupling Coupling by means of capacitance so that charges on one circuit influence another circuit because of capacitance between the two conductors.

Floating A device or circuit that is not grounded and not tied to any established potential.

Floating input An isolated input circuit not connected to ground at any point. (The maximum permissible voltage to ground is limited by electrical design parameters of the circuit involved.)

Frequency response The portion of the frequency spectrum which can be covered by a device within specified limits of amplitude error.

Guarded input An input that has a third terminal which is maintained at a potential near the input-terminal potential for a single-ended input–or near the mean input potential for a differential input. It is used to shield the entire input circuit.

Guard shield or "guard." An internal **floating** shield which surrounds the entire input section of an amplifier. Effective shielding is achieved **only** when the absolute potential of the guard is stabilized with respect to the incoming signal.

Ground (1) a point in a circuit used as a common reference or datum point in measuring voltages; (2) the conducting chassis or framework on which an electrical circuit is physically mounted and to which one point in a circuit is often connected; (3) the earth or low-resistance conductor connected to the earth at some point and having no potential difference from another conductor connected to the earth at the same point.

Ground loop The generation of undesirable signals within a ground conductor, owing to circulation currents within the conductor which originate from a second source of potential–frequently as a result of connecting two separate grounds to a signal circuit.

Hysterisis The summation of all effects, under constant environmental conditions, which cause the output of an instrument to assume different values at a given stimulus point when the point is approached first with increasing stimulus and then with decreasing stimulus.

Inductive pickup Signals generated in a circuit or conductor because of its mutual inductance with a disturbing source.

Impedance An indication of the total opposition that a circuit or device offers to the flow of alternating current at a particular frequency. Impedance "Z" is a combination of resistance "R" and reactance "X" (at designated frequency)–all expressed in ohms. $Z = (R^2 + X^2)^{1/2}$.

Linearity A relation such that any change of input signal is accompanied by a similar change in the output which is directly proportional to the input. The term "linearity" is often confused with the error which results from non-linearity in an instrument.

Low-level signal Very small variations in the amplitude, of a wave, serving to convey information or other intelligence. Variations in signal amplitude are frequently expressed in microvolts.

Low-pass filter A filter that transmits alternating currents **below** a given cutoff frequency and substantially attenuates all other currents.

Magnetic field Any space or region in which magnetizing forces are of significant magnitude with respect to conditions under consideration. A magnetic field is produced by a current-carrying conductor or coil, a permanent magnet, or by the earth itself.

Noise An unwanted electrical disturbance or spurious signal which modifies the transmission, measurement or recording of desired data.

Normal mode The expected or usual operating condition, such as the voltage which occurs **between** the two input terminals of an amplifier.

Off-ground The voltage above or below ground at which a device is operated.

Position feedback An essential part of a closed-loop servo system in which the mechanical position of the driven element is continuously monitored by a position sensor and compared with the input signal. Any discrepancy or error in position is amplified and used to drive the mechanical element precisely to the position dictated by the accuracy of the position sensing element and the ability of the drive mechanism to supply the necessary positioning forces.

Precision A term frequently associated with scientific measurements which refers to the repeatability of the instrument but does **not** cover other sources of error which may be inherent or present in the measuring system.

Repeatability The maximum deviation from the average of corresponding data points taken from repeated tests under identical conditions for any one stimulus value. The term is often extended to mean the difference in output for any given identically-repeated stimulus with no change in the remaining test conditions.

Resistance strain gage A metallic wire or foil grid that produces a resistance change which is directly proportional to its change in length.

Resolution The smallest change in applied stimulus that will produce a detectable change in the instrument output.

Shunting effect A reduction in signal amplitude caused by the load which an amplifier or measuring instrument imposes on the signal source. For d-c signals the shunting effect is directly proportional to the output impedance of the signal source and inversely proportional to the amplifier's input impedance.

Single-point grounding A grounding system that attempts to confine all return currents to a network which serves as the circuit reference and does **not** imply that the grounding system is limited to one earth connection. To be effective, no appreciable current is allowed to flow in the circuit reference.

Strain-gage based An instrument whose sensing element is composed of bonded or unbonded strain gages.

Thermal zero drift The maximum change or shift in pen zero resulting from changes in temperature. Specifically, the shift in pen zero when the instrument goes from one temperature to another.

Thermocouple A temperature-sensing device consisting of two dissimilar metal wires joined together at both ends. It develops a small electromotive force (emf) that is proportional to the **difference** in temperature between the "measuring junction" (located at the point of measurement) and the "reference junction" (usually located in the measuring instrument).

Transducer A device which converts energy from one form into another, retaining the characteristic amplitude variations of the energy being converted. Examples: a microphone which converts acoustical energy into electrical energy or a loudspeaker which does the reverse.

Transient A sudden signal change of short duration which, when plotted against time, would appear markedly different from the waveforms immediately preceding and following it.

Transposed An interchange in the relative positions of two or more objects. Most low-level signal transmission lines are carefully twisted to interchange the relative positions of conductors at regular intervals, so that the effects of inductive pickup will be neutralized.

References

1. Franks, Roger G. E., *Mathematical Modeling in Chemical Engineering.* John Wiley & Sons, New York, 1967.
2. Gould, Leonard A. *Chemical Process Control; Theory and Applications.* Addison-Wesley Pub. Co., Reading, Mass. 1969.
3. Eckman, D. P. *Industrial Instrumentation.* John Wiley & Sons, Inc., New York, 1950.
4. Roberts, Howard C. *Mechanical Measurements by Electrical Methods.* The Instruments Publishing Co., Inc., Pittsburgh, Pa. 1951.
5. Draper, C. S., Walter McKay and Sidney Lees. *Instrument Engineering,* vol. 3. McGraw-Hill Book Co., New York, 1955.
6. Lion, Kurt S. *Instrumentation in Scientific Research.* McGraw-Hill Book Co., New York, 1959.
7. Fribance, Austin E. *Industrial Instrumentation Fundamentals.* McGraw-Hill Book Co., New York, 1962.
8. O'Higgins, Patrick J. *Basic Instrumentation–Industrial Measurement.* McGraw-Hill Book Co., New York, 1966.
9. Kutz, Myer. *Temperature Control.* John Wiley & Sons, Inc., New York, 1968.
10. Benedict, Robert P. *Fundamentals of Temperature, Pressure, and Flow Measurements.* John Wiley & Sons, Inc., New York, 1969.
11. Norton, Harry N. *Handbook of Transducers for Electronic Measuring Systems.* Prentice-Hall, Inc., Englewood Cliffs, N. J., 1969.
12. *Instrument Engineers' Handbook,* vol. I. *Process Measurements,* vol. II. *Process Control,* Chilton Book Company, Philadelphia, Pa. (1970).
13. *Manual on Use of Thermocouples.* STP 470, ASTM; 1916 Race St., Philadelphia, Pa., 1971.
14. *Introduction to Transducers for Instrumentation.* Statham Instruments, Inc., 2230 Statham Boulevard, Oxnard, California.
15. Imsland, T. S. Level and Flow Measurements with ΔP Cells. *Instruments and Control Systems* (May 1969).

16. Shafer, Montgomery R. Performance Characteristics of Turbine Flowmeters. *J. Basic Eng.* (December 1962), p. 471.

17. Maryman, G. A. and H. Burlage, Jr. Expansion Coefficients for Orifice Meters in Pipes Less Than One Inch in Diameter. *J. Basic Eng.* (1961).

18. Cotton, K. C. and J. C. Wescott. Throat Tap Nozzles Used for Accurate Flow Measurements. *J. Eng. for Power*, p. 247, *Trans. ASME* (Oct. 1960).

19. Cortelyou, J. T. Centrifugal Flow Measurement. *Instruments and Control Systems* (February 1960). Manufactured by Fluidynamics, Inc., Monrovia, Calif.

20. Dodge, B. F. *Chemical Engineering Thermodynamics.* McGraw-Hill Book Co., 1944.

21. Carter, Don E. *Continuous Chromatography* (thesis), p. 70 and Fig. 6.3.2. Washington University, St. Louis, Missouri, Feb. 1964.

22. Arnberg, B. T. Review of Critical Flowmeters for Gas Flow Measurements. *J. Basic Eng.*, p. 447. *Trans. ASME* (Dec. 1962).

23. Smith, Jr., Robert E. and Roy J. Matz. A Theoretical Method of Determining Discharge Coefficients for Venturis Operating at Critical Flow Conditions. *J. Basic Eng.*, *Trans. ASME* (1962), p. 434.

24. Westbrook, M. H. and R. Munro. The Telemetering of Information from a Working Internal-Combustion Engine. *Journal of Engineering for Power*, *Trans. ASME* (1966).

25. Krassick, W. M. The Development of a Miniature, High-Speed Telemetry System for Dynamic Stress Analysis. *Journal of Engineering for Power*, *Trans. ASME* (January 1968), p. 56.

26. Budzilovich, D. N. Electrical Noise–Its Nature, Causes, Solutions. *Control Eng.* (May 1969), p. 74.

27. *Signal Conditioning.* Applications Booklet No. 101. Brush Instruments Div., Gould, Inc., Cleveland, Ohio, 1970.

28. *Elimination of Noise in Low-level Circuits.* Brush Instruments Div., Gould, Inc., Cleveland, Ohio.

8 Experimental Determination of Process Dynamics

8.1 TYPES OF FORCING

Methods for procuring dynamic information from existing processing systems may be classified according to the forcing imposed. These are (1) steady state, (2) random, and (3) transient.

Steady State "Steady state" means the application of an input which is periodic, each period having an identical time history. Steady state sinusoidal forcing is an example.

This method for acquiring dynamic descriptions from processes is usually impractical owing to the time required and the fact that the plant is in a state of continuous motion during the test period. In the early studies of process dynamics, sinusoidal forcing was used to the detriment of progress and acceptability of the "systems" approach within the processing industry.

For laboratory size processes with relatively rapid response or for testing instruments or control components, especially where only amplitude data are of interest, the technique can be used. Where computational facilities are not available or where the test data may be acquired and reduced in less than two hours, for example, there is some justification in considering direct sinusoidal forcing.

Descriptions of early process dynamics studies in which sinusoidal forcing was used may be found in the references at the end of this chapter, particularly *1* and *2*.

Random The use of naturally occurring random input disturbances to a plant as the excitation was considered as early as *1956* by Goodman and Reswick (*6*). With various ramifications, the method has been described from time to time since (*4, 5*). The assumption is made that the system is sufficiently excited by the random variations in the inputs and that the process performance can be found by analysis of input and response signals. The method appears attractive because no special inputs or signal generators are needed. On the other hand, a very large amount of data must be processed (*7*), via computers, and the amount of information retrieved is generally disappointing and fraught with uncertainty.

This method may be useful in those cases where it is impossible or undesirable to introduce known disturbances, but there seems to be little justification to use it for most process dynamics studies.

Transient Among the transient type of test inputs are (1) step, (2) aperiodic pulse train, (3) impulse, and (4) pulse.

Step forcing is a classical input that is useful for mathematical studies. As an input to real systems, it has many limitations. Among these are the following.

(1) A true step is extremely difficult to produce unless it involves merely closing a switch or manipulating a quick-reacting valve.

(2) If components, usually mechanical or electronic, are present which produce outputs which are derivatives of the input, these components, or those following, may be driven to saturation.

For example, pneumatic relays have a finite capacity for air flow, and pneumatic diaphragm valves can be forced to the limit of their response.

Under these conditions, the real input may differ from the intended step form.

(3) It is very difficult to extract the parameters of a multiordered system from step response data.

For example, it is almost impossible to distinguish the difference between two two-time constant systems unless there are substantial differences between the time constants of the two systems.

On the other hand, the step is useful to identify a system which is first order, to obtain an approximate estimate of dominant time constants, and to develop intuition in respect to the performance of a system.

In any event, the amount of information practically available from the step forcing of real systems appears limited.

Aperiodic pulse trains have been studied and, under ideal conditions, can be used to increase the reliability of data in specified frequency regions. From a practical point, the technique does not offer any great advantages over a single pulse.

An impulse is defined as a function which exists only at a point in time and is of infinite magnitude at that point. It is a mathematical abstraction useful for theoretical studies. Practically, it is impossible to produce a true impulse, but in certain special situations a useful approximation can be made to such an input.

About the only instances in which this kind of input can be approximated in the process industry is when a small volume of fluid containing a high concentration of a trace material or signal can be introduced almost instantaneously into a fluid stream. Some examples follow.

(1) Injection of a small quantity of high concentration dye into an inlet stream (or into the mixer itself) to study dispersion or efficacy of mixing.

(2) Addition of a short 'burst' of energy into a stream, via an electrical resistance element, to study the 'diffusion of temperature.'

(3) Injection of tracers such as radioactive materials or known solutes into liquid or gaseous streams for studying diffusion, measuring stream velocities or determining residence time.

Data processing is reduced if impulse forcing is used; only the output curve needs to be processed. The time response to an impulse is the weighting function of the process studied, and, from the result, data may be interpreted in the time domain or transferred to the complex frequency domain.

8.2 PULSE METHOD

The pulse testing procedure has proved uniformly satisfactory for many years and is especially useful for testing processes. Early experiences are described in Reference 3.

In conducting a *pulse* test, an input variable is changed in a pulse-like manner. This means that the variable is displaced from its equilibrium position for only a finite time. Before and after the duration of the pulse, this variable is held constant.

The outputs of a stable system will also behave in a pulselike manner, although some of them may exhibit oscillations before regaining their initial steady state values. The illustration shown as Figure 8.1 will serve to clarify the concept of a pulse.

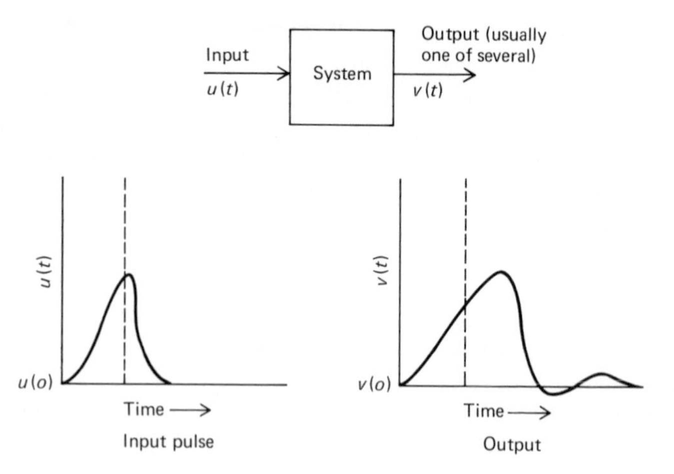

Figure 8.1. Illustration of pulse function excitation.

In a pulse test, the principal requirements are that the system be driven sufficiently hard so that the dynamics of the system are excited but not so hard that the capacity of the system to respond is exceeded.

From one, and only one, properly conducted pulse test, the frequency response characteristics of the system can be obtained. Thus, instead of conducting tests by the direct method at several discrete frequencies, only one test disturbance is used.

In a sense, the single pulse is designed to excite the system with all frequencies at once. Then, by appropriate computational techniques, the frequency response information is extracted therefrom.

Fourier Transform The method of converting pulse data to frequency response form utilizes the theory of Fourier transformations. The performance function is defined as the ratio of the Fourier transform of the output pulse to that of the input

$$[PF] = \frac{\int_{-\infty}^{\infty} e^{-j\omega t} f(t)_{\text{out}}\, dt}{\int_{-\infty}^{\infty} e^{-j\omega t} f(t)_{\text{in}}\, dt}. \tag{8.1}$$

In order to evaluate the integrals involved, summation approximations are required. This entails smoothing the curves and subdividing them at corresponding intervals of time.

When both input (independent) and output (dependent) variables are divided into equal time increments, a computer may be programmed to perform the operations indicated in the following formula for each of the selected frequencies:

$$[PF] = \frac{\sum_{k=1}^{k=n} v(k\Delta t)e^{-j\omega(k\Delta t)}}{\sum_{k=1}^{k=n} u(k\Delta t)\, e^{-j\omega(k\Delta t)}} = \frac{v}{u}(\omega) \tag{8.2}$$

where
$[PF]$ = the performance function relating the given pair of variables
k = the interval number
$v(k\Delta t)$ = the value of the dependent variable at time $k\Delta t$
$u(k\Delta t)$ = the value of the independent variable at time $k\Delta t$
ω = selected frequency
Δt = time increment
$j = \sqrt{-1}$

Since both numerator and denominator are complex numbers, each may be resolved into its corresponding trigonometric and amplitude and angle forms:

$$[PF] = \frac{\sum_{k=1}^{k=n} A_n\,[\cos\beta - j\sin\beta]_n}{\sum_{k=1}^{k=n} A_d\,[\cos\beta - j\sin\beta]_d} = \frac{A_n, \underline{/N}}{A_d, \underline{/D}}$$

$$= [DAR], \underline{/DRA}\,. \tag{8.3}$$

where $[DAR]$ denotes the amplitude ratio (gain) or dynamic amplitude ratio and $[DRA]$ indicates the phase angle or dynamic response angle.

In order to define concisely the concept of frequency response and to show that Fourier transformation of pulses in the time domain may be used to yield results identical with those procured by direct sinusoidal forcing, the following analysis is given.

Assume a system whose behavior is described by an nth order linear differential equation with constant coefficients. Let $y(t)$ be the process variable (dependent) which will vary with time in response to some disturbance (independent variable) introduced to the system. Let this disturbance, or input, vary sinusoidally and assume that, initially, the first $n - 1$ derivatives of the variable, including $y(t)$, are zero. Then

$$\sum_0^n a_k \frac{d^k y(t)}{dt^k} = A \sin \omega t$$

$$y^{n-1}(0) = y^{n-2}(0)$$

$$= \ldots . y^1(0) = y(0) = 0 . \tag{8.4}$$

When the Laplace transform is introduced,

$$\int_0^\infty e^{-st} y(t) dt = Y(s)$$

and, if this is applied to Equation (8.4), yields the polynomial in s:

$$\left(\sum_0^n a_k s^k\right) Y(s) = \frac{A\omega}{s^2 + \omega^2} . \tag{8.5}$$

If we let $G(s) = \sum_0^n a_k s^k$,

$$Y(s) = \left(\frac{A\omega}{s^2 + \omega^2}\right) \frac{1}{G(s)} . \tag{8.6}$$

If $G(s)$ is a Hurwitz polynomial, it is possible to obtain the dynamic properties of the system from the steady state solution:

$$Y_{ss}(t) = \sum Res \left. \frac{A\omega e^{st}}{G(s)(s^2 + \omega^2)} \right|_{s=-j\omega}^{s=+j\omega}$$

$$= \left. \frac{A\omega e^{st}}{2sG(s)} \right|_{s=+j\omega} + \left. \frac{A\omega e^{st}}{2sG(s)} \right|_{s=-j\omega}$$

$$= \frac{Ae^{j\omega t}}{2jG(j\omega)} - \frac{Ae^{-j\omega t}}{2jG(-j\omega)} . \tag{8.7}$$

Each complex function can be resolved into a magnitude and a phase angle

$$G(j\omega) = |G(j\omega)| e^{j\phi(\omega)}$$

$$G(-j\omega) = |G(j\omega)| e^{-j\phi(\omega)}$$

so

$$Y_{ss}(t) = \left| \frac{A}{G(j\omega)} \right| \sin \left[\omega t - \phi(\omega) \right] . \tag{8.8}$$

Theoretically, sinusoidal forcing is not necessary, the same information being obtainable by pulse forcing. Assume that in the neighborhood of the operating conditions the system behaves linearly and that an arbitrary input $x(t)$ is used. Equation (8.6) then becomes

$$\frac{Y(s)}{X(s)} = \frac{1}{G(s)}$$

or

$$\frac{\displaystyle\int_0^\infty e^{-st}\, y(t)\,dt}{\displaystyle\int_0^\infty e^{-st}\, x(t)\,dt} = \frac{1}{G(s)} . \tag{8.9}$$

Suppose both $y(t)$ and $x(t)$ are continuous functions of a bounded variation which return to their initial value after a finite time and remain so as time progresses. Such functions may be called *pulses* (Figure 8.1). If $s = j\omega$, (8.9) becomes

$$\frac{\displaystyle\int_0^{T_u} e^{-j\omega t}\, y(t)\,dt}{\displaystyle\int_0^{T_u} e^{-j\omega t}\, x(t)\,dt} = \frac{1}{G(j\omega)}. \tag{8.10}$$

Since both pulses are assumed to close, the integrals exist and they may be evaluated for any value of ω. The results are identical to those obtained through direct sinusoidal forcing.

The integrals may be numerically evaluated by approximating the curves as the tops of a number of trapezoids whose bases subdivide the abscissa into equal increments. A typical approximation is

$$\int_0^{T} e^{-j\omega t}\, y(t)\,dt \cong \left\{\frac{\sin\dfrac{\omega\Delta t}{2}}{\dfrac{\omega\Delta t}{2}}\right\} \times \sum_{k=1}^{k=n-1} y(k\Delta t)\,e^{-j\omega k\Delta t}\,\Delta t \tag{8.11}$$

where Δt is a sectionally fixed increment width.

The ratio of the Fourier transforms (the performance function) is

$$[PF]\,(j\omega) = \frac{\displaystyle\sum_{k=1}^{k=n-1} y(k\Delta t)\,e^{-j\omega k\Delta t}}{\displaystyle\sum_{k=1}^{k=n-1} x(k\Delta t)\,e^{-j\omega k\Delta t}}$$

$$= |G(j\omega)|^{-1}\, e^{-j\phi(\omega)}. \tag{8.12}$$

A detailed derivation of a convenient form for computing Fourier transforms using the trapezoidal approximation is given in Appendix 3.

The steps necessary for procuring pulse data and reducing these to frequency response form can now be listed.

(1) Prepare for the tests by assembling, installing, and calibrating the measuring systems and placing the processing system in the desired mode of operation.

Usually, measuring elements must be quite sensitive and highly responsive. The same demands are made on the devices used to convert and record the output signals from the primary measurement elements.

(2) The mechanism for properly pulsing the desired input variable must be assembled and tested. In some cases, special generating devices may be required, especially if the temperature or composition of a stream must be pulsed. In other cases, simply positioning a valve may suffice.

(3) Initial experimentation is made to check the operation of the measuring system and to become familiar with the response of the system. This helps to establish the optimum height and width of the forcing pulse.

(4) The actual test is made with the chosen pulse. Continuous records are obtained of the input and of as many outputs as may be desirable. Wherever possible, all records appear together on multichannel strip charts or equivalent.

The input and one of the output signals obtained might appear as shown in Figure 8.2 if continuous (analog) recording is used.

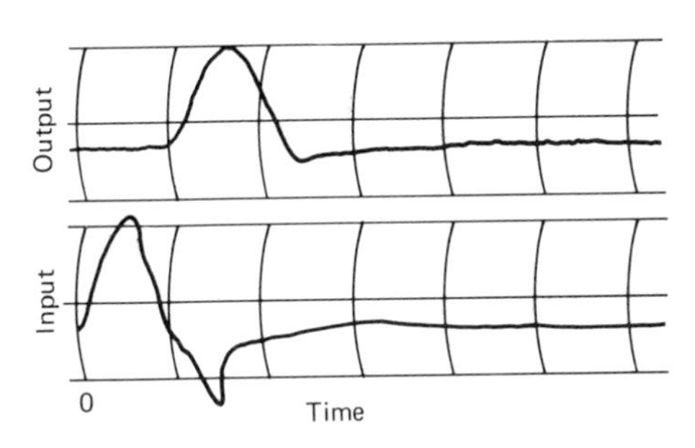

Figure 8.2. Typical input and output records obtained in pulse testing.

8.3 EVALUATION OF THE PULSE METHOD

Several questions arise when the pulse technique is to be evaluated.

(1) Is there an optimum pulse shape?

(2) How do the pulse height and width influence the results obtainable?

(3) In what manner does the increment width used in the summation approximations of the Fourier integrals affect the results?

(4) Can one readily ascertain the regions in which the reduced

TABLE 8.1 SUMMARY OF SOME PROPERTIES OF PULSE FUNCTIONS

Name	Time History	Time Equation	Fourier Transform	Maximum Relative Magnitude and Frequency at Which It Occurs	Frequency at Which Zeros Occur
Rectangle	1, f(t), t→, T	$f(t) = 1$ $0 < t < T$	$T \dfrac{\sin \frac{\omega T}{2}}{\frac{\omega T}{2}} e^{\frac{-j\omega T}{2}}$	T $\omega = 0$	$\omega = \dfrac{2n\pi}{T}$ $n = 1, 2, 3,$
Triangle	1, f(t), 0, 0, t→, T	$f(t) = \dfrac{2}{T} t$ $0 \leq t \leq \dfrac{T}{2}$ $f(t) = 2 - \dfrac{2}{T} t$ $\dfrac{T}{2} \leq t \leq T$	$T \left[\dfrac{1 - \cos \frac{\omega T}{2}}{\left(\frac{\omega T}{2}\right)^2} \right] e^{\frac{-j\omega T}{2}}$	$\dfrac{T}{2}$ $\omega = 0$	$\omega = \dfrac{4n\pi}{T}$ $n = 1, 2, 3,$
Ramp	1, f(t), 0, t→, T	$f(t) = \dfrac{t}{T}$ $0 \leq t \leq T$	$\dfrac{1}{\omega} \sqrt{1 + \dfrac{\sin^2 \frac{\omega T}{2}}{\left(\frac{\omega T}{2}\right)^2} - 2\left(\dfrac{\sin \omega T}{\omega T}\right)} e^{i\theta}$ $\tan \theta = \dfrac{\omega T \cos \omega T - \sin \omega T}{\cos \omega T + \omega T \sin \omega T = 1}$	$\dfrac{T}{2}$ $\omega = 0$	No Zeros

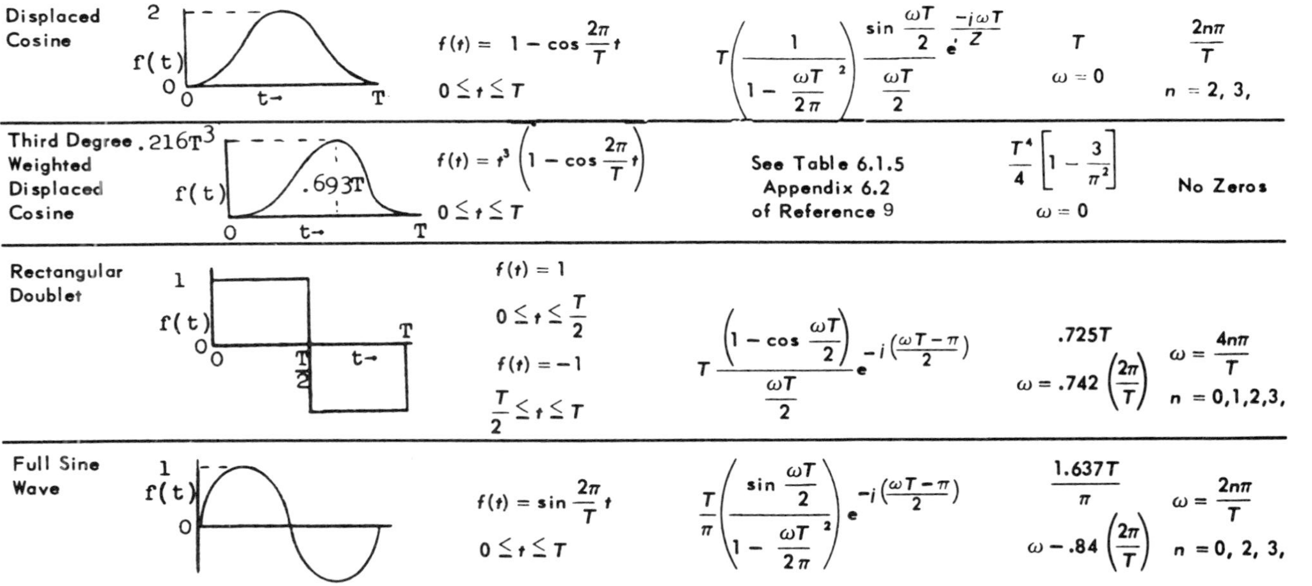

Displaced Cosine	$f(t) = 1 - \cos \frac{2\pi}{T} t$, $0 \leq t \leq T$	$T \left(\frac{1}{1 - \left(\frac{\omega T}{2\pi}\right)^2} \right) \frac{\sin \frac{\omega T}{2}}{\frac{\omega T}{2}} e^{\frac{-i\omega T}{2}}$	T, $\omega = 0$	$\frac{2n\pi}{T}$, $n = 2, 3,$
Third Degree Weighted Displaced Cosine	$f(t) = t^3 \left(1 - \cos \frac{2\pi}{T} t\right)$, $0 \leq t \leq T$	See Table 6.1.5 Appendix 6.2 of Reference 9	$\frac{T^4}{4}\left[1 - \frac{3}{\pi^2}\right]$, $\omega = 0$	No Zeros
Rectangular Doublet	$f(t) = 1$, $0 \leq t \leq \frac{T}{2}$; $f(t) = -1$, $\frac{T}{2} \leq t \leq T$	$T \frac{\left(1 - \cos \frac{\omega T}{2}\right)}{\frac{\omega T}{2}} e^{-i\left(\frac{\omega T - \pi}{2}\right)}$	$.725T$, $\omega = .742 \left(\frac{2\pi}{T}\right)$	$\omega = \frac{4n\pi}{T}$, $n = 0,1,2,3,$
Full Sine Wave	$f(t) = \sin \frac{2\pi}{T} t$, $0 \leq t \leq T$	$\frac{T}{\pi} \left(\frac{\sin \frac{\omega T}{2}}{1 - \left(\frac{\omega T}{2\pi}\right)^2} \right) e^{-i\left(\frac{\omega T - \pi}{2}\right)}$	$\frac{1.637T}{\pi}$, $\omega - .84 \left(\frac{2\pi}{T}\right)$	$\omega = \frac{2n\pi}{T}$, $n = 0, 2, 3,$

Reprinted from Joel O. Hougen, "Experiences and Experiments with Process Dynamics, American Institute of Chemical Engineers Monograph Series" 60 (1964), no. 4.

data become unreliable, and how does signal corruption or noise contribute to the uncertainty of the final results?

(5) How can smoothing of rough data be best accomplished, and what uncertainties are involved in smoothing processes?

(6) Are there simple criteria which may be applied to the raw records in order to evaluate their information content prior to processing by the digital computer?

(7) Are there limitations in the computer program per se?

(8) Does the pulse method give unique results regardless of pulse shape and length, all else being equal?

First, it is well to consider the effect of pulse shape on the nature of the forcing function. It is obvious that the form of the time function will determine the values of the Fourier transform at discrete frequencies. When the time function conforms to some mathematical form, it is frequently possible to derive exact relations for the transform. Although in carrying out an actual field test one rarely wishes to be restricted to producing an input signal corresponding to an exact mathematical form, it is highly instructive to investigate some known shapes. For then it becomes possible to evaluate the quality of the input, in terms of harmonic content, and to know which regions of the test results may be expected to be excellent or where they may be suspect.

Analysis of Various Pulse Functions The harmonic content of various mathematical pulses has been studied by a number of investigators, notably Lees (*8*) and Dreifke (*9*). The most comprehensive appears to be that of Dreifke.

The shapes which have been investigated may be placed in two categories, one and two sided. One-sided pulses which have been studied include rectangular, triangular, displaced cosine, weighted displaced cosines, and ramp (a right triangle). Two-sided pulses which have been investigated are rectangular doublet, full sine, and damped sine. Table 8.1 summarizes the important features of some of these pulses. From a study of these results, some interesting conclusions can be made.

(1) One-sided pulses which are symmetrical about their maxima all yield identical Fourier transform phase angles—that is, $(-\omega T)/(2)$ radians. Presumably this is true regardless of the time history of the pulse as long as it satisfies the above condition.

(2) Pulses such as the rectangular doublet or full sine have phase angles which lag behind those above by 90 degrees.

(3) All one-sided pulses exhibit their maximum Fourier transform

amplitudes at zero frequency, and those which are symmetrical about the maximum pulse amplitude exhibit one or more zeros in their Fourier transform amplitudes.

(4) As the one-sided symmetrical pulses become smoother in their initial and final time histories (that is, tend to exhibit zero initial and final first derivatives), the magnitude of the Fourier transform amplitude is maintained at higher levels over a wider range of frequency.

(5) Unsymmetrical one-sided pulses may have no zero amplitudes in their transform.

(6) As one-sided pulses become more and more unsymmetrical by returning more quickly to zero than they depart from it, the amplitude of the Fourier transform diminishes less rapidly. The ultimate is displayed by the so-called *ramp pulse.*

(7) Two-sided equal-weighted pulses such as the rectangular doublet and full sine forms shown in Table 8.1 have Fourier transform amplitudes of zero at zero frequency and exhibit a maximum at some higher frequency.

(8) A damped 1-cycle sine wave pulse has a finite Fourier transform amplitude at zero frequency but exhibits its maximum value at a higher frequency.

(9) The implication to be drawn from the last two observations is that pulses having properties similar to the last three can be used for maximum system excitation in selected frequency regions. Thus these forms may be particularly useful for diagnostic purposes.

8.4 DATA PROCESSING AND ANALYSIS

Over the years a number of studies have been made of the pulse testing method. Some of these are summarized below. References at the end of this chapter should be consulted for details.

(1) The accuracy of the computational routine for converting pulse-test data into frequency response form is entirely satisfactory as long as a reasonable number of experimental observations are used in the approximation. For example, amplitudes associated with the equivalent harmonics of a half-sine pulse can be computed with an error of less than one percent with only ten increments in the approximation. This indicates that the amount of data required to adequately describe a pulse should always be nominal. Computed amplitudes of other known pulse shapes such as the saw tooth, rectangular, and displaced cosine functions bear out these conclusions.

The computer routine produces no error in calculating the phase angles (arguments) of the harmonics associated with *symmetrical* pulse shapes; hence, such results cannot be used as criteria of accuracy in these cases.

(2) The analysis of analog-computer-generated single pulses was equally satisfactory. An apparently constant error of about two percent appeared in the phase angles of a displaced cosine function, regardless of increment width and frequency. This is an indication of the magnitude of reading and machine errors.

(3) In the computing of frequency response results from analog-computer-generated inputs and outputs with a simulated first-order system, excellent results can be achieved, compared with theory.

Dreifke (*9*) has conclusively demonstrated that good results can be computed on either side or between frequencies at which the input exhibits a zero in its Fourier transform amplitude.

(4) Premature termination of slowly decaying response data (truncation of output) can introduce serious errors in computed frequency response results and can lead to erroneous interpretations for *heavily damped* systems. Results of truncation, however, depend on the nature of the system studied, and Dreifke, Hougen, and Mesmer (*10*) have shown that for *lightly damped* systems as much as 50 percent of the time history may be discarded without appreciably affecting the accuracy of the recovered information.

(5) By comparison with theory, the pulse testing technique is capable of satisfactorily predicting the frequency response of a first- over second-order linear system having well-separated time constants.

Dreifke (*9*) has extended this to fourth- over sixth-order systems.

(6) Properly conducted pulse tests on real systems yield frequency response data in excellent agreement with those obtained by direct sinusoidal forcing.

Time data can be used directly in determining parameters of simple systems being forced with well-defined pulses. Draper, McKay, and Lees (*15*) demonstrate how this is done for first- and second-order systems using rectangular and displaced cosine pulses. For example, the damping ratio and undamped natural frequency may be found if the ratio of time to reach peak amplitudes and the ratio of peak magnitudes are known. Graphs for first- and second-order systems have been computed.

For more complicated unknown systems, it is perhaps impossible to procure complete information from time data alone; however, pulse data may be used for diagnostic purposes. Figure 8.3 is pre-

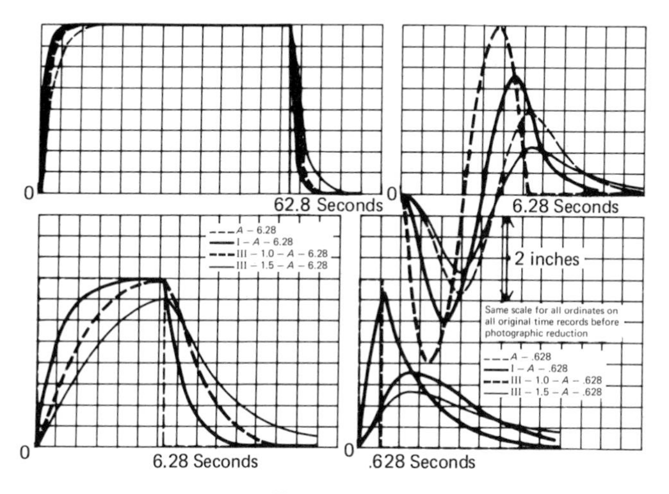

Figure 8.3. Comparison of time histories of first and second-order systems with various pulse forcings.

sented to indicate the difference between the time histories of first- and second-order systems with different damping ratios as a function of the nature of the forcing pulse. The following notation is used in the code on this figure and those immediately following.

A Roman numeral indicates the physical system.

I = simple first-order lag

III = second order

The arabic number following the Roman numeral specifies the damping ratio for the second-order systems.

The letter following either the Roman numeral or damping ratio indicates shape of forcing pulse.

A = rectangle

B = triangular

H = full sine

F = fifth-degree weighted displaced cosine

The terminal number is the pulse duration in seconds.

The two sets of time data on the left-hand side of Figure 8.3 clearly show that rectangular pulses of long duration (equivalent to step forcing) give little opportunity to distinguish between first- and second-order critically or over damped systems. Distinctions begin to appear as the pulse width is decreased, these made especially clear in the vicinity of the termination of the pulse, or shortly thereafter, as shown by the time histories in the lower right-hand portion of Figure 8.3. The shortest pulse data, lower right, leaves no doubt which is a first- and which is a second-order system and, of course, easily distinguishes differences in damping. As shown in the upper right of Figure 8.3, a full-sine pulse is capable of revealing much more information concerning dynamic behavior than a rectangular pulse of the same duration.

As expected, long pulses fail to extract high-frequency information, but, if a long pulse is used, it is better to employ a pulse with abrupt terminal sections, such as a rectangle, at least for first-order systems. Figure 8.4 compares results from a rectangular pulse with a weighted displaced cosine pulse. Both pulses of the duration chosen in Figure 8.4 are of little use in recovering dynamic data from first-order systems since computed information deteriorates rapidly with

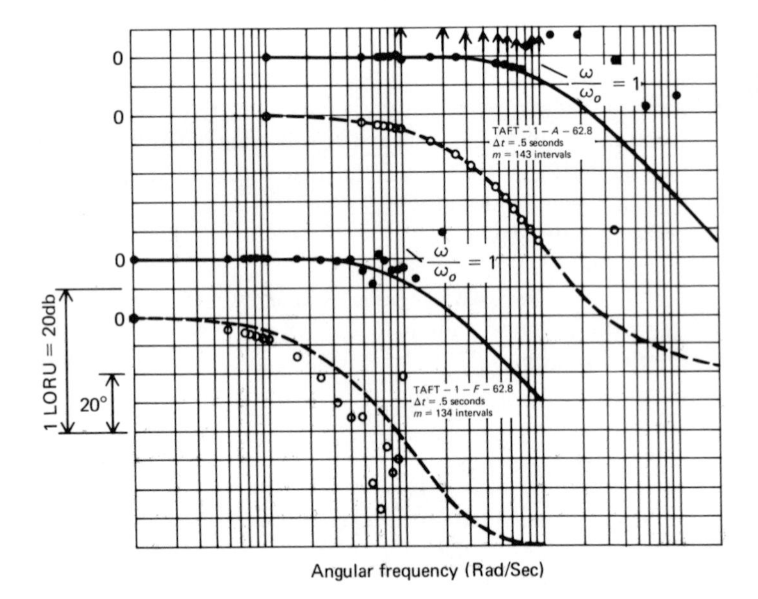

Figure 8.4. Inferior frequency response data obtained from pulses of long duration.

frequency. It is of interest, however, to note that information can be extracted at frequencies between those for which the transform of the input has zero amplitude, the frequency at which zeros exist being denoted by arrows.

As the pulse width is reduced, the frequency range over which reliable information can be extracted increases. Figure 8.5 presents re-

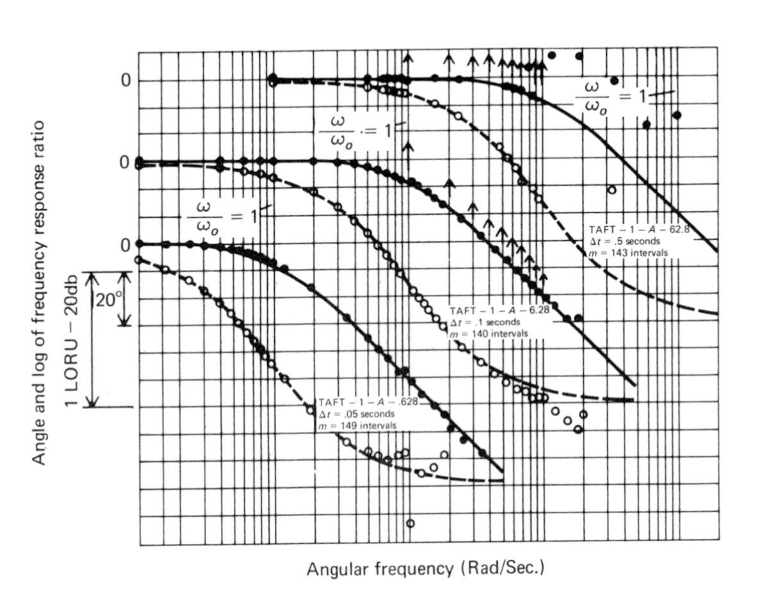

Figure 8.5. Improved frequency response data obtained by decreasing width of forcing pulse.

sults for a first-order system excited with a rectangular pulse varying in width from 62.8 to 0.628 seconds. The sets of curves are shifted by a decade from one another in order to avoid overlapping. Once again the ability to retrieve data beyond the first zero and between subsequent zeros is clearly indicated.

Figures 8.6 and 8.7 are included to show the quality of amplitude ratio information extractable with short pulses to a first-order system. The code letters indicate the following pulse shapes: A = rectangular, B = triangular, C = ramp, D = first degree weighted dis-

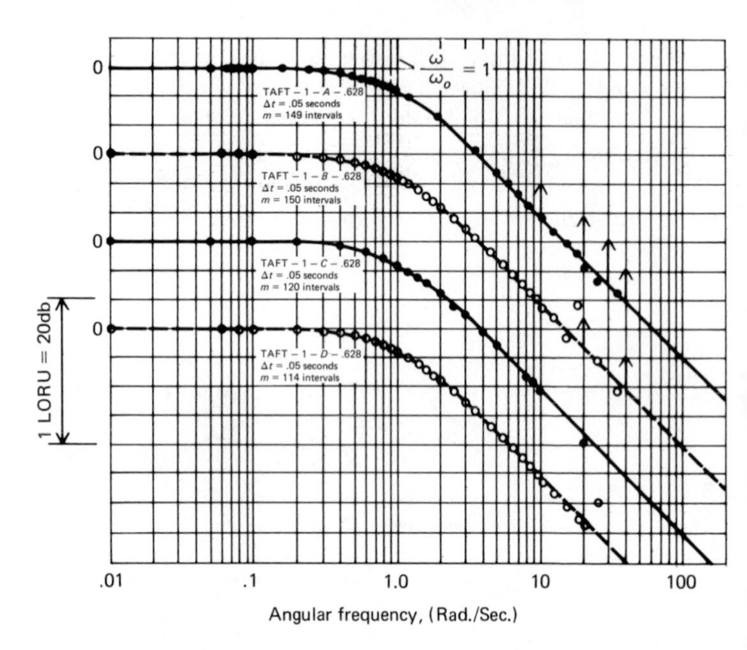

Figure 8.6. Comparison of frequency response data obtained using forcing pulses of different shapes (rectangular, triangular, ramp, first degree weighted displaced cosine pulse inputs).

placed cosine, E = third degree weighted displaced cosine, F = fifth degree weighted displaced cosine, G = rectangular doublet, H = full sine.

Figure 8.8 demonstrates that two-sided pulses having identical positive and negative shapes cannot yield reliable low frequency information since their Fourier transform amplitudes become zero at zero frequency. This is an important point to bear in mind, since sometimes oscillating inputs are the only kind which can be conveniently injected and great uncertainty may sometimes exist in low frequency results.

Except for the limitations indicated above, the ability to extract useful information about simple systems by pulse testing is amply demonstrated.

The following summary describes work done by Dreifke (*9*) in investigating complex systems by the pulse method. A system having the transfer function

$$\frac{X_2}{Y_1} = \frac{[1 + j\omega T_1]\left[1 - \left(\frac{\omega}{\omega_a}\right)^2 + j\frac{2\zeta_a}{\omega_a}\omega\right]}{\left[1 - \left(\frac{\omega}{\omega_{01}}\right)^2 + j\frac{2\zeta_1}{\omega_{01}}\omega\right]\left[1 - \left(\frac{\omega}{\omega_{01}}\right)^2 + j\frac{2\zeta_2\,\omega}{\omega_{02}}\right]\left[1 - \left(\frac{\omega}{\omega_{03}}\right)^2 + j\frac{2\zeta_3\,\omega}{\omega_{03}}\right]} \tag{8.13}$$

was simulated on an analog computer. For this system the characteristic equation was

$$s^6 + 0.275s^5 + 1.51875s^4 + 0.2125s^3 + 0.50156s^2 + 0.01093s + 0.01562 = 0. \tag{8.14}$$

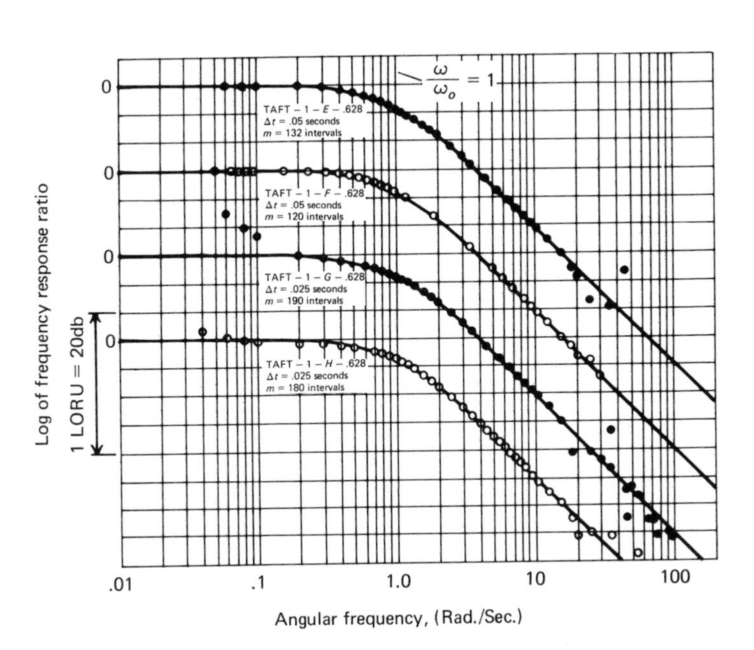

Figure 8.7. Comparison of frequency response data obtained using forcing pulses of different shapes (third degree weighted displaced cosine, fifth degree weighted displaced cosine, rectangular doublet, full sine).

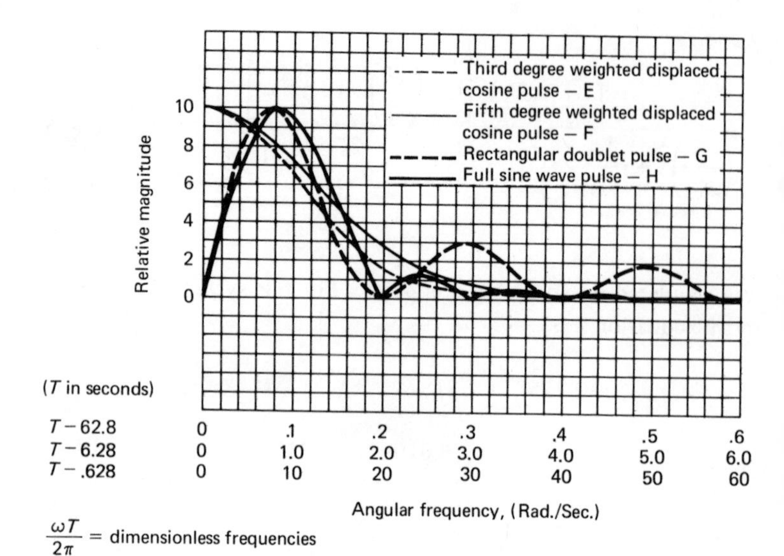

Figure 8.8. Harmonic content of pulses of various shapes.

The roots of this equation are

$$s_{1,2} = -0.00486 \pm j0.1866$$

$$s_{3,4} = -0.0618 \pm j0.657$$

$$s_{5,6} = -0.0708 \pm j1.011. \tag{8.15}$$

Thus

$$\frac{X_2}{Y_1}(j\omega) = \frac{[1 + j0.500\,\omega]\left[1 - \left(\frac{\omega}{0.500}\right)^2 + j0.200\,\omega\right]}{\left[1 - \left(\frac{\omega}{0.1866}\right)^2 + j0.2255\,\omega\right]\left[1 - \left(\frac{\omega}{.660}\right)^2 + j0.284\,\omega\right]\left[1 - \left(\frac{\omega}{1.013}\right)^2 + j0.1361\,\omega\right]} \tag{8.16}$$

where various parameters and constants are

$$\omega_{01} = 0.1866 \qquad \omega_{02} = 0.660 \qquad \omega_{03} = 1.013$$

$$\zeta_1 = 0.0260 \qquad \zeta_2 = 0.0937 \qquad \zeta_3 = 0.0699$$

$$\frac{2\zeta}{\omega_{01}} = 0.2255 \qquad \frac{2\zeta_2}{\omega_{02}} = 0.284 \qquad \frac{2\zeta_3}{\omega_{03}} = 0.1361$$

$$\omega_a = 0.500 \qquad T_1 = 0.500$$

$$\zeta_a = 0.050 \qquad T_2 = 0$$

$$\frac{2\zeta_a}{\omega_a} = 0.200. \tag{8.17}$$

The time data are shown in Figure 8.9, and the frequency response for the ratio X_2/Y_1 is shown in Figure 8.10 with a triangular forcing function for y_i. The fidelity with which the experimental results agree with the theory is clearly indicated, and the critical frequencies $\omega_{01} = 0.1866$, $\omega_{02} = 0.660$, and $\omega_{03} = 1.013$ can be discerned and estimated with precision sufficient for most engineering applications.

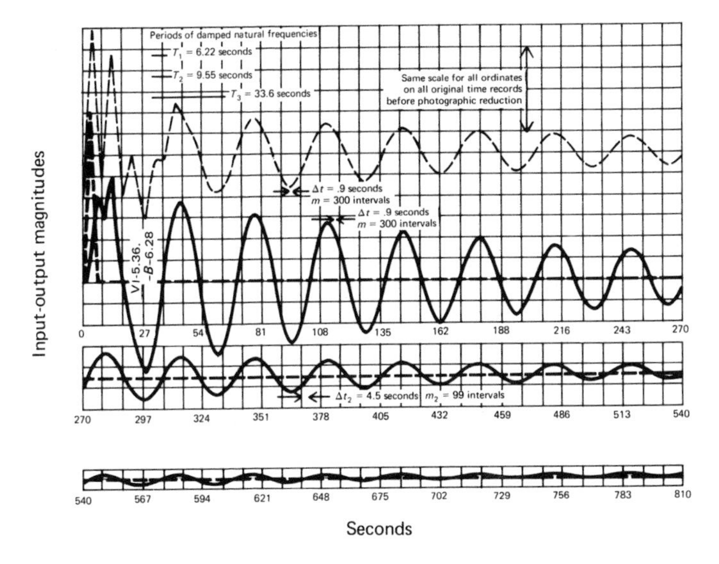

Figure 8.9. Time history of complex lightly damped system from triangular pulse forcing.

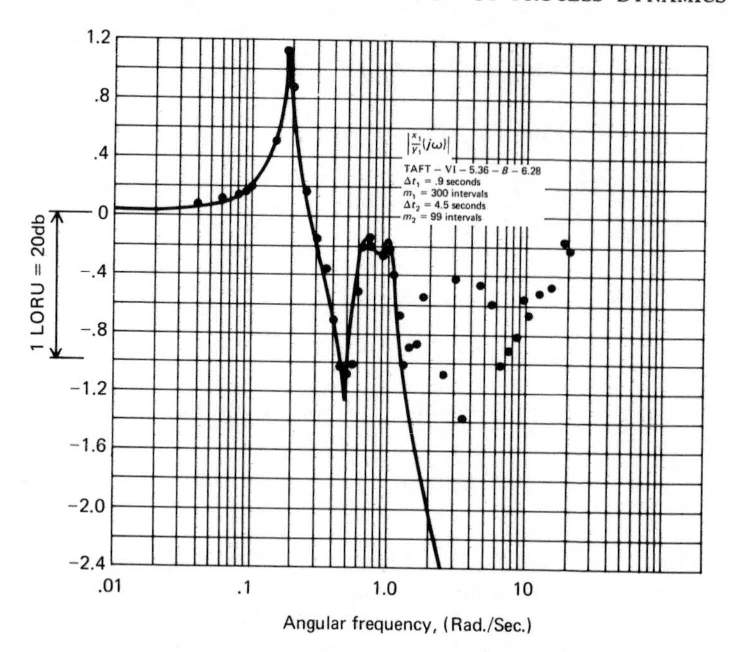

Figure 8.10. Illustration of quality of system identification achieved through single pulse excitation technique.

The results of an exhaustive evaluation of the pulse technique for extracting dynamic behavior of linear systems can be found in the work of Dreifke (9). The conclusions he has drawn are given here verbatim.

(1) *Experimental Instrumentation.* The experimental instrumentation in many cases is simple compared to that for other methods which yield about the same amount of information.

(2) *Time Required for Actual Experimentation.* The time required for actual experimentation is uniquely small. One properly executed pulse test implicitly contains all the dynamic response data for the system in a practical sense. Once such pulse test data exist, values of the frequency response for any frequencies of interest may be obtained at any time without further testing. Values for additional frequencies by the direct method require additional testing.

(3) *Data Processing Machines.* Digital computers are required for processing the data as hand processing is unduly time consuming.

(4) *Simplicity of Data Reduction.* It is not necessary to assume an analytic form for the time response before processing the data as in some other methods. Thus, expert judgment or prior knowledge

is not required to process data by the pulse method. On the other hand, standard curves are available for use in the frequency domain for quickly obtaining linear approximations.

(5) *Complete Spectrum Coverage.* On completely unknown systems, judiciously chosen pulses can cover any desired portions of the entire frequency spectrum, thus ensuring that all the system dynamics will be excited.

(6) *Direct Time Domain Analysis.* Direct time domain analysis is enhanced by proper choice of pulse shape and width. Fail-safe dynamic testing is possible.

(7) *Types of Input Pulses.* The actual input pulses of this study represent types of pulses that are useful. In general, of course, combinations and extensions of these particular types should be used.

(8) *Detection of Nonlinearities.* Distortion due to nonlinearities may be determined by use of multiple amplitudes of a given pulse or by processing data for different pulse shapes.

(9) *Pulse Strength Concept.* The concept of the strength of the pulse as the area under the curve is not meaningful to the degree that greater strength gives greater response. For a given area, the useful frequency range more nearly varies inversely as the first moment of the area for at least certain pulses.

(10) *Experimental Criteria.* For a rough guide and allowing for about 25 percent maximum error in the experimental frequency response, the following criteria are given:

$$|F_1\ (j\omega)| > 8e$$

$$|F_2\ (j\omega)| > 8e$$

$$\omega_{\max}\ \Delta t < \frac{\pi}{2}$$

$$\Delta t \leqslant \frac{T_1}{10} \tag{8.18}$$

where T_1 is the smallest characteristic time of interest in the system and e is the estimated ordinate reading error in the time domain.

Extensive searches of the literature have revealed considerable interest in pulse testing [as discussed in Dreifke's work]. On the other hand, vast segments of the engineering field seem to have made negligible use of the idea. It appears that it would have great competitive advantage for some phases of experimental work on such divergent physical systems as (a) audio devices, (b) electronic amplifiers, (c) continuous (distributed) elastic members for determination of first few natural frequencies and related mode shapes, (d) automatic control systems, (e) chemical processes, (f) the common hydraulic, electric, pneumatic and mechanical systems and lines. While the parameters of the systems are considered to be the unknowns [in Dreifke's study], there are, of course, many interesting systems that have the input or output data as the unknown.

Aside from its potential application in the many fields of engineering in the vein indicated, it seems that recognition of spectral contents of the various pulse shapes may add considerable sophistication and utility to those applications in the communications field that use pulse coding in electronic signal transmission facilities.

Finally, as with experiments in any physical science, care and precaution are urged when using the method. Awareness of nonlinearities, instrument dynamics, and limitations of the procedure itself are essential to its application. In experimental research, it is easy to make mistakes, and there is a great human tendency to neglect inconsistencies. Test and retest until all known possible questions are answered.

It has been shown that the requirement for pulse closing can be eliminated by additional data processing with little increase in the digital program. Input and output signals therefore may be supposed to appear as in Figure 8.11. Since the time histories have been assumed to reach steady state at times T_1 and T_2, the derivatives of these curves at these points will be zero, and thus $f'(t)$ and $g'(t)$ are pulses in the original sense of the term. In practice it may be difficult to ascertain exactly the values of T_1 and T_2, but one may assume that, at some later time, μT_1 and $v T_2$, the derivatives of each curve, become zero.

The following ratios of transforms can be formed:

$$PF(s) = \frac{\int_0^\infty g(t)e^{-st}\,dt}{\int_0^\infty f(t)e^{-st}\,dt} = \frac{\int_0^\infty g'(t)e^{-st}\,dt}{\int_0^\infty f'(t)e^{-st}\,dt}. \tag{8.19}$$

The first ratio is the definition of the performance function. The second follows from the fact that $f'(o) = g'(o) = 0$.

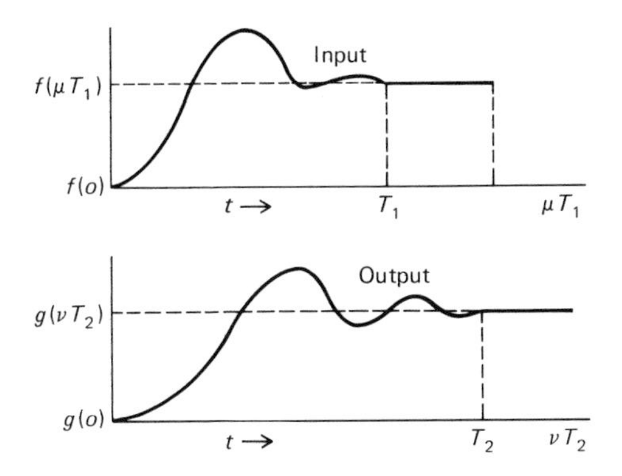

Figure 8.11. Pulse-like time histories which do not return to original values.

Integration by parts yields

$$PF(s) = \frac{\int_0^{\upsilon T_2} e^{-st} g'(t)\,dt}{\int_0^{\mu T_1} e^{-st} f'(t)\,dt} = \frac{e^{-s\upsilon T_2} g(\upsilon T_2) + s\int_0^{\upsilon T_2} e^{-st} g(t)\,dt}{e^{-s\mu T_1} g(\mu T_1) + s\int_0^{\mu T_2} e^{-st} f(t)\,dt}. \tag{8.20}$$

The last quotient is completely finite and, moreover, is evaluated from the original time history data. When $j\omega$ is substituted for s, the frequency response function is obtained.

This method of data reduction has been found to be particularly useful for handling data procured from transient tests in which time histories do not close. Thus, step or modified step response data may be used to procure frequency response.

Frequently, processes or apparata possess legitimate integration properties, and the response to a pulse input cannot close. For example, a controller which imparts a reset or integration action exhibits a nonclosing pulse if excited by a closing pulse. In such instances, data processed in accordance with (8.20) have led to excellent dynamic interpretations.

References 11, 12, 13 and 14 are devoted to evaluations of various numerical methods for obtaining Fourier transforms.

Composition of Linear Forms Associated with the normal solutions of linear differential equations with constant coefficients is the Laplace transform of the ratio of output to input variables. This ratio is commonly referred to as the *transfer function*; or in this work, it is sometimes called the *performance function*.

Substitution of $j\omega$ for s in the transfer function gives the steady state sinusoidally forced response relationship in the time domain. If the transfer function is known, these frequency response characteristics are usually easily derived graphically, particularly if the transfer function can be expressed as the ratio of first- or second-order factors as illustrated below.

Assume a system described by the differential expression in y forced by the differential expression in x,

$$\frac{d^3 y}{dt^3} + \frac{bd^2 y}{dt^2} + \frac{cdy}{dt} + dy = Ax + \frac{Bdx}{dt} + \frac{Cd^2 x}{dt^2} .$$

Where initial conditions are zero,

$$(s^3 + bs^2 + cs + d)\, y\,(s) = (A + Bs + Cs^2)\, x\,(s)$$

or

$$\frac{y(s)}{x(s)} = \frac{(A + Bs + Cs^2)}{(s^3 + bs^2 + cs + a)} = \frac{K\,[a' s^2 + b' s + 1]}{[as^3 + bs^2 + cs + 1]} .$$

Presumably, the numerator term can be considered a quadratic factor of the form $\frac{s^2}{\omega_n'^2} + \frac{2\xi'}{\omega_n'} s + 1$ or the product of two first-order terms $(1 + \tau_1' s)(1 + \tau_2' s)$. Likewise, the denominator may be written as

$$(1 + \tau_1 s)(1 + \tau_2 s)(1 + \tau_3 s) \quad \text{or}$$

$$\left(\frac{s^2}{\omega_n^2} + \frac{2\xi}{\omega_n} s + 1\right)(1 + \tau s) .$$

The transfer function may therefore be written as $\dfrac{\Pi^i[\;\;]_i}{\Pi^j[\;\;]_j}$

where $\Pi^i[\;\;]_i$ and $\Pi^j[\;\;]_j$ are products of first- and second-order polynomial terms.

Bode and Nyquist Diagrams. Whether or not it is possible to describe systems by linear differential equations, it is very useful to relate the frequency response characteristics determined experimentally, as presented on a Bode diagram, with commonly occurring transfer function forms. Several of the most useful will be described.

(1) τs.

With $s = j\omega$, this becomes $j\tau\omega$. A linear complex plane polar plot of this function coincides with the positive imaginary axis. The amplitude is $\tau\omega$, and the phase angle is $\tan^{-1} \tau\omega/0$ or $+90°$ for all frequencies. The linear polar complex plane plot (Nyquist diagram) and Bode diagram representations are shown in Figure 8.12. The slope of the amplitude line on the Bode diagram is +1 and crosses unity amplitude at the frequency $1/\tau$.

(2) $1/\tau s$.

With $s = j\omega$, this becomes $1/j\omega\tau$, a complex number with a purely imaginary denominator. The phase angle of $\dfrac{1}{j\tau\omega}$ is $-\tan^{-1} \dfrac{\tau\omega}{0} = -90$

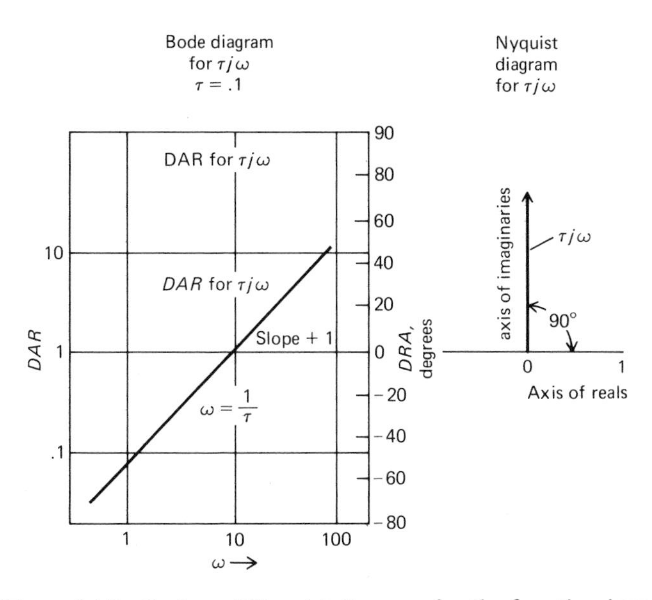

Figure 8.12. Bode and Nyquist diagrams for the function $j\tau\omega$.

for all frequencies. Since $\frac{1}{j\tau\omega} = \frac{-j}{\tau\omega}$, the amplitude on the complex plane lies along the negative imaginary axis. The amplitude is $\frac{1}{\tau\omega}$ and, on the Bode diagram, has a slope of -1. The line crosses unity where $\omega = \frac{1}{\tau}$. Figure 8.13 shows the two representations.

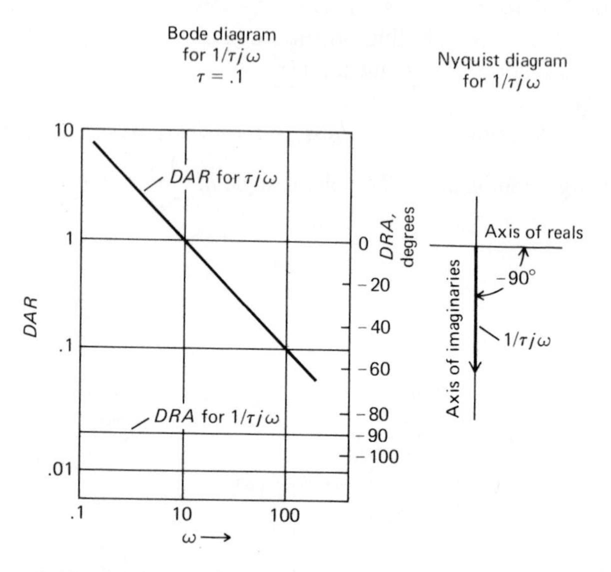

Figure 8.13. Bode and Nyquist diagrams for the function $1/j\tau\omega$.

(3) $1 + \tau s$.
With $s = j\omega$, this becomes $1 + j\tau\omega$ which may be written as

$$\sqrt{1 + (\tau\omega)^2}\ e^{j\theta} \quad \text{or} \quad \sqrt{1 + (\tau\omega)^2},\ \underline{/\tan^{-1}\tau\omega}.$$

The complex plane representation and Bode diagrams are shown in Figure 8.14. Since $\log_{10}$ Amp $= 1/2 \log[(1 + (\tau\omega)^2]$, at high frequencies, where $\tau\omega >> 1$, log Amp $= +\log\tau\omega$. Thus, the slope of the amplitude curve approaches unity at sufficiently high values of frequency. The extrapolation of this line of unity slope intersects

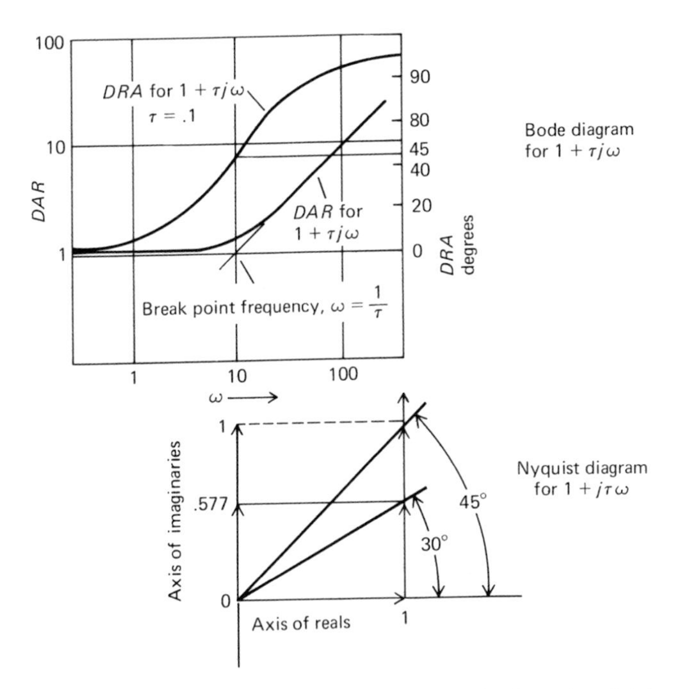

Figure 8.14. Bode and Nyquist diagrams for the function $1 + j\tau\omega$.

unity amplitude at $\omega = \dfrac{1}{\tau}$. This frequency is commonly denoted as the break point or corner frequency, for obvious reasons.

(4) $\dfrac{1}{1 + \tau s.}$

With $s = j\omega$, this becomes $1/1 + j\omega\tau$, which may be written as

$$\frac{1 - j\omega\tau}{1 + (\omega\tau)^2} = \frac{1}{\sqrt{1 + (\omega\tau)^2}} e^{-j\theta} \quad \text{or} \quad \frac{1}{\sqrt{1 + (\omega\tau)^2}}, \underline{/-\theta} \text{ where } \theta = \tan^{-1} \omega\tau.$$

The frequency response representation, Fig. 8.15, is a reflection of the corresponding curves of Fig. 8-14 around the zero phase angle and unity amplitude axes. The phase begins at zero and approaches $-90°$ as ω takes on values from zero to infinity. When $\omega = \tau$ the phase is $-45°$. Since $\log_{10}$ DAR $= \log \dfrac{1}{\sqrt{1 + (\omega\tau)^2}} = -\dfrac{1}{2}$ log

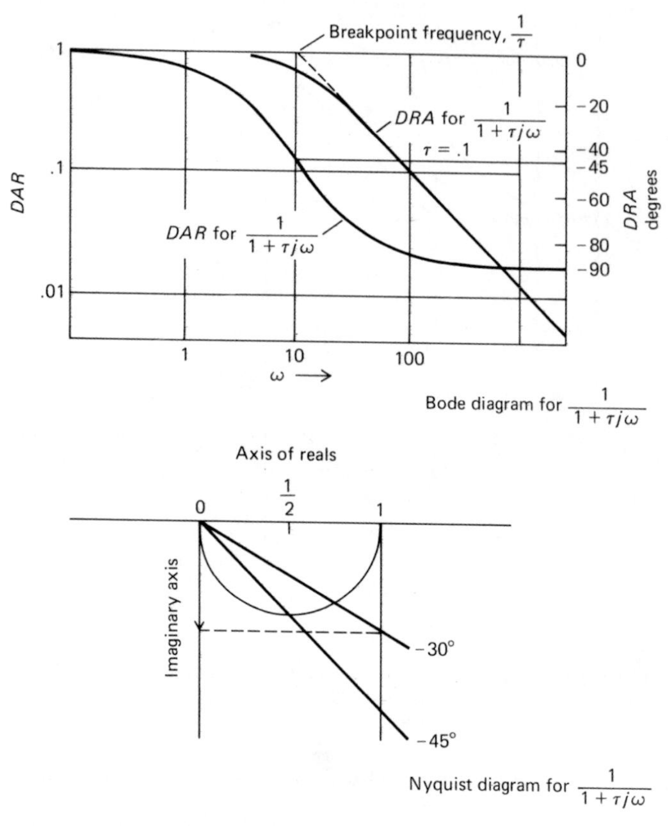

Figure 8.15. Bode and Nyquist diagrams for $1/(1 + j\tau\omega)$.

$[1 + (\omega\tau)^2]$, it follows that when $\omega\tau >> 1$ the slope of the amplitude versus frequency becomes -1. Extrapolation of this slope to the unity amplitude axis gives an intersection at $\omega = 1/\tau$, the break point frequency. Since $\frac{1}{1+\tau j\omega} = \frac{1-\tau j\omega}{1+(\tau\omega)^2} = \frac{1}{1+(\tau\omega)^2} - j\frac{\tau\omega}{1+(\tau\omega)^2}$, the function is seen to be the sum of the real number $\frac{1}{1+(\tau\omega)^2}$ and the imaginary number $\frac{j\tau\omega}{1+(\tau\omega)^2}$.

The complex polar plot is also shown in Figure 8.15.

The locus is a semicircle with its center at 0.5 on the axis of reals and a radius of 0.5.

Thus, if it is assumed that the equation of the locus is

$$y^2 + (x - 0.5)^2 = 0.5^2$$

and if $x = \dfrac{1}{1 + (\tau\omega)^2}$

then

$$\begin{aligned} y &= \sqrt{0.5^2 - (x - 0.5)^2} \\ &= \sqrt{0.25 - \left[\left(\frac{1}{1 + (\tau\omega)^2}\right)^2 - \left(\frac{1}{1 + (\tau\omega)^2}\right) + 0.25\right]} \\ &= \sqrt{\frac{-1 + (\tau\omega)^2 - 1}{[1 + (\tau\omega)^2]^2}} = \sqrt{\frac{(\tau\omega)^2}{[1 + (\tau\omega)^2]^2}} = \frac{\tau\omega}{1 + (\tau\omega)^2}. \end{aligned}$$

This is precisely the magnitude of the imaginary part of the function.

(5) $\left(\dfrac{1 + \alpha\tau s}{1 + \tau s}\right)$

With $s = j\omega$, this ratio becomes

$$\frac{1 + j\alpha\tau\omega}{1 + j\tau\omega} = \frac{\sqrt{1 + (\alpha\tau\omega)^2}}{\sqrt{1 + (\tau\omega)^2}} e^{j(\theta_1 - \theta_2)}$$

where $\theta_1 = \tan^{-1} \alpha\tau\omega$ and $\theta_2 = \tan^{-1} \tau\omega$. This function is obviously a combination of forms similar to 3 and 4 above. The Bode plot is easily constructed by combining curves such as Figure 8.14 and Figure 8.15, recalling that on a log scale products are obtained by addition and on the uniform scale phase angles are additive.

When α is unity, the phase is zero and the amplitude is unity for all frequencies.

If $\alpha < 1$, the amplitude and phase are always unity or less. If α is greater than unity, the amplitude and phase are always unity or greater. The frequency response for $\alpha = 10$ is shown in Figure 8.16 as a Bode plot. As frequency goes from zero to infinity, the amplitude changes from unity to α and the phase from zero passing through a maximum or minimum depending upon whether α is

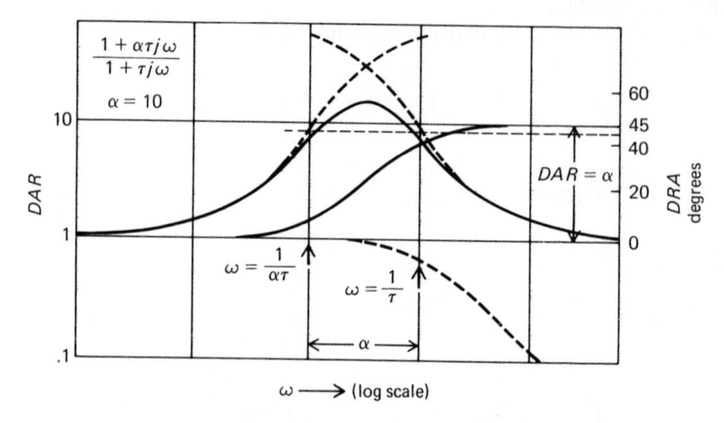

Figure 8.16. Bode diagram for $\left(\dfrac{1+\alpha\tau j\omega}{1+\tau j\omega}\right)$ with $\alpha = 10$.

greater or less than unity, and returns to zero as frequency approaches infinity. The frequency at which the maximum phase angle is attained ($\alpha > 1$) is given by

$$\omega_{\text{max phase}} = \frac{1}{\tau}\sqrt{\frac{1}{\alpha}}\,.$$

and the maximum phase may be found from the relation;

$$[DRA]_{\max} = \tan^{-1}\sqrt{\alpha} - \tan^{-1}\sqrt{1/\alpha}\,.$$

TABLE 8.2 Maximum Phase Angle for the Function $[(1+\alpha\tau s)/(1+\tau s)]$ for Various Values of α Greater than Unity

α	*[DRA], degrees*	*% of 90°*
5	43	48
10	55	61
15	61	68
20	65	72
30	69	77
50	74	82
100	78	86

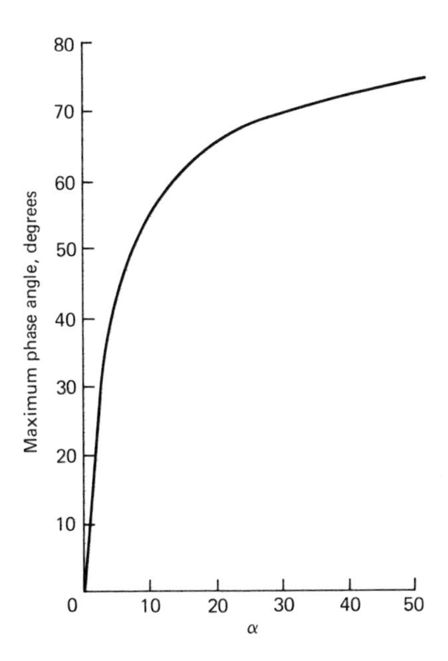

Figure 8.17. Maximum phase angle of $\left(\frac{1+\alpha\tau j\omega}{1+\tau j\omega}\right)$.

That is, the maximum phase angle for this function occurs where the tangent is equal to the cotangent.

Figure 8.17 and Table 8.2 show the dependence of $[DRA]_{max}$ upon α. It will be observed that the phase lead contribution of this function increases rather slowly for values of α greater than 20.

Figure 8.18 is the complex polar plot of $\frac{1+\alpha\tau j\omega}{1+\tau j\omega}$ with $\alpha = 10$.

(6) $\frac{1}{(1+\tau_1 s)(1+\tau_2 s)}$.

With $s = j\omega$, the result is

$$\frac{1}{(1+j\tau_1\omega)(1+j\tau_2\omega)} = \frac{1}{[1+(\tau_1\omega)^2]\ [1+(\tau_2\omega)^2]}\ e^{-j(\theta_1+\theta_2)}$$

where $\theta_1 = \tan^{-1}\omega\tau_1$ and $\theta_2 = \tan^{-1}\omega\tau_2$.

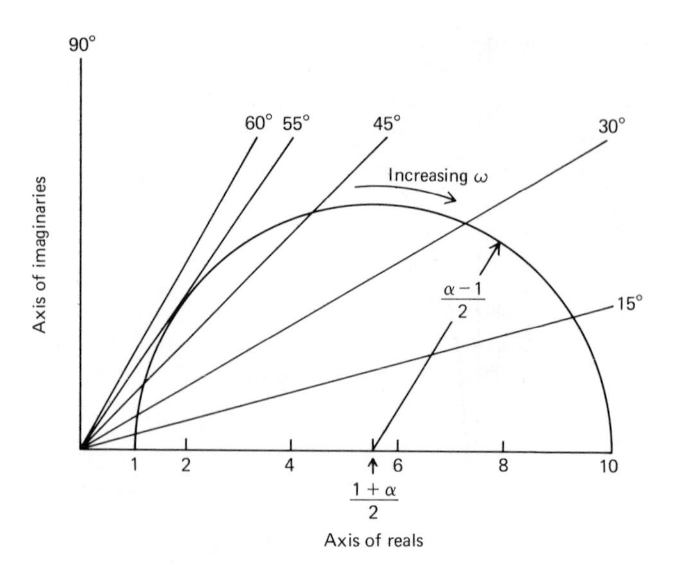

Figure 8.18. Complex polar plot (Nyquist diagram) of $\left(\dfrac{1+\alpha\tau j\omega}{1+\tau j\omega}\right)$ with $\alpha = 10$.

The frequency response diagram is constructed by adding the amplitude of $\dfrac{1}{1+j\tau_1\omega}$ to that of $\dfrac{1}{1+j\omega\tau_2}$ on the log scale and the phase angles θ_1 and θ_2 on the uniform scale. The result is shown in Figure 8.19 where the time constants τ_1 and τ_2 are separated by 1 decade–i.e., $\tau_1 = 10\,\tau_2$ or $\omega_2 = 10\,\omega_1$.

For this function, the amplitude monotonically decreases from unity and the phase angle decreases from zero to $-180°$ as frequency increases from zero to infinity.

(7) $$\frac{1}{\left(\dfrac{s^2}{\omega_n{}^2}+\dfrac{2\xi s}{\omega_n}+1\right)}$$

With $s = j\omega$, this second-order form becomes

$$\frac{1}{\left[1-\dfrac{\omega^2}{\omega_n^2}\right]+j\,\dfrac{2\omega\xi}{\omega_n}} = \frac{1}{\sqrt{\left[1-\left(\dfrac{\omega}{\omega_n}\right)^2\right]^2+\left(\dfrac{2\omega\xi}{\omega_n}\right)^2}}\,e^{-j\theta},$$

where $\theta = \tan^{-1} \dfrac{2(\omega\xi/\omega_n)}{\left[1 - \left(\dfrac{\omega}{\omega_n}\right)^2\right]}$.

As ω approaches infinity, the phase angle goes from zero to $-180°$. Where $\omega = \omega_n$, the phase angle is $-90°$.

Amplitude is unity at $\omega = 0$, and it decreases monotonically as frequency increases. At intermediate values of frequency, the ampli-

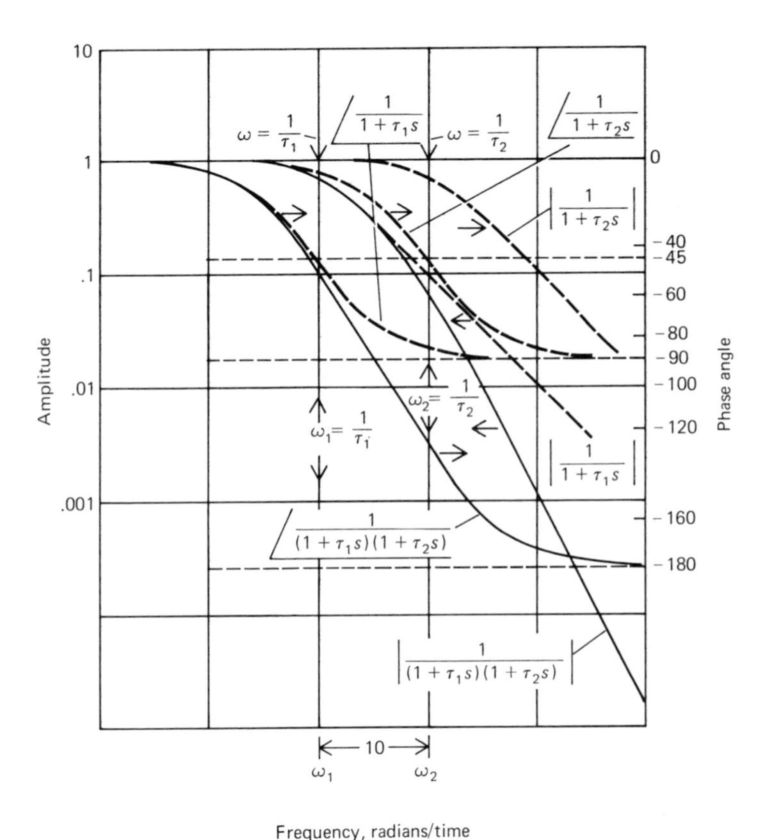

Figure 8.19. Bode plot for the function $\dfrac{1}{(1 + \tau_1 s)(1 + \tau_2 s)}$ for $s = j\omega$.

tude may be more or less than unity depending on the value of ξ. At high values of ω, the slope of the amplitude curve approaches -2 since

$$\log_{10} \text{Amp} = \log_{10} \frac{1}{\left\{\left[1 - \left(\frac{\omega}{\omega_n}\right)^2\right]^2 + \left(\frac{2\xi}{\omega_1}\right)^2\right\}^{1/2}}$$

$$\cong \frac{1}{2} \log_{10} \left[1 - \left(\frac{\omega}{\omega_n}\right)^2\right]^2 = -2 \log_{10} (\omega/\omega_n).$$

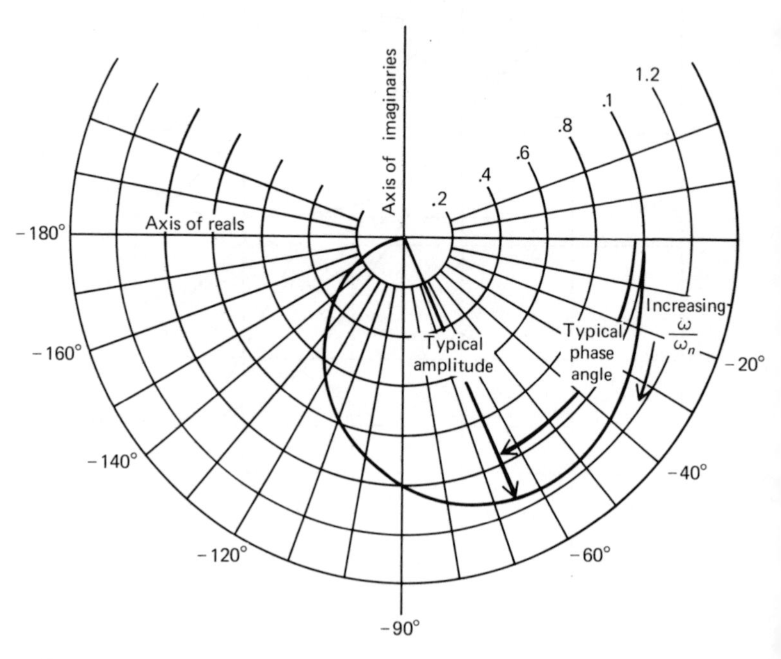

Figure 8.20. Nyquist or complex polar plot of the function $\dfrac{1}{\left[\dfrac{s^2}{\omega_n^2} + \dfrac{2\xi s}{\omega_n} + 1\right]}$ for $\xi = 0.5$ and $s = j\omega$.

Bode diagrams for various values of ξ are shown in Figures 5-3 and 5-4. In Figure 8.20 is shown the Nyquist plot for the case for $\xi = 0.5$ as ω/ω_n takes on values from zero to infinity.

8.5 RESOLUTION OF BODE PLOTS

Sometimes the problem is encountered of deducing the form of a transfer function from frequency response information which may have been derived in one of a number of ways. This is particularly desirable if the system characteristics are to be compared with theoretically derived relations or if it is desirable to correlate experimentally determined parameters with system parameters.

This may be easily and rapidly accomplished with a set of templates or profiles corresponding to well defined theoretical forms. These profiles may be purchased or can be constructed from plastic or from the graphs themselves (such as Figures 5.3 and 5.4) used as underlays. A convenient size is such that on log scales the ordinate, *DAR*, and the abscissa, frequency, are both 2.5 inches per cycle. This corresponds to 20 decibels change in [*DAR*] per decade where $db = 20 \log_{10} [DAR]$. The uniform scale for [*DRA*] is, conveniently, 20° per inch. The procedure for extracting a linear description by fitting standard profiles to experimental data is illustrated in Figure 8.21.

The following steps are recommended.

(1) Fit the amplitude data as far out in frequency as possible using a first-order curve, unless second-order profiles for both amplitude and phase fit the data fairly well.

In Figure 8.21 is presented the frequency response data obtained by pulse testing a process, and computing the Fourier transforms. The results are shown as the curves labelled [*DAR*] and [*DRA*]. The amplitude coordinate is uniform, $\log_{10}$ of the dynamic amplitude being plotted rather than decibels which are 20 times greater. The first-order profile fits the low-frequency data if the break point, indicated by a scribe mark on the plastic template, coincides with a frequency of 1.36×10^{-2}. This corresponds to a time constant of $\left(\frac{1}{1.36}\right) \times 10^2$ or 73.5 seconds. This is curve 1 in Figure 8.21.

(2) Mark the position of the break point frequency (or ω_n), and note the agreement with the phase angle corresponding to the first- (or second-) order form.

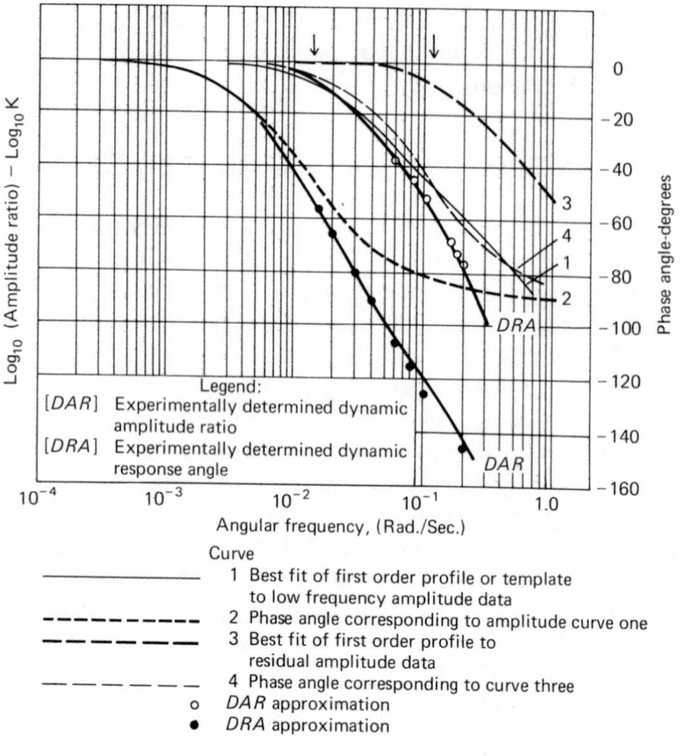

Figure 8.21. Resolution of experimental frequency response data into linear components.

With the scribe marks corresponding to the break point frequency and 45° lag ($DRA = -45°$), a reasonable fit in the low-frequency range for the example is obtained as shown by Curve 2. That is, for the example, fair agreement between amplitude and phase data occurs in the low-frequency region using first-order profiles.

(3) If the experimental phase angle data deviate less than $-10°$ from the first-order fit at the break point, the amplitude curve probably should by shifted slightly towards the high frequencies. The nature of the amplitude data will dictate if this is feasible.

If the deviation is more than $-10°$, then a second-order profile should be considered.

Usually, with some practice, a consistent fit can be obtained. The greatest difficulty occurs if a numerator term is present. In these cases, a ratio such as $\left(\frac{1+as}{1+bs}\right)$ will occur, and, if a/b is 5 or less, it becomes difficult to satisfy both amplitude and phase, especially if another denominator term with a time constant not far removed from either a or b is present.

In the example, the phase angle deviation is about -10°.

(4) Note the deviations of the amplitude data from the best fit to the profiles finally selected, and plot these deviations.

For the example, the plot of these amplitude deviations is shown as Curve 3.

(5) Fit a profile (as above) to the amplitude deviation data, locating the appropriate break point frequency. Note the fit of the phase angle deviations to the phase angles corresponding to the amplitude profile used in 4.

In Figure 8.21, the deviation data fit a first-order amplitude profile fairly well if the break point frequency is 1.1×10^{-1} radians per second. (Curve 3) The phase angles corresponding to this break point frequency are shown as Curve 4. The fit to the phase angle deviations is quite satisfactory, no subsequent deviations exceeding 5° for frequencies as high as 0.2.

(6) If the phase data are consistently low, consider introducing pure delay time, although this should be very small if it is removed from the output data prior to processing, which is highly recommended.

This procedure, which is not as arbitrary as might appear, can usually resolve experimental frequency response data in 15-20 minutes.

It may be argued that the results are not reproducible or consistent and that the assumed linearity is invalid. In actual practice, however, the procedure yields useful information and frequently lends insights into the physical phenomena which occur in the process under study.

The results for the example of Figure 8.21 indicate that the frequency dependent relation between output and input can be approximated by the second-order form

$$\left(\frac{1}{1 + 73.5s}\right)\left(\frac{1}{1 + 9.1s}\right).$$

In this case, the two time constants $\tau_1 = 73.5$ and $\tau_1 = 9.1$ seconds could be related to the physics of the system which consisted of a cascaded pneumatic resistance-capacitance process.

One of the most potentially useful aspects of dynamic testing is verification of theoretical 'models'. In these instances where a differential equation can be Laplace transformed and where initial conditions introduce no difficulties, substitution of $j\omega$ for s permits the derivation of expressions for a dynamic amplitude ratio and a dynamic response angle as functions of frequency. If then it is possible to pulse test the real system, an experimental frequency response relation may be quickly obtained via a Fourier transform computation routine.

Comparison of theoretical performance with experimental results, using both amplitude and phase data, provides stringent criteria for substantiating theoretical forms. The fact that forcing pulses of different shapes or types can be readily used enables an experimenter to diagnose erroneous formulations and to locate sensitive parameters.

References

1. Young, A. J. *An Introduction to Process Control System Design.* Longmans Green Co., New York, 1955.
   Early experiences with direct frequency response testing are described.
2. Oldenburger, Rufus, ed. *Frequency Response.* The Macmillan Co., New York, 1956.
   Reviews and documents early studies.
3. Hougen, J. O. *Experiences and Experiments with Process Dynamics.* American Institute of Chemical Engineers Monograph Series No. 4, vol. 60, 1964.
4. Izawa, K. and K. Furata. *Simultaneous identification of multi-input and -output systems.* Proceedings of IFAC Tokyo Symposium, pp. 224-236, 1965.
5. Pelegrin, M. J. Application of statistical techniques to the servomechanism field, in *Automatic and Manual Control* (A. Tustin, ed.). Butterworths Publications Ltd., London, England, 1951.
6. Goodman, T. P. and J. B. Reswick. Determination of system characteristics from normal operating records. *Trans. Amer. Soc. Mech. Eng.* 78 (1956), p. 259.
7. Gallier, P. W., C. M. Sliepcevich and T. H. Puckett. *Chemical Engineering Progress.* Symposium Series 57, No. 36, pp. 59–68, 1961.

8. Lees, Sidney. *Interpreting Dynamic Measurements of Physical Systems.* Massachusetts Institute of Technology Report R-128, Feb. 1957.

9. Dreifke, Gerald E. *Effects on input pulse shape and width on accuracy of dynamic system analysis from experimental pulse data.* Dissertation presented to Sever Institute of Washington University, June, 1961.

   This thesis is a classic in its field.

10. Dreifke, G. E., G. Mesmer and J. O. Hougen. Effects of truncation on time to frequency domain conversion. *Trans. Instrum. Soc. Amer.* **1**, no. 4 (October 1962), pp. 353–368.

    This paper is derived from the above thesis by Dreifke.

11. Clements, W. C., Jr. and K. B. Schnelle, Jr. *I&EC Proc. Des. Develop.* **2**, no. 2 (1953), pp. 94 -102.

12. Lewis, C. I., D. F. Bruley and D. H. Hunt. *I&EC Proc. Des. Develop* **6**, no. 3 (1967), pp. 281–286.

13. Stewart, R. R. and D. F. Bruley. *Amer. Inst. Chem. Eng. J.* **13**, no. 793 (1967) and **15**, no. 220 (1969).

14. Zolner, W. J. and R. R. Stewart. Paper in preparation. Northeastern University, Boston, Mass.

15. Draper, C. S., Walter McKay and Sidney Lees. *Instrument Engineering*, vol. 2. McGraw-Hill Book Co., 1953.

    Chapter 25, "Relating function forms from pulse function responses," gives details of pulse data reduction. When the system being tested is known to be either first or second order, the system parameters can be found from a single rectangular or displaced cosine input pulse test by referring to Figures 25-10, 25-11, 25-12 or 25-14 and 25-16.

9
Industrial Control Components; Electronic Controllers, Pneumatic Controllers and Pneumatic Transmission Lines

The majority of industrial controllers utilize either pneumatic or electrical circuits to generate the desired functions. Currently, sales of each type are roughly equal. Electronic types are preferred for maximum compatibility with supervising digital control systems, but evidently pneumatics continue to be specified for many new facilities.

9.1 ELECTRONIC CONTROLLERS

Modern electronic controllers take advantage of the properties of high-gain amplifiers, feedback principles and the convenience and small space requirements of printed and/or integrated circuits.

The high-gain amplifier is the principal component. It is an electronic amplifier with linear properties, excellent frequency response and high impedance. Gains are in the range of 10^5 to 10^6 with an impedance of 10^5 to 10^7 ohms. As a result, the amplifier draws almost no current. The usual amplifier inverts the sign of the applied voltage so that to preserve the sign an additional inverting amplifier with unity gain is used.

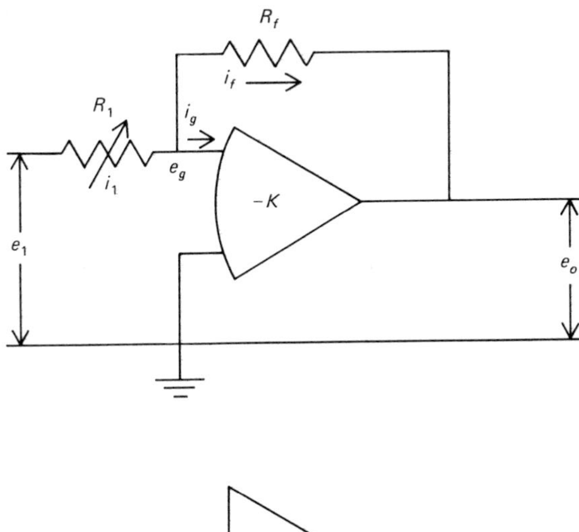

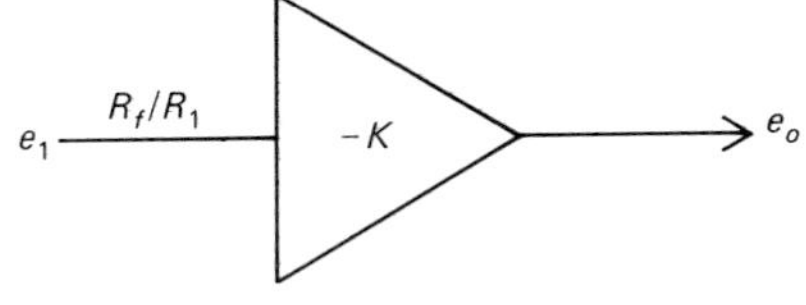

Figure 9.1. (a) Schematic diagram of variable gain circuit using a high gain amplifier (b) simplified representation of variable gain circuit.

Because of the high gain of the amplifier, the voltage appearing at the input to it, when part of a circuit, is vanishingly small.

Figure 9.1a shows a variable gain circuit employing a high-gain operational amplifier. The analysis of the circuit is outlined below.

Voltage e_1, relative to some reference value, is imposed across the input terminals. The very small voltage, e_g, appearing at the amplifier input, is amplified to produce output voltage e_0. The voltage $e_g - e_0$, across feedback resistor, R_f, gives rise to current i_f. Because of the sign inversion, $e_0 = -Ke_g$, but, since K is very high, in order for e_0 to be a useful signal, e_g must be very small indeed. Since amplifier impedance is high, i_g is negligible. Thus

$$e_1 - e_g \cong e_1 = i_1 R_1$$

$$e_g - e_0 \cong -e_0 = i_f R_f$$

and

$$i_1 \cong i_f.$$

Therefore,

$$\frac{e_1}{R_1} = \frac{-e_0}{R_f},$$

or

$$e_0 = \frac{-R_f}{R_1} e_1 .$$

The ratio is usually changed by adjusting the resistor R_1. An equivalent representation of the circuit is shown in Figure 9.1b.

The principle may be extended to obtain a summing circuit as shown in Figure 9.2a.

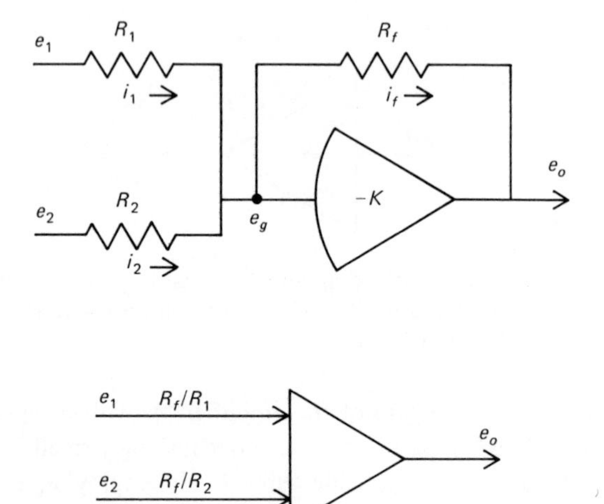

Figure 9.2. (a) Operational amplifier circuit for use as summing device (b) simplified representation of a summer.

If it is again assumed that $e_g \cong 0$ and that there is no current through the amplifier,

$$e_1 = i_1 R_1 ,$$

$$e_2 = i_2 R_2 ,$$

$$-e_0 = i_f R_f \text{ and}$$

$$i_1 + i_2 = i_f ;$$

therefore,

$$\frac{e_1}{R_1} + \frac{e_2}{R_2} = \frac{-e_0}{R_f},$$

so that,

$$e_0 = -\left[\frac{R_f}{R_1} e_1 + \frac{R_f}{R_2} e_2\right].$$

The equivalent representation is shown in Figure 9.2b.

Integrating Circuit Replacing the feedback resistor, R_f, with a capacitor produces an integrating circuit. Figure 9.3a and b,

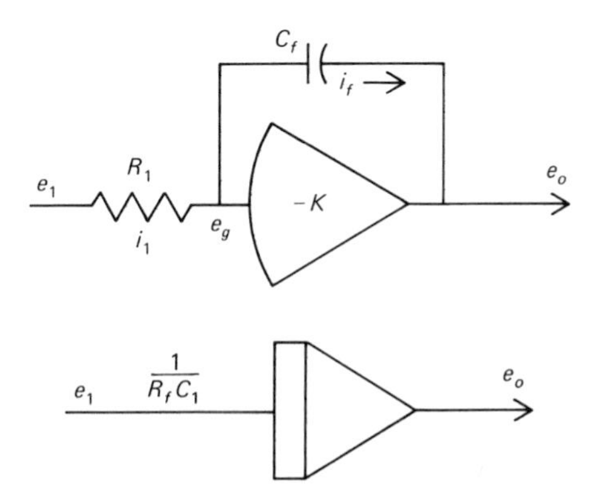

Figure 9.3. (a) Integrating circuit (b) simplified representation of integrator.

are equivalent circuits. In this case,

$$e_1 = i_1 R_1$$

$$-e_0 = \frac{1}{C_f}\int i_1\, dt = \frac{1}{C_f}\int \frac{e_1}{R_1}\, dt = \frac{1}{R_1 C_f}\int e_1\, dt.$$

If R_1 and C_f are expressed in megohms and microfarads, respectively, the integration constant, $R_1 C_f$, is in seconds.

In operational form, assuming zero initial conditions,

$$e_0(s) = -\frac{1}{R_1 C_f s},$$

where s is the complex Laplace operator and e_0 is now a function of s. In analog circuitry, the initial condition can be inserted as a voltage taken from a variable potentiometer.

Practical Differentiating Circuit In a similar manner, a differentiating circuit is constructed by substituting a capacitor for the input resistor, as in Figure 9.4:

$$e_1 = \frac{1}{C_1}\int i_1\,dt,$$

$$-e_0 = i_f R_f,$$

$$i_1 = i_f,$$

$$\frac{de_1}{dt} = \frac{i_1}{C_1} = \frac{-e_0}{C_f R_f},$$

$$E_0 = R_f C_1 \frac{de_1}{dt},$$

or

$$e_0\,(s) = -R_f C_1\, e_1\, s.$$

Considering frequency response for which $s = j\omega$, it is apparent that very high output voltages and possible amplifier overload could occur if a high frequency input were imposed. Because true dif-

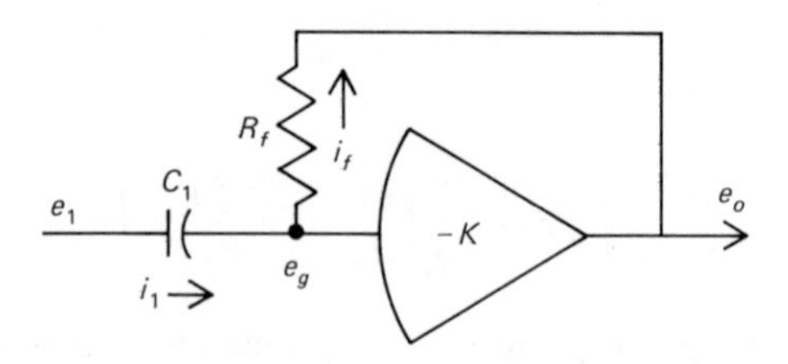

Figure 9.4. Pure differentiating circuit.

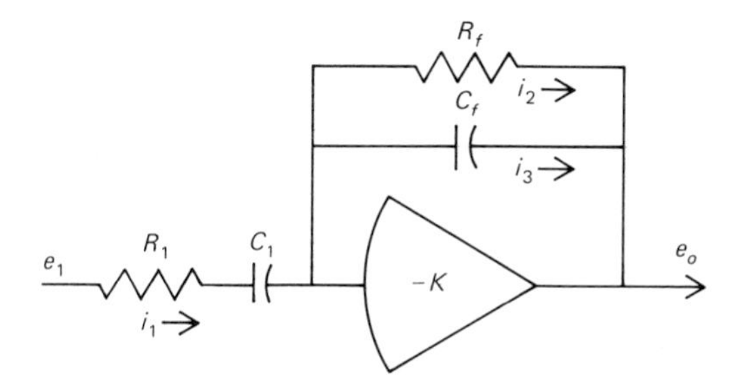

Figure 9.5. Modified differentiating circuit.

ferentiating circuits are sensitive to rapidly varying input signals, which may arise from signal corruption (noise), they are not in common use. Circuit modifications are employed to eliminate this undesirable aspect of the pure differentiator. One such modification is shown in Figure 9.5. The analysis follows:

$$e_1 = R_1 i_1 + \frac{1}{C_1}\int i_1\, dt \quad \text{or} \quad e_1(s) = \left[\frac{1+R_1 C_1 s}{C_1 s}\right] i_1(s)$$

$$-e_0 = R_f i_2 \quad \text{or} \quad i_2(s) = \frac{-e_0}{R_f}$$

$$-e_0 = \frac{1}{C_f}\int i_3\, dt \quad \text{or} \quad i_3(s) = -e_0 C_f s\ .$$

Then, since

$$i_1 = i_2 + i_3,\ i_2(s) + i_3(s) = -e_0\left[\frac{1}{R_f} + C_f s\right],$$

or

$$i_1(s) = -e_0\left[\frac{1+R_f C_f s}{R_f}\right].$$

Therefore, in operator form,

$$e_1(s) = -\left[\frac{1+R_1 C_1 s}{C_1 s}\right]\left[\frac{1+R_f C_f s}{R_f}\right] e_0$$

or
$$e_0(s) = \frac{-R_f C_1 s}{(1 + R_1 C_1 s)(1 + R_f C_f s)} \cdot e_1(s). \qquad (9.1)$$

Assuming a sign inversion through an amplifier of unity gain and the appropriate choice of resistors and capacitors, the frequency response of the above circuit could appear as shown in Figure 9.6. For this figure, $R_f = R_1$, $R_f C_1 = 1$, $R_f C_f = 0.05$ or $C_f/C_1 = 0.05$. A gain coefficient of 1 is used so that the ratio of e_0 to e_1 is

$$\frac{e_0}{e_1}(s) = \left[\frac{s}{1+s}\right]\left[\frac{1}{1+.05s}\right]. \qquad (9.2)$$

It is apparent that, in the frequency range of $\omega = .01$ to 5, amplification and phase lead, characteristic of a differentiating circuit, are, in some measure, achieved.

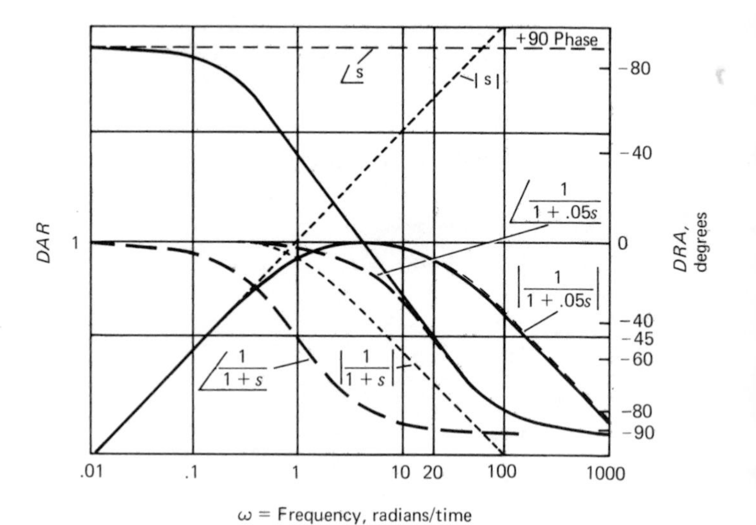

Figure 9.6. Bode diagram of the function $\left(\frac{s}{1+s}\right)\left(\frac{1}{1+.05s}\right)$ and the component functions.

Controller Circuits The generalized circuit, employed for computing purposes appears in Figure 9.7, from which the relationship between e_0 and e_1 is

$$\frac{e_0}{e_1} = \frac{-Z_f}{Z_1}, \tag{9.3}$$

where Z_f and Z_1 are impedances corresponding to the circuits represented by the Z's.

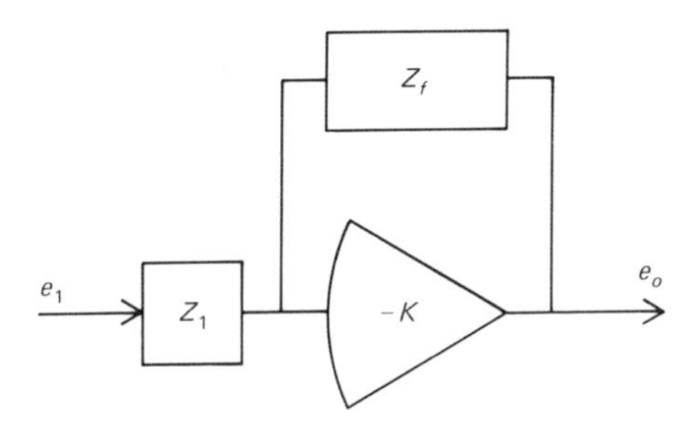

Figure 9.7. Generalized representation of an analog computing circuit employing a high gain operational amplifier.

Tables of functions produced from various networks may be found; for example, see References 1 and 2 at the end of this chapter. The parallel resistance-capacitance network which appears in the feedback path of the circuit shown in Figure 9.5 has an impedance

$$Z_f = \frac{R_f}{R_f C_f s + 1},$$

while the element consisting of a resistor and capacitor in series in that same circuit has the impedance

$$Z_f = \frac{R_1 C_1 s + 1}{C_1 s}.$$

If the relationship shown as (9.3) is applied,

$$\frac{e_0}{e_1} = \frac{-Z_f}{Z_1} = \frac{-R_f C_1 s}{(1 + R_f C_f s)(1 + R_1 C_1 s)} \tag{9.4}$$

a result identical to (9.1).

The partial electronic circuit for a popular analog type controller (Bell & Howell, Control Division Bridgeport, Conn.) is given in Figure 9.8.

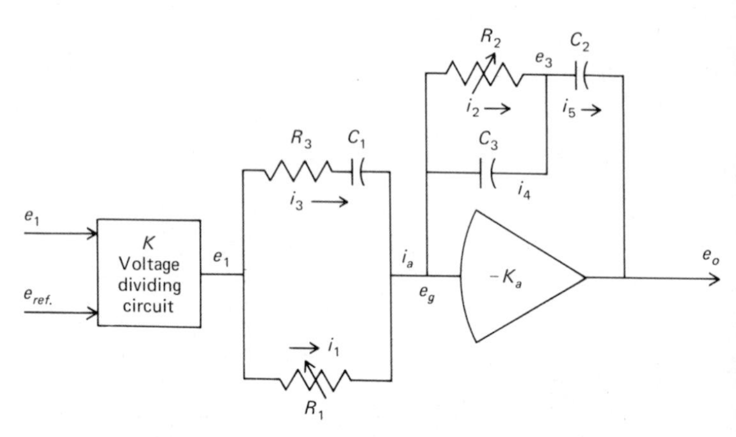

Figure 9.8. Circuit diagram for Bell & Howell three-term controller.

A voltage dividing network in the first block permits changing the factor K, which is called the gain of the controller.

The analysis of the latter portions of this circuit will be outlined below. Use is made of the facts that $i_1 + i_3 = i_a$, $i_2 + i_4 = i_5$, $i_a = i_5$, and, because of the presence of the operational amplifier (having a high gain, $-K_a$), $e_g \cong 0$.

For convenience, final equations are written in operational form assuming zero initial conditions.

For the first section, excluding the block K,

$$i_1 + i_3 = i_a,$$

$$e_1 - e_g = i_3 R_3 + \frac{1}{C_1}\int i_3\, dt. \tag{9.5}$$

Since $e_g \cong 0$ and $\frac{1}{C_1}\int i_3\,dt \Leftrightarrow \frac{i_3(s)}{C_1 s}$ in operator form,

$$e_1(s) = i_3(s)\left[R_3 + \frac{1}{C_1 s}\right] = i_3(s)\left[\frac{R_3 C_1 s + 1}{C_1 s}\right],$$

or

$$i_3(s) = \frac{(C_1 s)e_1}{[R_3 C_1 s + 1]}. \tag{9.6}$$

Also,

$$e_1 - e_g = i_1 R_1,$$

or

$$i_1 = \frac{e_1}{R_1} \tag{9.7}$$

since

$$e_g \cong 0.$$

Substituting (9.6) and (9.7) into (9.5) gives

$$i_a = e_1\left[\frac{1}{R_1} + \frac{C_1 s}{R_3 C_1 s + 1}\right] = \left[\frac{R_3 C_1 s + 1 + R_1 C_1 s}{R_1(R_3 C_1 s + 1)}\right] e_1,$$

or

$$i_a = \left[\frac{(R_3 + R_1)C_1 s + 1}{R_1(R_3 C_1 s + 1)}\right] e_1. \tag{9.8}$$

In block diagram form, the relationship may be shown as

$$e_1 \longrightarrow \boxed{\frac{(R_3 + R_1)C_1 s + 1}{R_1(R_3 C_1 s + 1)}} \longrightarrow i_a.$$

For the second section,

$$e_g - e_3 = i_2 R_2, \tag{9.9}$$

$$e_g - e_3 = \frac{1}{C_3}\int i_4\,dt, \tag{9.10}$$

$$e_3 - e_0 = \frac{1}{C_2} \int i_5 \, dt. \tag{9.11}$$

In operational form, and if $e_g = 0$,

$$i_2 = -e_3/R_2 \text{ and} \tag{9.12}$$

$$i_4 = -e_3 C_3 s . \tag{9.13}$$

Since

$$i_5 = i_2 + i_4 , \tag{9.14}$$

$$i_5 = -e_3 \left[\frac{1}{R_2} + C_3 s \right] = - \left[\frac{1 + R_2 C_3 s}{R_2} \right] e_3 . \tag{9.15}$$

From (9.11)

$$e_3 = e_0 + \frac{i_5}{C_2 s} . \tag{9.16}$$

Substituting into (9.15) gives

$$i_5 = - \left[e_0 + \frac{i_5}{C_2 s} \right] \left[\frac{1 + R_2 C_3 s}{R_2} \right] \quad \text{or}$$

$$R_2 C_2 s \, i_5 = - (i_5 + e_0 C_2 s)(1 + R_2 C_3 s) .$$

Expanding and rearranging results in

$$R_2 C_2 s \, i_5 = - [i_5 + R_2 C_3 s \, i_5 + C_2 e_0 s + R_2 C_2 C_3 e_0 s^2],$$

$$(R_2 C_2 s + R_2 C_3 s + 1) i_5 = -(C_2 s) [R_2 C_3 s + 1] e_0)$$

or

$$i_5 = \frac{-C_2 s \, [R_2 C_3 s + 1] e_0}{[R_2 \, (C_2 + C_3) s + 1]} . \tag{9.17}$$

In block diagram form, this is shown as

$$e_0 \longrightarrow \boxed{\frac{-C_2 s [R_2 C_3 s + 1]}{R_2 (C_2 + C_3) s + 1}} \longrightarrow i_5 .$$

Since $i_5 = i_a$,

$$\left[\frac{(R_3 + R_1)C_1 s + 1}{R_1(R_3 C_1 s + 1)}\right] e_1 = -C_2 s \left[\frac{(R_2 C_3 s + 1)}{R_2(C_2 + C_3)s + 1}\right] e_0 . \tag{9.18}$$

or, after rearrangement,

$$\frac{e_0}{e_1} = -\left[\frac{1 + (R_1 + R_3)C_1 s}{R_1 C_2 s}\right]\left[\frac{1 + R_2(C_2 + C_3)s}{1 + R_2 C_3 s}\right]\left[\frac{1}{1 + R_3 C_1 s}\right]. \tag{9.19}$$

The Bell and Howell (Bell and Howell, Controls Division, Bridgeport, Connecticut) fast-range 3-term blind controller circuit uses components with the following specifications:

R_1 and R_2 : variable from about 0.3 megohms to infinity (adjustable)
R_3 : 10,000 ohms or 0.01 megohms.
$C_1 = C_2$: 1 microfarad, (mfd)
C_3 : 0.1 mfd.

Thus

$$\frac{e_0}{e_1} = -\left[\frac{1 + (R_1 + 0.01)s}{R_1 s}\right]\left[\frac{1 + R_2(1.1)s}{1 + R_2(0.1)s}\right]\left[\frac{1}{1 + 0.01s}\right].$$

Because $R_1 \gg 0.01$, $R_1 + 0.01 \cong R_1$. Also, practically, $1 \gg 0.01s$, so the relationship simplifies to

$$\frac{e_0}{e_1} = -\left[\frac{1 + R_1 s}{R_1 s}\right]\left[\frac{1 + 1.1R_2 s}{1 + 0.1R_2 s}\right]. \tag{9.20}$$

For convenience, the following terms are defined:

$$\tau_i = R_1$$
$$\tau_d = 0.1R_2$$
$$\alpha\tau_d = 1.1R_2$$

Therefore, $\alpha = \frac{\alpha\tau_d}{\tau_d} = \frac{1.1R_2}{0.1R_2} = 11.0$ for this circuit. After introducing the gain constant, the controller function becomes

$$\frac{e_0}{e_i} = -K\left[\frac{1+\tau_i s}{\tau_i s}\right]\left[\frac{1+\alpha\tau_d s}{1+\tau_d s}\right]. \tag{9.21}$$

The sign of the function is readily reversed in practice by passing the output through an inverting amplifier.

This type of control function is very commonly supplied in process controllers. It is called proportional plus integral plus deriva-

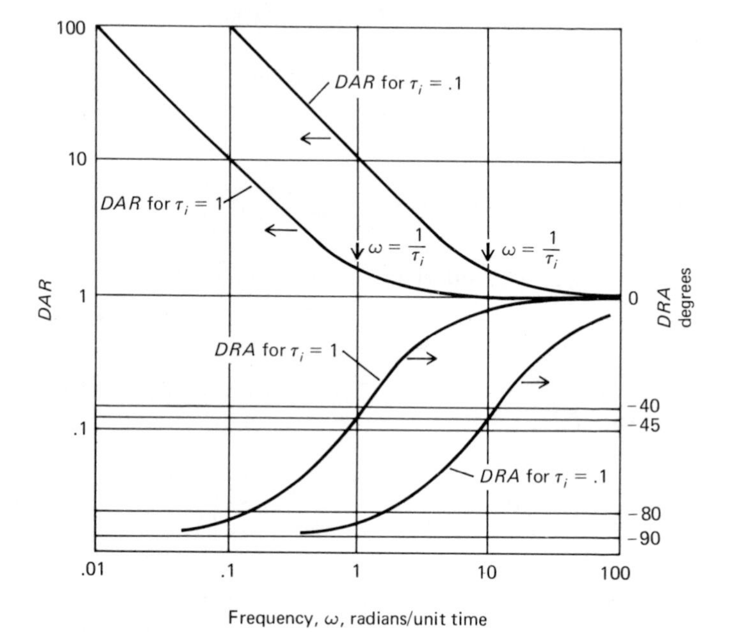

Figure 9.9. Frequency response of the "integral" component, $\frac{1+\tau_i s}{\tau_i s}$ for electronic controller with $\tau_i = 1$ and $\tau_i = 0.1$.

tive, the *PID* controller. The various parts correspond to those names as indicated below:

$$\frac{e_0}{e_i} = \underbrace{K}_{\substack{\uparrow \\ P \\ \text{Proportional}}} \underbrace{\left[\frac{1+\tau_i s}{\tau_i s}\right]}_{\substack{\uparrow \\ I \\ \text{"Integral"}}} \underbrace{\left[\frac{1+\alpha\tau_d s}{1+\tau_d s}\right]}_{\substack{\uparrow \\ D \\ \text{"Derivative"}}}. \tag{9.22}$$

Figures 9.9 and 9.10 show the frequency response characteristics of the 'Integral' and 'Derivative' components for various values of the parameters.

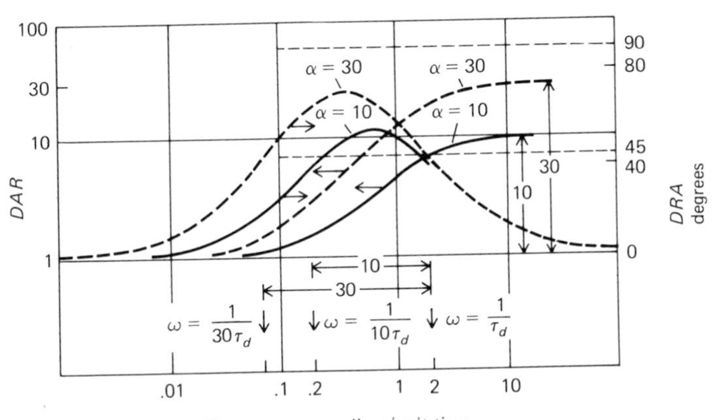

Figure 9.10. Frequency response of the "derivative" component, $\frac{1+\alpha\tau_d s}{1+\tau_d s}$, for an electronic controller with $\tau_d = 0.5$ and α of 10 and 30.

Calibration of Electronic Controller Parameters.

a. The gain factor, K. Calibration of gain is generally very easily accomplished either by making $\tau_i = \infty$ and $\tau_d = 0$ or by making connections which by-pass the *I* and *D* elements. The change in e_0 is then observed for given changes in e_i (or their equivalents) for various gain adjustments, usually called Proportional Band settings. The sensitivity at each setting will be the slope of the plot of e_0 versus e_i on rectilinear graph paper. The sensitivity is inversely related to

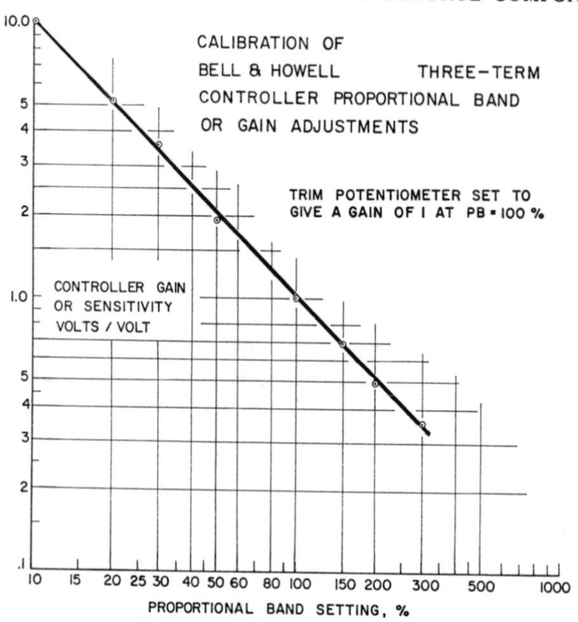

Figure 9.11. Proportional band or sensitivity calibration of an electronic controller.

the Proportional Band adjustment. A typical result is shown in Figure 9.11.

The results will generally become uncertain in the region of low PB values (< 10 percent) because of the very high gain of the system and the increasing dependence of performance on the quality of the components.

The term Proportional Band had its origin and is well entrenched in process-control vernacular. It was conceived to express a relationship between the deviation of the pen on a controller chart and the displacement of a final control element, such as a motor valve. If the sensitivity of the controller was such that an excursion of ± 50 percent of full deflection (0-100 percent) of the pen on the chart recording the variable of interest was sufficient to fully stroke the valve, then the PB = 100 percent. As PB is reduced, a smaller excursion of the pen from the set-point is required to completely stroke the valve.

b. Reset action. To find the 'integration' constant, τ_i, shown in (9.22) it is recommended that the derivative function $(1 + \alpha\tau_d s)/(1 + \tau_d s)$ be rendered ineffective. To do this, R_2 is made zero so that $\tau_d = 0$. The controller function then becomes, in operator notation,

$$e_0(s) = K\left[\frac{1+\tau_i s}{\tau_i s}\right] e_i(s)\ . \tag{9.23}$$

The objective is to choose a forcing which, when applied at the input, will produce a transient response which is simple to analyze and from which τ_i (and K) can be found.

In this case, a step function input appears to be useful.

Let $e_i(t) = E$, a step change in the input. Then, since $e_i(s) = \frac{E}{s}$, partial fraction expansion gives

$$e_0(s) = K\left[\frac{1+\tau_i s}{\tau_i s}\right]\frac{E}{s} = \frac{A}{s^2} + \frac{B}{s}\ . \tag{9.24}$$

The constants A and B are determined in the usual way:

$$A = EK\left[\frac{1+\tau_i s}{\tau_i}\right]_{s=0} = \frac{EK}{\tau_i}\text{, and}$$

$$B = EK\left[\frac{1+\tau_i s}{\tau_i s}\right] - \frac{A}{s} = EK\ .$$

Therefore,

$$e_0(s) = \frac{EK}{\tau_i s^2} + \frac{EK}{s}\ .$$

The normal solution in the time domain is

$$e_0(t) = \frac{EKt}{\tau_i} + EK\ . \tag{9.25}$$

The response will be a step function of magnitude EK followed by a ramp function with a slope of $\frac{EK}{\tau_i}$. The controller gain, K, is found as the magnitude of the output step divided by E, the input step. The integration time constant, τ_i, is found as EK/slope, the slope being measured from the time history of the response.

Conversely, this technique is useful in determining if a component can be described by a function of this kind.

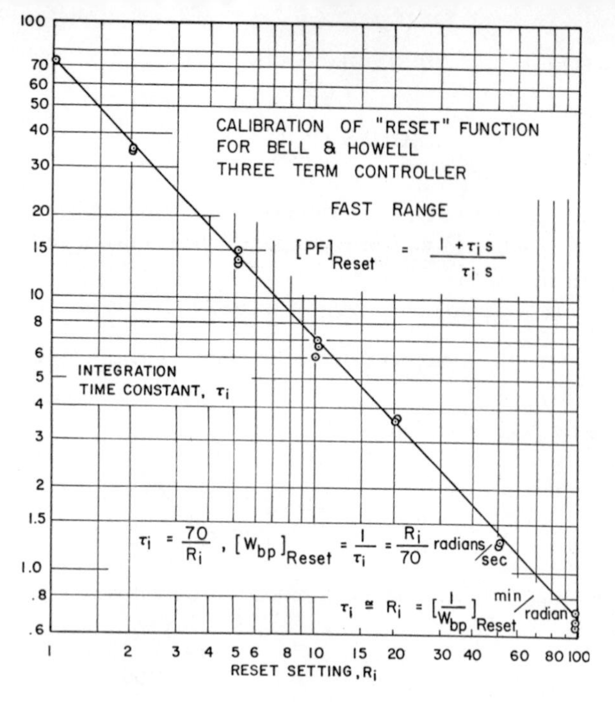

Figure 9.12. Calibration of the integral component for an electronic controller.

Typical relations between τ_i and controller settings obtained by this technique are shown in Figure 9.12. Frequency response characteristics are shown in Figure 9.9.

c. Derivative action. If the integration component is inactivated (by making the equivalent of R_1 infinite), the controller function becomes

$$\frac{e_0}{e_i}(s) = K\left[\frac{1 + \alpha\tau_d s}{1 + \tau_d s}\right]. \tag{9.26}$$

Once again a step forcing in the time domain appears to have merit. Thus, for initial conditions of zero,

$$e_0(s) = K\left[\frac{1 + \alpha\tau_d s}{1 + \tau_d s}\right]\frac{E}{s} = \frac{a}{1 + \tau_d s} + \frac{b}{s}. \tag{9.27}$$

By the usual procedure,

$$a = EK\tau_d(\alpha - 1) \quad \text{and} \quad b = EK,$$

so that

$$e_0(s) = \frac{EK\,(\alpha - 1)}{\left[\dfrac{1}{\tau_d} + s\right]} + \frac{EK}{s},$$

and the time solution becomes

$$e_0(t) = EK\,(\alpha - 1)e^{-t/\tau_d} + EK\,. \tag{9.28}$$

Note that, when $t = 0$, $e_0(0) = EK\alpha$. This indicates that the time response to a step function is a spike at time zero of magnitude $EK\alpha$ followed by the exponential decay. The larger the value of τ_d, the more slowly the decay.

Because the output of the controller rises so rapidly, the recording system may not be sufficiently responsive to obtain $EK\alpha$ from the time history. This difficulty is circumvented by replotting the data.

The equation is rearranged to give

$$\left[\frac{e_0(t)}{KE}\right] - 1 = (\alpha - 1)e^{-t/\tau_d}\,. \tag{9.29}$$

Hence,

$$\ln\left[\frac{e_0(t)}{KE} - 1\right] = \ln\,(\alpha - 1) - \frac{t}{\tau_d},$$

or

$$\log_{10}\left[\frac{e_0(t)}{KE} - 1\right] = \frac{\log_{10}}{2.3}(\alpha - 1) - \frac{t}{\tau_d}\,. \tag{9.30}$$

A plot of $\log_{10}\left[\dfrac{e_0(t)}{KE} - 1\right]$ versus t will yield, for various values of τ_d, straight lines with slopes of $-1/\tau_d$ and a common intercept at $t = 0$ of $\dfrac{(\alpha - 1)}{2.3}$.

This technique will enable determination of both τ_d and α. Typical results appear in Figure 9.13.

Conversely, the time history response to a step can be used to determine if a controller has this form of action.

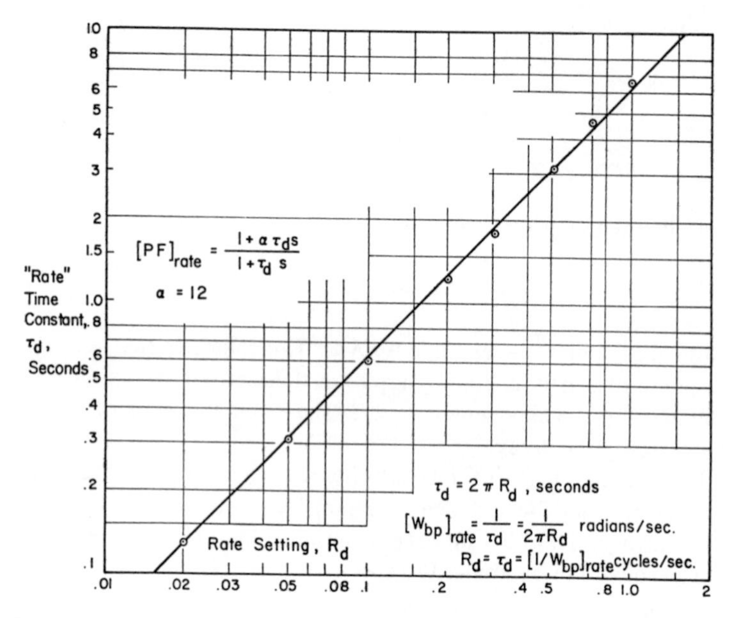

Figure 9.13 Calibration of the derivative component for an electronic controller.

Of course other forcing functions, such as sinusoidal or pulse, may be used and in some cases may be preferable. Experience with the method described has been very satisfactory.

Frequency response characteristics of this function are shown in Figure 9.10 with values of α of 10 and 30.

9.2 PNEUMATIC CONTROLLERS

All pneumatic controllers make use of the fixed-variable orifice as a detecting mechanism. This consists of an orifice to which is supplied air at a constant pressure, followed by a nozzle. A baffle, actuated by the variable of interest, restricts the flow through the nozzle. Nozzle back pressure becomes a measure of the variable. Figure 9.14 illustrates a typical scheme whereby a pressure-sensitive mechanism serves to displace a baffle thus changing the separation between it and a nozzle. The pressure of the air supply, p_s, is usually regulated at about 20 psig.

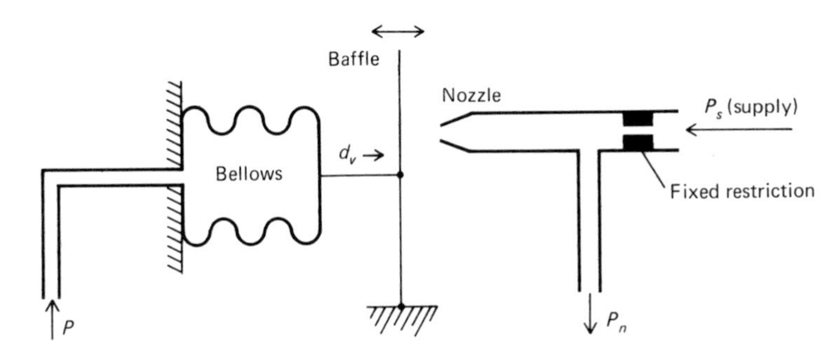

Figure 9.14. Fixed and variable nozzle-baffle assembly.

The relation between nozzle back pressure, p_n and baffle displacement is somewhat as shown in Figure 9.15a.

Nozzle-baffle assemblies have two great disadvantages.

(1). *The sensitivity is too great.* The change in nozzle backpressure is so large that p_n varies from near p_s to near zero as the gap, d, changes a few thousandths of an inch. A valve, being actuated by p_n, would therefore be essentially open or closed; i.e. control would be ON-OFF.

(2). *The capacity of the nozzle for air flow is too small* which means that final control elements such as valve motors, having large volumes over their diaphragms, would not move very rapidly.

The first of these difficulties is overcome by introducing a sensitivity reduction mechanism (negative feedback). This is shown in Figure 9.16, where it is assumed that the nozzle assembly may be moved by virtue of bellows B.

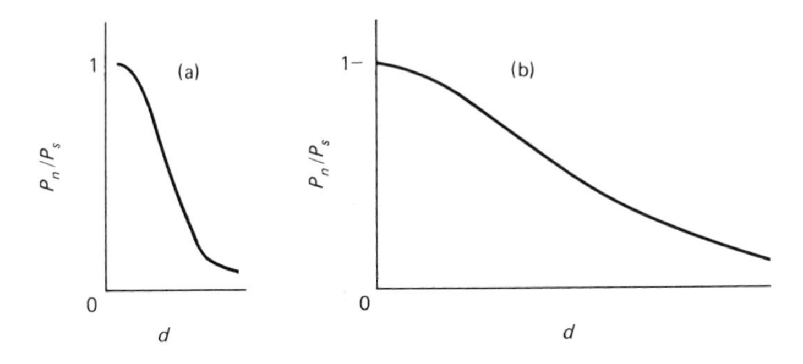

Figure 9.15. Sensitivity of nozzle-baffle assembly with and without negative feedback.

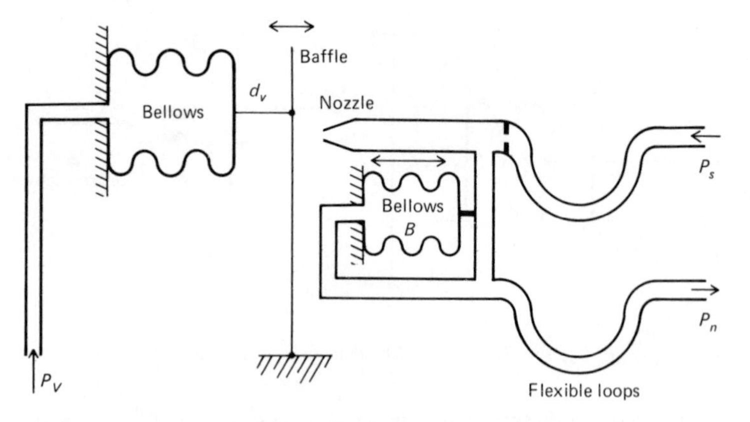

Figure 9.16. Nozzle-baffle assembly provided with negative feedback to give sensitivity reduction.

As the baffle approaches the nozzle, backpressure, p_n, increases. The pressure in the bellows, B, increases forcing the nozzle mechanism away from the baffle. With proper design, the decreased sensitivity produces smooth throttling over a much increased change of variable, p_v, as shown in Figure 9.15b.

The block diagram for the nozzle-baffle system revised in this way appears in Figure 9.17. The ratio $\dfrac{p_n}{d_v} = \dfrac{S_n}{1 + S_n S_{nfbb}}$, shows that, when $S_n S_{nfbb} \gg 1$, $\dfrac{p_n}{d_v} \cong \dfrac{1}{S_{nfbb}}$, which is independent of the nozzle-baffle sensitivity. In this way, as long as $S_n S_{nfbb}$ is suf-

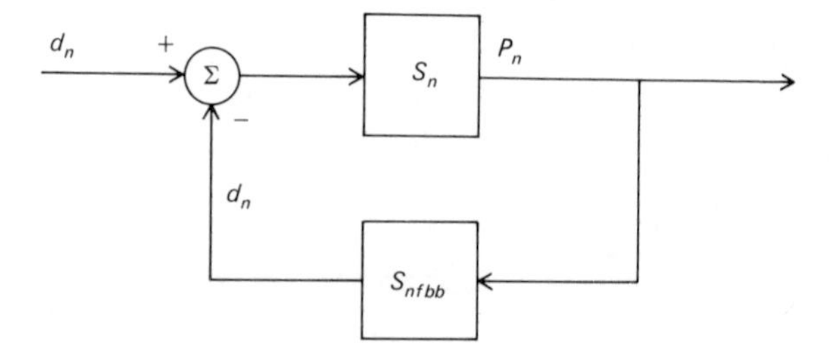

Figure 9.17. Block diagram for nozzle-baffle assembly provided with negative feedback mechanism.

ficiently great, the nozzle-baffle assembly need not be strictly linear, and performance depends largely upon the negative feedback bellows mechanism.

The second difficulty is overcome by using a pneumatic amplifier or, as it is commonly called, a relay. The nozzle back pressure, p_n is used to activate the relay valve which has a much higher capacity than the fixed orifice. A schematic diagram of a direct acting relay associated with a nozzle-baffle assembly is shown in Figure 9.18. Depending upon the construction, relays may be either direct acting or reverse acting. Block diagrams and relationships are given in Figure 9.19.

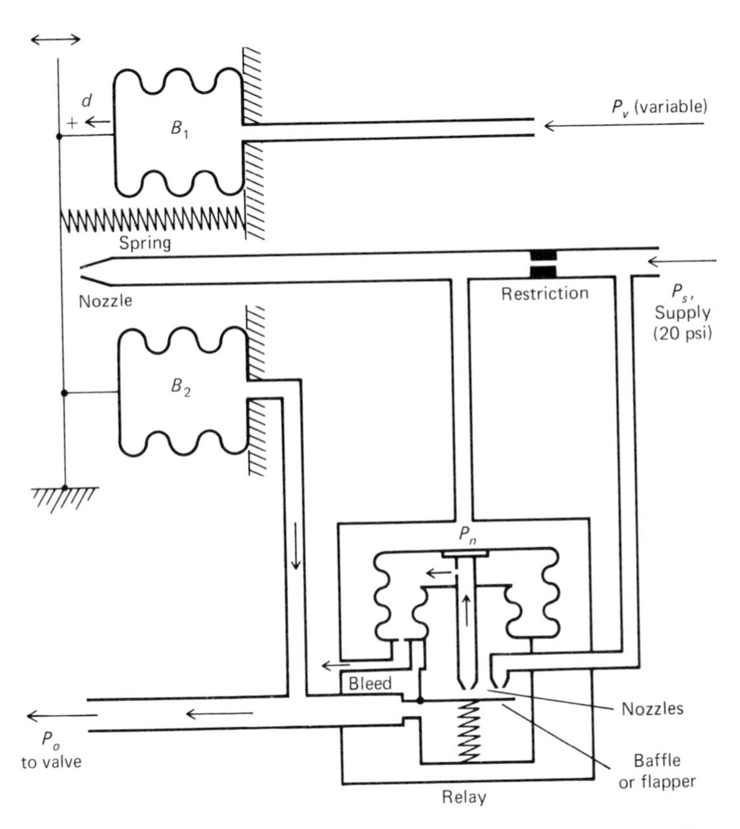

Figure 9.18. Nozzle-baffle assembly provided with negative feedback through a direct acting relay.

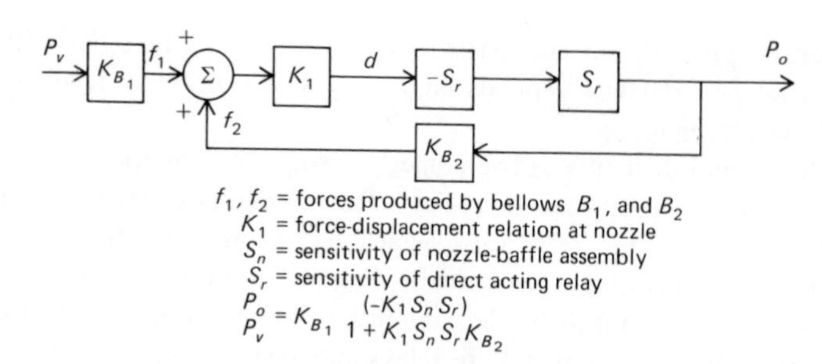

Figure 9.19. Block diagram and relationships for nozzle-baffle system provided with negative feedback and direct acting relay.

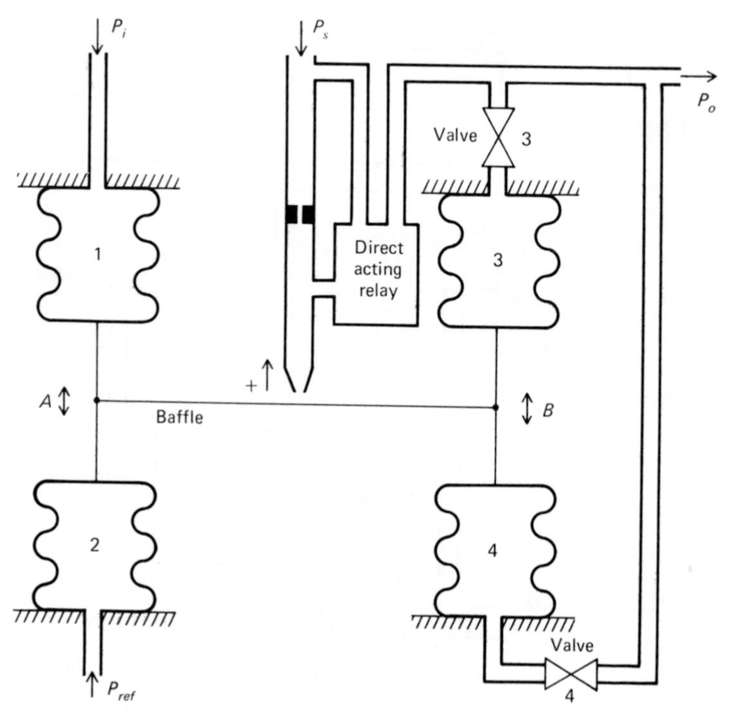

Figure 9.20. Functional diagram of a three-term pneumatic controller.

Three-term controller A functional diagram of a common type *three-term* pneumatic controller is shown in Figure 9.20. It is called three-term because it produces *Proportional* + *Integral* + *Derivative* (PID) action of sorts. It is instructive to first examine the mechanics of a pair of opposed bellows such as 1 and 2 on the left in Figure 9.20 and as shown in Figure 9.21.

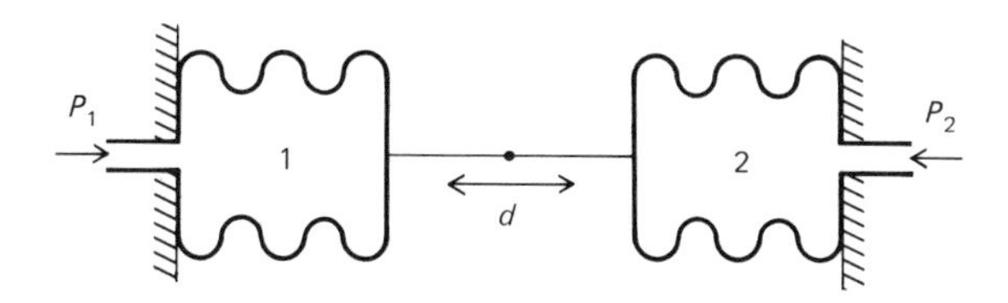

Figure 9.21. Opposed bellows assembly.

If we assume that each bellows is slightly compressed and has spring constants k_1 and k_2 and areas A_1 and A_2, at equilibrium, the net force produced by the bellows on the left is

$$F_l = p_1 A_1 - k_1 (l_{0_1} - l_1),$$

while the net force produced by the right-hand bellows is

$$F_r = p_2 A_2 - k_2 (l_{0_2} - l_2),$$

where l_{0_1} and l_{0_2} are the free lengths. Consequently,

$$p_1 A_1 - k_1 (l_{0_1} - l_1) = p_2 A_2 - k_2 (l_{0_2} - l_2). \qquad (9.31)$$

If p_1 is increased, the connecting mechanism moves to the right. Let this displacement be d. Then

$$(\Delta p_1 + p_1) A_1 - k_1 [l_{0_1} - (l_1 + d)] = p_2 A_2 - k_2 [l_{0_2} - (l_2 - d)]. \qquad (9.32)$$

Subtracting (9.31) from (9.32) gives

$$d = \left[\frac{A_1}{k_1 + k_2}\right] \Delta p_1 .$$

Similarly, if a change Δp_2 occurs in p_2.

$$d = \left[\frac{-A_2}{k_1 + k_2}\right] \Delta p_2.$$

If the pressures p_1 and p_2 are equal and allowed to change by the same amount, the equilibrium position of the mechanism may be shifted either to the left or right, depending upon the design. Thus, with pressure p in both bellows,

$$pA_1 - k_1 [l_{o_1} - l_1] = pA_2 - k_2 [l_{o_2} - l_2]. \tag{9.33}$$

Then if displacement, d, to the right is assumed,

$$(p + \Delta p) A_1 - k_1 [l_{o_1} - (l_1 + d)] \\ = (p + \Delta p) A_2 - k_2 [l_{o_2} - (l_2 - d)]. \tag{9.34}$$

Subtracting 9.33 from 9.34 gives

$$d = \left[\frac{A_2 - A_1}{k_1 + k_2}\right] \Delta p. \tag{9.35}$$

This shows that, as the equilibrium pressure in a pair of opposed bellows (each pressure being equal) is changed, it is possible to displace the interconnecting linkage and produce a displacement d.

One more feature of the control mechanism shown in Figure 9.20 is important. It will be noted that each right-hand bellows has an adjustable valve in the air line leading to it. These assemblies enable the controller to contribute dynamic compensation.

Consider a bellows-valve assembly represented in Figure 9.22a. The following assumptions are valid.

(1) Flow through valve is viscous; i.e. flow is proportional to pressure drop.

(2) The bellows volume does not change appreciably since the displacement, d, is *very* small.

(3) Temperature is constant.

For viscous flow across the valve, the flow rate in moles/unit time, for example, is

$$\frac{dN}{dt} = K (p_0 - p_b).$$

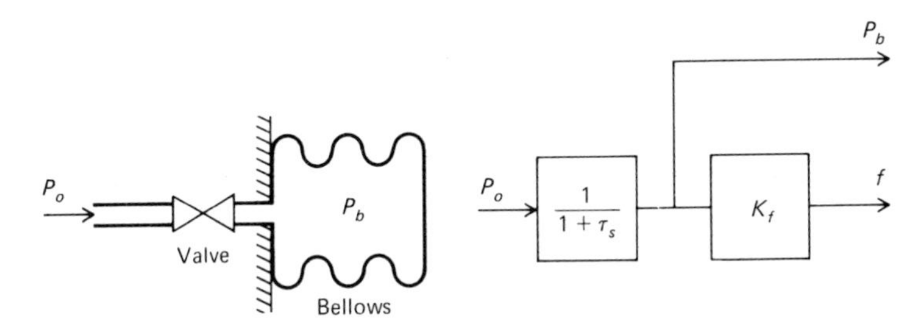

Figure 9.22. Dynamics of a bellows-valve assembly.

The change in inventory in the bellows is

$$\frac{dN}{dt} = \frac{V}{RT}\frac{dp_b}{dt}.$$

Combining the above,

$$\frac{V}{KRT}\frac{dp_b}{dt} + p_b = p_o,$$

or, in operator notation,

$$p_b = \left(\frac{1}{1+\tau s}\right) p_0 \text{ where } \tau = \frac{V}{KRT}.$$

If a linear spring constant is assumed,

$$p_b A = kd$$

or

$$d = \frac{p_b A}{k} = \frac{A}{k}\left(\frac{1}{1+\tau s}\right) p_o.$$

The block diagram appears in Figure 9.22b. If the output is to be considered a force and if $F = k_f p_b$,

$$F = \left[\frac{k_f}{1+\tau s}\right] p_o.$$

K depends upon the adjustment of the valve in the line to the bellows and is inversely related to the resistance to flow through the valve. If the valve is closed, $K = 0$ and $\tau = \infty$; if the valve is open, $K = \infty$ and $\tau = 0$.

The complete block diagram for the pneumatic circuit shown in Figure 9.20 is given in Figure 9.23.

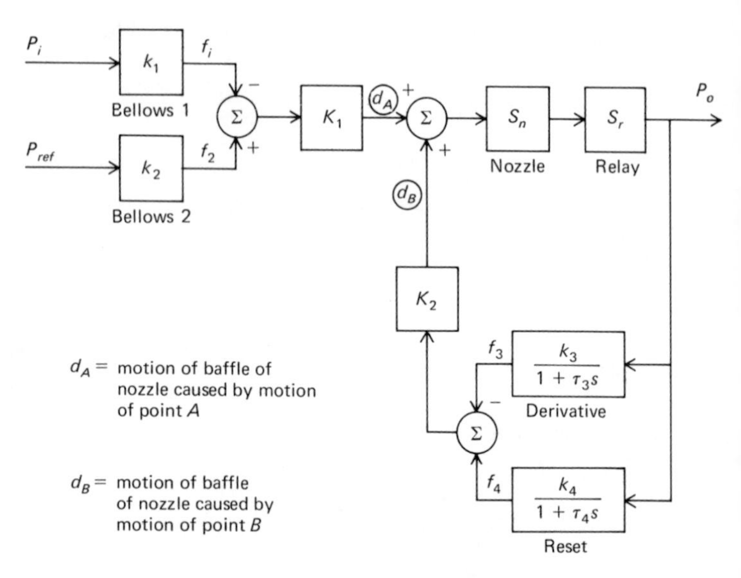

Figure 9.23. Block diagram of three-term pneumatic controller circuit.

A pressure, p_i, assumed to be a measure of the variable to be controlled, is imposed on Bellows 1. Likewise a pressure, assumed to be a measure of the desired value of the variable (set-point), is imposed on Bellows 2. The opposed forces are subtracted by the force summing member (baffle), and the resultant motion is transmitted from Point A to the nozzle location by the baffle, the conversion indicated by the block labelled K_1.

With upward motion of the baffle considered positive, the nozzle-baffle gain, S_n, will be positive. The same holds true for the direct acting relay with gain S_r. The output pressure, p_o, will thus increase as the input pressure, p_i, decreases.

Proportional Mode. To produce the negative feedback action necessary to obtain smooth proportional action, Bellows 3 is provided, the output of which is a force tending to move the force summing member (baffle) in a direction opposite to that caused by a change in p_i. When used in a proportional mode, Valve 3 is wide open ($\tau_3 = 0$), Valve 4 is closed ($\tau_4 = \infty$), and Bellows 4 is inactive.

For this situation, the performance function becomes, assuming $k_1 = k_2 = k$,

$$p_0 = \frac{kK_1 S_n S_r}{1 + S_n S_r K_2 k_3} (p_{\text{ref}} - p_i) .$$

Since it is likely that $S_n S_r K_2 k_3 >> 1$,

$$\left[\frac{p_0}{\Delta p}\right]_P \cong \frac{kK_1}{k_3 K_2} \qquad \text{where} \qquad \Delta p \equiv (p_{\text{ref}} - p_i) .$$

The latter relations shows that the gain of the controller is virtually independent of the gains of the nozzle-baffle assembly and relay but depends mostly on the components in the feedback path.

Suppose that p_i is a measure of the temperature of the effluent stream from a heat exchanger in which a fluid is being heated from 100°F. Further, suppose that, when the effluent temperature is 200°F, p_i is 10 psig, the output pressure, p_o, is 10 psig and the valve regulating the flow of hot fluid to the heat exchanger is 50 percent open. Under these conditions, assume that $p_i = p_{Ref}$.

If the controller is operating in the *proportional* mode, outlet pressure, p_0, will appear within Bellows 3, Valve 3 will be wide open, Valve 4 will be closed.

Imagine that the flow rate of fluid being heated increases (plant *load* increases). Immediately, the effluent temperature decreases, and the controller output increases in an effort to open the control valve and admit a greater flow of heating medium to the heat exchanger.

With purely proportional control, however, this valve positions itself in proportion to the temperature and cannot recognize that the plant load has changed. Thus, while the valve opens, it cannot open sufficiently to bring p_i back into agreement with p_{Ref}. An off-set or steady-state error will always exist if the load changes on a plant provided with only proportional control.

To circumvent this difficulty, early designers of pneumatic controllers provided a positive feedback mechanism shown as Bellows 4 in Figure 9.20. This supplies the means of permanently shifting point B in such a direction that with virtually the same value of p_i (and p_{ref}) the output pressure, p_o, will have been changed appropriately. By proper choice of bellows areas and spring constants, the opposed Bellows 3 and 4 can accomplish this, as was pointed out previously.

It should also be apparent that, with both Bellows 3 and 4 active, the negative feedback action provided by Bellows 3 is virtually removed by the positive feedback action of Bellows 4 so that the overall gain of the controller becomes very high. Thus, the steady state (zero frequency) error tends to disappear when the controller forms part of a process control system.

In practice, the time constant associated with Bellows 4 is always kept larger than that of Bellows 3 so that during a transient the negative feedback action predominates and the controller gain is prevented from becoming excessive.

Proportional/Derivative Mode. To produce proportional plus derivative action ($P + D$), Valve 4 is closed ($\tau_4 = \infty$) and Valve 3 is throttled (τ_3 is finite) to give a delayed negative feedback action. The performance function then becomes

$$\left[\frac{p_o}{\Delta p}\right]_{P+D} = \frac{kK_1 S_n S_r}{1 + \dfrac{S_n S_r k_3 K_2}{1 + \tau_3 s}} = \frac{kK_1 S_n S_r (1 + \tau_3 s)}{1 + \tau_3 s + S_n S_r k_3 K_2}$$

$$= \frac{kK_1 S_n S_r}{1 + S_n S_r k_3 K_2} \left[\frac{(1 + \tau_3 s)}{1 + \dfrac{\tau_3 s}{1 + S_n S_r k_3 K_2}}\right]$$

$$= S \left[\frac{1 + \alpha\tau_d s}{1 + \tau_d s}\right] \tag{9.36}$$

where

$$S = \left[\frac{kK_1 S_n S_r}{1 + S_n S_r k_3 K_2}\right]$$

$$\alpha\tau_d = \tau_3$$

$$\tau_d = \frac{\tau_3}{1 + S_n S_r k_3 K_2}$$

and $$\alpha = 1 + S_n S_r k_3 K_2 \ .$$

Note that, when $s = 0$, $\left[\frac{p_0}{\Delta p}\right]_{P+D} = S$ and, when $s = \infty$,

$$\left[\frac{p_0}{\Delta p}\right]_{P+D} = \alpha S = kK_1 S_n S_r .$$

Proportional/Integral Mode. To achieve proportional + integral (or reset), control Valve 3 is opened wide ($\tau_3 = 0$) and Valve 4 is throttled. This gives delayed positive feedback action. The performance function becomes

$$\left[\frac{p_0}{\Delta p}\right]_{P+I} = \frac{kK_1 S_n S_r}{1 - S_n S_r K_2 \left[\frac{k_4}{1 + \tau_4 s} - k_3\right]}$$

$$= \frac{kK_1 S_n S_r}{1 + S_n S_r K_2 \left[\frac{k_3 (1 + \tau_4 s) - k_4}{1 + \tau_4 s}\right]}$$

$$= \frac{kK_1 S_n S_r (1 + \tau_4 s)}{1 + \tau_4 s + S_n S_r K_2 \left[k_3 (1 + \tau_4 s) - k_4\right]}$$

$$= \frac{kK_1 S_n S_r (1 + \tau_4 s)}{1 + S_n S_r K_2 (k_3 - k_4) + (1 + S_n S_r K_2 k_3) \tau_4 s}$$

$$= \left[\frac{kK_1 S_n S_r}{1 + S_n S_r K_2 (k_3 - k_4)}\right] \left[\frac{1 + \tau_4 s}{1 + \frac{1 + S_n S_r K_2 k_3 \tau_4 s}{1 + S_n S_r K_2 (k_3 - k_4)}}\right].$$

Since $k_3 \cong k_4$, it follows that

$$\left[\frac{p_0}{\Delta p}\right]_{P+I} = (kK_1 S_n S_r) \left[\frac{1+\tau_4 s}{1+(1+S_n S_r K_2 k_3)\tau_4 s}\right]$$

$$= S_{P+I} \left[\frac{1+\tau_i s}{1+\beta\tau_i s}\right] \tag{9.37}$$

where $S_{P+I} = kK_1 S_n S_r$,

$$\tau_i = \tau_4$$

$$\beta\tau_i = (1 + S_n S_r K_2 k_3)\tau_4$$

and $\beta = (1 + S_n S_r K_2 k_3) = \alpha.$

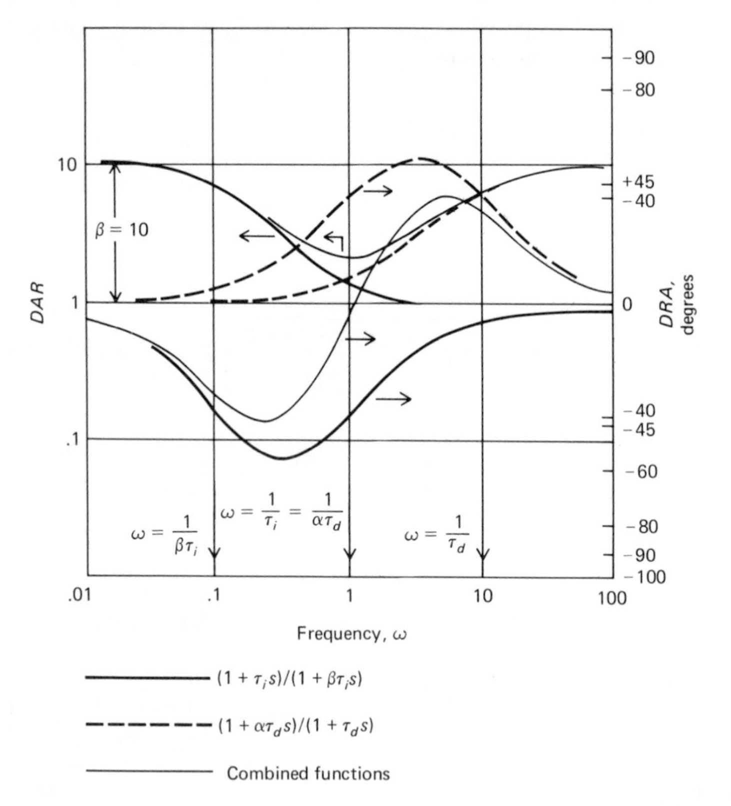

Figure 9.24. Frequency response of typical pneumatic controller function.

Note that, when $s = 0$, $\left[\dfrac{p_0}{\Delta p}\right]_{P+I} = S_{P+I} = kK_1 S_n S_r$

and when $s = \infty$, $\left[\dfrac{p_0}{\Delta p}\right]_{P+I} = \dfrac{S_{P+I}}{\beta} = \dfrac{kK_1 S_n S_r}{1 + S_n S_r K_2\, k3} = S.$

The frequency response which the $P + D$ and $P + I$ action produce are shown in Figure 9.24. Since the positions of the component functions can be shifted on the frequency axis in accordance with τ_i or τ_d, the shape and position of the combined curve will depend on the parameters selected.

When both bellows systems are active, the resulting mathematical form becomes more complicated and the performance is difficult to predict.

$$\left[\frac{P_0}{\Delta P}\right]_{P+I+D} = [kK_1 S_n S_r] \bigg/ \left\{1 - S_n S_r K_2 \left[\frac{k_4}{1+\tau_4 s} - \frac{k_3}{1+\tau_3 s}\right]\right\}$$

$$= [kK_1 S_n S_r] \bigg/ \left\{1 + S_n S_r K_2 \left[\frac{k_4\,(1+\tau_3 s) - k_3\,(1+\tau_4 s)}{(1+\tau_4 s)\,(1+\tau_3 s)}\right]\right\}$$

$$= [kK_1 S_n S_r (1+\tau_4 s)(1+\tau_3 s)]/[(1+\tau_4 s)(1+\tau_3 s)$$
$$+ S_n S_r K_2 k_4 (1+\tau_3 s) - S_n S_r K_2 k_3 (1+\tau_4 s)]$$

$$= [kK_1 S_n S_r (1+\tau_3 s)(1+\tau_4 s)]/[\tau_3\tau_4 s^2 + (\tau_3+\tau_4)s + 1$$
$$+ S_n S_r K_2 k_4 + S_n S_r K_2 k_4 \tau_3 s - S_n S_r K_2 k_3 - S_n S_r K_2 k_3 \tau_4 s]$$

$$= [kK_1 S_n S_r (1+\tau_3 s)(1+\tau_4 s)]/\{\tau_3\tau_4 s^2$$
$$+ [\tau_3 + \tau_4 + S_n S_r K_2 (k_4\tau_3 - k_3\tau_4)]\, s + S_n S_r K_2 (k_4 - k_3) + 1\}$$

Since $k_4 \approx k_3$,

$$\left[\frac{P_0}{\Delta P}\right]_{P+I+D} = \frac{[kK_1 S_n S_r (1+\tau_3 s)\,(1+\tau_4 s)]}{\{\tau_3\tau_4 s^2 + [(1+S_n S_r K_2 k_4)\tau_3 + (1 - S_n S_r K_2 k_3)\tau_4]\, s + 1\}}. \tag{9.38}$$

When $s = 0$,

$$\left[\frac{P_0}{\Delta P}\right]_{P+I+D} = kK_1 S_n S_r, \qquad \text{as for } P + I.$$

When $s = \infty$,

$$\left[\frac{P_0}{\Delta P}\right]_{P+I+D} = \frac{kK_1 S_n S_r \tau_3 \tau_4 s^2}{\tau_3 \tau_4 s^2} = kK_1 S_n S_r,$$

as for $P + D$.

The form of the performance function will be

$$\left[\frac{P_0}{\Delta P}\right]_{P+I+D} = \frac{K(1+\tau_3 s)(1+\tau_4 s)}{(1+\tau_a s)(1+\tau_b s)}. \tag{9.39}$$

since, for practical reasons, the time constants of the denominator must be real and distinct. τ_a and τ_b will be dependent upon *both* τ_3 and τ_4.

Equating the denominators of (9.38) and (9.39) gives

$$\tau_a \tau_b = \tau_3 \tau_4 \qquad \text{and}$$

$$(\tau_a + \tau_b) = [(1 + S_n S_r K_2 k_4)\tau_3 + (1 - S_n S_r K_2 k_3)\tau_4] .$$

It follows that

$$\tau_a^2 + \tau_a \tau_b = \tau_a[(1 + S_n S_r K_2 k_4)\tau_3 + (1 - S_n S_r K_2 k_3)\tau_4]$$

or $\quad \tau_a^2 - \tau_a[(1 + S_n S_r K_2 k_4)\tau_3 + (1 - S_n S_r K_2 k_3)\tau_4] + \tau_3 \tau_4 = 0$

and hence that

$$\tau_a, \tau_b = \frac{1}{2}[(1 + S_n S_r K_2 k_4)\tau_3 + (1 - S_n S_r K_2 k_3)\tau_4]$$

$$\pm \sqrt{\frac{[(1 + S_n S_r K_2 k_4)\tau_3 + (1 - S_n S_r K_2 k_3)\tau_4]^2}{4} - \tau_3 \tau_4}\,.$$

Since τ_b must be less than τ_4 to produce the 'derivative' action and τ_a must be greater than τ_3 to create the integration action, the negative radical must be associated with τ_b and the positive sign with τ_a.

By using the techniques described for determining the parameters of electronic controllers, the constants $(1 + S_n S_r K_2 k_3)$ and $(1 + S_n S_r K_2 k_4)$ and, for various settings of the controller, the parameters τ_3 and τ_4 may be found experimentally with only the derivative or integral mode active. Presumably, then, for any settings. where τ_3 and τ_4 are known, the parameters τ_a and τ_b can be calculated for the three-term controller.

Limits are imposed on the relative values of τ_3 and τ_4 since under no conditions must the term under the radical become negative.

Some pneumatic controllers, notably the Taylor Tri-Act stack type, have been designed to achieve independent 'reset' and 'rate' adjustments. The performance function of these will be approximated by forms such as (9.22) or (9.39).

9.3 TRANSMISSION LINE DYNAMICS

The design of pneumatic control systems demands a knowledge of the dynamic behavior of the systems by which the pneumatic signals are transmitted from controller to final control device. Of greatest concern are the limitations which a pneumatic transmission line may impose on the overall ensemble. Specifically, the designer would like to be able to predict the important characteristics of the transmission line and thus select a configuration which will assure that the line dynamics will not contribute to unacceptable system performance. This implies the need to predict the dominant time constants of pneumatic transmission lines.

Many studies of transmission line dynamics have been made (References 5a-5g at end of this chapter). The results described in Reference 5a appear to be most easily applied for the purposes mentioned above.

In this study, it was found that the relation below describes a wide selection of pneumatic transmission line configurations (various tube sizes, lengths and terminal volumes):

$$\frac{P(L,s)}{P_1(s)} = \frac{1}{1 + \dfrac{2\xi}{\omega_n} s + \dfrac{s^2}{{\omega_n}^2}},$$

where

$$\xi = \frac{RL}{2\rho c}\sqrt{\frac{1}{2} + \frac{Q}{aL}}$$

is the equivalent second-order damping factor,

$$\omega_n = \frac{c}{L\sqrt{\frac{1}{2} + \frac{Q}{aL}}}$$

is the equivalent second-order undamped natural angular frequency, and the resistance $R = \frac{32\mu}{d^2} = \frac{8\pi\mu}{a}$.

The various symbols are defined as follows:

L = tube length,
ρ = fluid density,
c = velocity of sound in fluid,
Q = terminal volume,
a = cross-sectional area of tube,
$\frac{Q}{aL}$ = ratio of terminal volume to volume of tubing,
μ = fluid viscosity,
d = diameter of conduit (internal),
P_i = pressure at input point, and
P_o = pressure at output point.

If

$$\xi >> 1, \xi + \sqrt{\xi^2 - 1} \cong 2\xi,$$

$$\xi - \sqrt{\xi^2 - 1} \approx \frac{1}{2\xi},$$

and

$$\frac{P(L,s)}{P_i(s)} \cong \frac{1}{1 + \left[\frac{2\xi}{\omega_n}\right] s} = \frac{1}{1 + \tau s},$$

where

$$\tau = \frac{2\xi}{\omega_n}.$$

Inspection of these relations, which describe the experimental data out to a frequency well beyond $\frac{1}{\tau}$ and somewhat higher than ω_n, shows that, with constant terminal volume Q, the undamped natural angular frequency, ω_n, decreases and the damping factor, ξ, increases with line length. Similarly, with a constant length of line, as the terminal volume increases, ξ increases and ω_n decreases. It should also be noted that, while ξ depends upon several fluid properties, ρ, c, and μ, ω_n depends on only one fluid property, c, the velocity of sound in the fluid.

The designer has restrictions on line length, fewer restrictions on line diameter and fewer yet on choice of terminal volume. Once the fluid and its average pressure and temperature are selected (e.g., air at 9 psig and 85°F), the acoustic velocity can be estimated. Then, using the estimated tube length, ω_n can be computed for a given tubing size and terminal volume. If ω_n is about 10 times greater than the reciprocal of the dominant process time constant, the tubing dynamics will not appreciably affect the system performance. The damping characteristics of the line are then estimated by calculating ξ. If $\xi \ll 1$, it may be desirable to increase Q, with care being taken to keep $1/\omega_n$ ten times the process dominant time constant.

If $\xi \gg 1$ (3 or more, for example), the equivalent first-order time constant of the pneumatic transmission system can be estimated as $\dfrac{2\xi}{\omega_n}$. It is desirable that this be one-tenth or less of the dominant system time constant. A minimum value of 0.7 for ξ is recommended.

Table 9.1 lists the dimensions and resistances of commonly used pneumatic transmission lines.

Figure 9.25 is a plot of $\dfrac{1}{\sqrt{1/2 + Q/aL}}$ versus Q/aL. ω_n is found as $c/L\left[\dfrac{1}{\sqrt{1/2 + Q/aL}}\right]$.

The second-order form may also be written as

$$\frac{P(L,s)}{P_i(s)} = \frac{1}{\left[1 + \dfrac{s}{\omega_n(\xi + \sqrt{\xi^2 - 1})}\right]\left[1 + \dfrac{s}{\omega_n(\xi - \sqrt{\xi^2 - 1})}\right]}$$

$$= \frac{1}{(1 + \tau_2 s)(1 + \tau_1 s)}$$

Table 9.1 Dimensions of Tubing Used for Transmitting Industrial Pneumatic Control Signals

Nominal size	Wall thickness	Material	I.D. (inches)	Cross section		Volume per 100 ft		Resistance, $R = \frac{32\mu}{d^2} = \frac{8\pi\mu}{a}$ Temp. °F				
				in^2	$ft^2 \times 10^4$	in^3	$ft^3 \times 10^2$	−32	64	104	129	165
1/4" O.D.	0.040	Polyethylene	0.170	0.0227	1.575	27.22	1.575	1.59	1.96	2.02	2.08	2.25
5/16" O.D.	0.062	"	0.189	0.0281	1.948	33.67	1.948	1.29	1.59	1.64	1.68	1.82
3/8" O.D.	0.062	"	0.251	0.0495	3.436	59.38	3.436	0.73	0.90	0.93	0.96	1.03
1/2" O.D.	0.062	"	0.375	0.1110	7.711	133.24	7.711	0.33	0.40	0.41	0.42	0.46
1/4" O.D.	0.030	Copper	0.190	0.02845	1.969	34.02	1.969	1.27	1.56	1.62	1.67	1.80
3/8" O.D.	0.032	"	0.311	0.0760	5.275	91.06	5.275	0.48	0.58	0.61	0.62	0.67
1/2" O.D.	0.035	"	0.430	0.1452	10.085	174.20	10.085	0.25	0.31	0.32	0.33	0.35
1/4" O.D.	0.032	Aluminum	0.186	0.02721	1.887	32.61	1.887	1.33	1.63	1.69	1.74	1.88
1/2" O.D.	0.049	"	0.402	0.1269	8.814	152.31	8.814	0.28	0.35	0.36	0.37	0.40

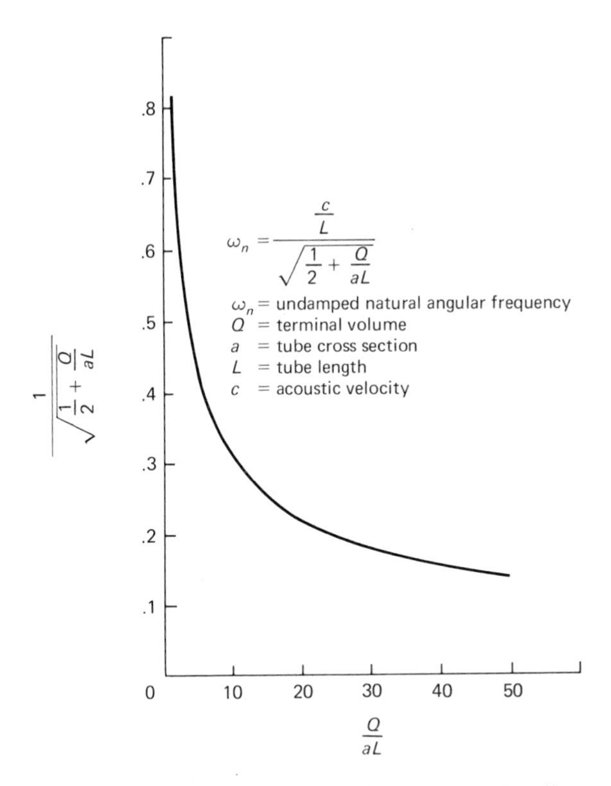

Figure 9.25. Properties of pneumatic transmission lines.

where
$$\tau_1 = \frac{1}{\omega_n(\xi - \sqrt{\xi^2 - 1})}$$

and
$$\tau_2 = \frac{1}{\omega_n(\xi + \sqrt{\xi^2 - 1}} .$$

It follows that
$$\frac{\tau_1}{\tau_2} = \frac{\xi + \sqrt{\xi^2 - 1}}{\xi - \sqrt{\xi^2 - 1}} = \beta$$

and
$$\xi = \frac{1 + \beta}{2\sqrt{\beta}} .$$

β is a measure of the separation of time constants for an over-damped ($\xi > 1$) second-order system. Table 9.2 shows the relation between β and ξ.

Table 9.2 Equivalent damping coefficients as a function of separation of time constants

$\beta = \tau_1/\tau_2$	ξ
1	1.00
4	1.25
9	1.67
16	2.13
25	2.60
36	3.08

References

1. Tyner, Mack and Frank P. May. *Process Engineering Control.* The Ronald Press Company, New York, 1968.
   This book is a valuable reference for those concerned with process control. Table on p. 461 is a table showing the functions produced by various passive networks.

2. Grabbe, Eugene, Simon Ramo and Dean E. Wooldridge, eds. *Handbook of Automation, Computation and Control*, vol. 1. John Wiley & Sons, Inc., New York, 1958.
   Tables 3-7 on pp. 29-41 in chapter 23 show many electrical networks useful for compensation and computation.

3. Tustin, A. ed. *Automatic and Manual Control.* Butterworths Publications, Ltd., London, England, 1951.
   Early papers on the analysis of pneumatic controllers include the following two from the above book.
   Aikman, A. R. and C. I. Rutherford. *The characteristics of air-operated controllers*, p. 175.
   Janssen, J. M. L. *Analysis of pneumatic controllers*, p. 189.

4. Technical papers have been prepared by various manufacturers of industrial controllers describing their performance. Among these are Taylor Instrument Companies, Foxboro, Fischer and Porter. Information is available upon request.

5. Pneumatic transmission line studies have been reported in the following publications.

(a) Hougen, J. O., R. A. Walsh and O. R. Martin. Dynamics of pneumatic transmission lines. *Control Eng.* (September 1963), pp. 114–117.
(b) Nichols, N. B. Linear properties of pneumatic transmission lines. *ISA Transactions* (January 1962).
(c) Schuder, C. B. and R. C. Binder. The response of pneumatic transmission lines to step inputs. *J. Basic Eng., ASME Transactions* (December 1959).
(d) Iberall, A. S. *Attenuation of Oscillatory Pressures in Instrument Lines.* U. S. Dept. of Commerce, National Bureau of Standards Research Paper RP 2115, vol. 45, July 1950.
(e) Ansari, J. A. and Rufus Oldenburger. Propagation of disturbance in fluid lines. *J. Basic Eng., ASME Transactions* (June 1967), pp. 415–422.
(f) Karam, J. T. Jr., and M. E. Franke. The frequency response of pneumatic lines. *J. Basic Eng., ASME Transactions* (June 1967), pp. 371–378.
(g) Buckley, Page and W. L. Luyben. Designing long line pneumatic control systems. *Instrum. Technol.* (April 1969), p. 61.

10
Controller Function Selection

10.1 THE SYNTHESIS PROBLEM

As previously stated, the purpose of a controller is to endow the complete system, of which it is part, with desirable performance characteristics. This usually means that the control variables should be restored to acceptable values following either a change in the reference values (set points) or the appearance of disturbances at any of a number of points in the system. Figure 10.1a and b show the simplest arrangement for a single input-single output feedback control system emphasizing each aspect. The system represented by G_T includes the sensor of the input; G'_T excludes this item; i.e., $G_T = G'_T \cdot G_S$.

In terms of these diagrams, the function of the controller is to assure that the output C is satisfactory, either changing to follow changes in *Ref.* or remaining constant despite disturbances.

In the first instance, if it is assumed that disturbances are absent, it is desired that

$$\frac{C}{Ref.} = \frac{G_C G_T}{1 + G_C G_T} \cong 1$$

and, in the second instance, if it is assumed that changes in *Ref.* are absent, the objective is to have

$$\frac{C}{d} = \frac{G_S}{1 + G_C G_T} \cong 0.$$

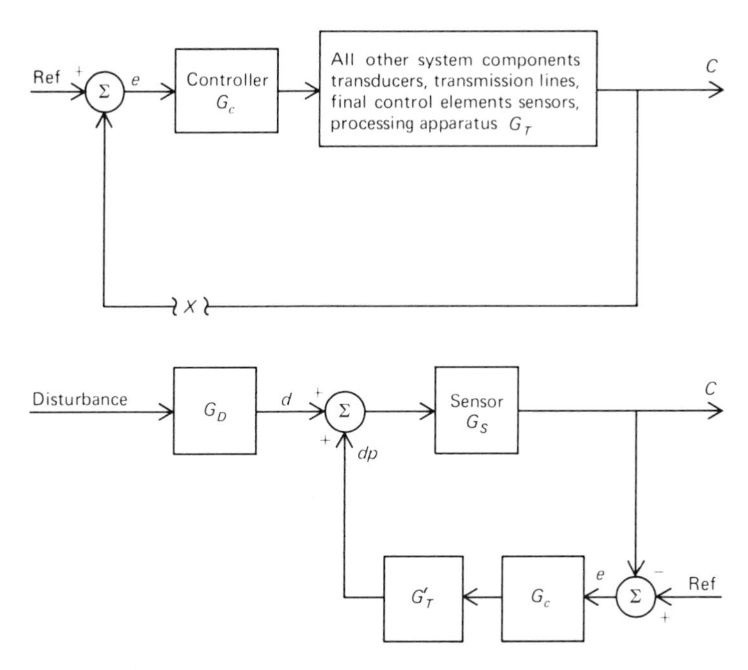

Figure 10.1. Simplified block diagrams indicating role of the controller. (a) Block diagram of single input-single output controlled system (feedback path shown broken at x). (b) Block diagram arranged to emphasize disturbances.

In both cases, the conditions can apparently be achieved by simply increasing the magnitude of the controller function, G_C.

While in some instances this is true (in principle), undesirable oscillations of the output of the closed loop system usually occur as the gain of the controller is increased. The reason for this is that, as controller gain is increased, the dynamic characteristics of the system are altered such as to continuously increase the deviation, e, rather than drive it towards zero.

Stability Criteria With reference to Figure 10.1a, it follows that

$$\frac{e}{Ref.} = \frac{1}{1 + G_C G_T}.$$

If at a given frequency $G_C G_T$ is a vector of unity length with a phase angle of $-\pi$, (-180°), then $G_C G_T = -1$ and $\frac{e}{Ref.} = \frac{1}{0} = \infty$. This is a condition of instability. The closer $G_C G_T$ approaches the $1, -180^\circ$ point, the more oscillatory the closed loop system becomes.

The objective of the design is to choose G_C such that e is reduced to zero in a satisfactory manner.

For linear systems, the symbols G_C and G_T represent differential equations which can be of high order. It can be appreciated that the mathematical labor required to determine a satisfactory form for G_C could be an imposing undertaking. Many ingenious techniques have been developed which simplify the work.

Since it is time consuming and sometimes rather questionable to derive an equivalent linear form for a system for which the frequency response data have been obtained experimentally, methods of selecting the controller function by nonrigorous methods are popular (*1-7*).

About 26 years ago, Bode (*9*) formulated a procedure, based on theoretical studies, which enables satisfactory selection of the controller function needed for compensation in the high frequency region. Subsequently, these have been refined by Oldenburger (*10*). This method applies to those systems classified as "non-minimum phase systems." Since chemical processing systems almost always fall in this class, the method is of particular interest to process engineers.

Design Approach The objective is to determine a satisfactory controller function by working in the frequency domain. Moreover, this is done using open loop frequency response information.

Satisfactory control, on the other hand, usually implies specified time domain response. Consequently the desideratum is to design in the frequency domain using open loop data but nonetheless achieve acceptable closed loop time domain characteristics.

Satisfactory time response is a somewhat nebulous term since it depends on the particular system and criteria chosen by the designer. Process control system specifications are usually poorly defined and not particularly demanding. However, in instances where fairly precise control is required, the procedure recommended here produces a practical, near-optimum design satisfactory for most process engineering purposes.

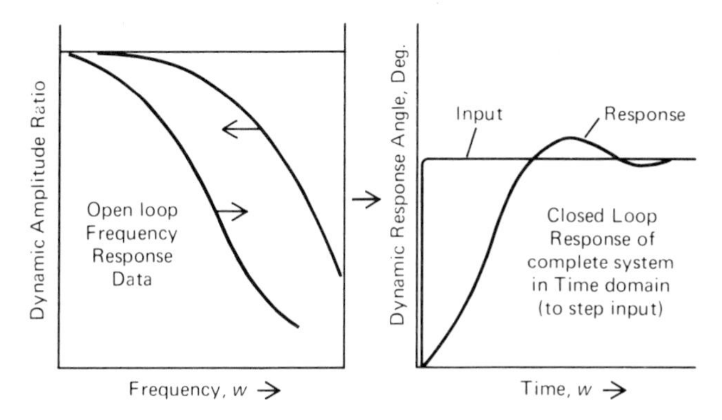

Figure 10.2. Design objectives: proceed from open loop system dynamics to desirable closed loop performance in the time domain.

It is emphasized that the objective is to proceed from the open loop frequency response to the closed loop time response as indicated in Figure 10.2.

Design Procedure Procedures for designing feedback control systems for existing continuous chemical processes are relatively simple because the frequency response of such systems is almost always relatively simple suggesting rather simple equivalent linear forms. With appropriate values for K_T and the τ's the linear form

$$G_T = \frac{\pm K_T(1 + \tau_4 s)}{(1 + \tau_1 s)(1 + \tau_2 s)(1 + \tau_3 s)}$$

can be fitted to the frequency response data for most processes encountered in the chemical industry. This has been found to be true for a large number of industrial processes, systems and subsystems. Very frequently, even simpler forms have been found. The dead time factor, e^{-DTs}, a rather common occurrence, has not been included at this point but will be discussed later.

Based on this model, it is clear that at low frequencies constant amplitude ratio and zero phase angle are approached.

The closed loop form of a series compensated feedback control system is, as has been seen,

$$\frac{C}{R} = \frac{G_C G_T}{1 + G_C G_T}.$$

where G_T denotes all system components except the controller, G_C. As frequency decreases, the dynamic effects of most processes are of diminishing concern, and the objective becomes one of achieving a high gain. The low frequency requirement of G_C is to impart this. At sufficiently high gain, $\frac{C}{R}$ approaches unity. A low frequency component of G_C of the form $\frac{k}{s}$, which approaches infinity as $s = jw$ approaches zero, would accomplish the desired objective. This is a pure integration action which removes the steady state error or 'off-set' which would occur without it.

In practice, two modified forms are commonly used,

$$\frac{1 + \tau_i s}{\tau_i s} \quad \text{and} \quad \frac{1 + \tau_i s}{1 + \beta_i \tau_i s}$$

where τ_i is an adjustable integration rate constant, commonly associated with the 'reset rate.' The frequency response of these forms is shown in Figure 10.3.

Normally the design problem is to select τ_i such that the integration component is properly combined with G_T. There may be some advantage in being able to alter β_i; however, this option is not available on standard controllers where β_i is fixed at about 10-15.

Integration Function To indicate the purpose of the 'integration' function, the low frequency properties of a closed loop system employing the control function $K \frac{1 + \tau_i s}{\tau_i s}$ will be compared with a control function which imparts only purely proportional action, K.

With purely proportional control and assuming

$$G_T = \frac{1}{(1 + \tau_1 s)(1 + \tau_2 s)},$$

$$\frac{C}{Ref.} = \frac{G_C G_T}{1 + G_C G_T} = \frac{K}{(K+1)} \left[\frac{1}{\frac{\tau_1 \tau_2 s^2}{K+1} + \frac{(\tau_1 + \tau_2)s}{K+1} + 1} \right].$$

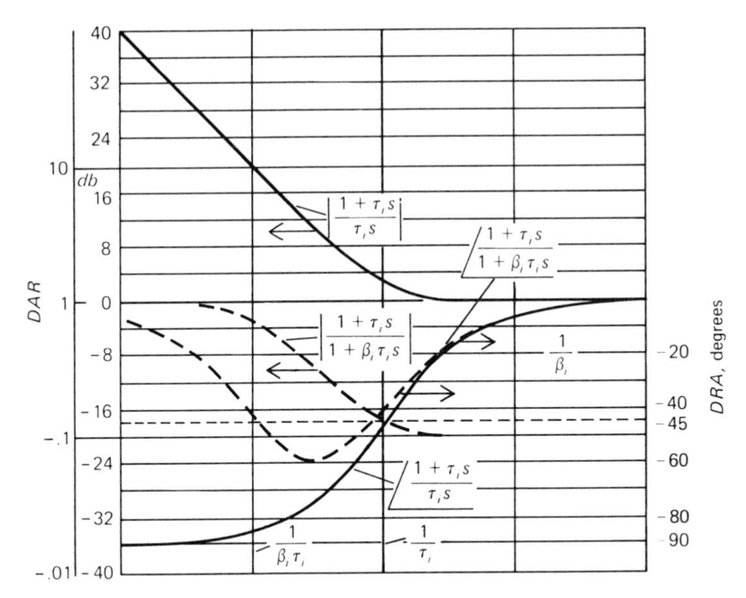

Figure 10.3. Frequency response of two controller functions commonly used for low frequency compensation. (The interval between each ordinate represents a ten-fold increase in frequency.)

As s approaches zero, $\frac{C}{Ref.}$ approaches $\frac{K}{K+1}$ and hence the ratio $\frac{C}{Ref.}$ can never be unity. This is indicative of the steady state error which occurs if a purely proportional control system is used. Since there is usually an upper bound on K above which excessive system oscillations occur, the ratio is usually appreciably less than unity.

If the controller function is $K\frac{(1+\tau_i s)}{\tau_i s}$, then, for the same process,

$$\frac{C}{Ref.} = \frac{(1+\tau_i s)}{\left[\frac{\tau_i \tau_1 \tau_2 s^3}{K} + \frac{\tau_i(\tau_1 + \tau_2)s^2}{K} + \tau_i\left(1+\frac{1}{K}\right)s + 1\right]}$$

so that, when $s \longrightarrow 0, \dfrac{C}{Ref.} \longrightarrow 1$.

The 'integration' has eliminated steady state error.

It is in the high frequency region that Bode's design procedure is particularly useful for process control systems. The essence of the method is embodied in two criteria:

(1) the slope of the *fully compensated* open loop system frequency response plotted on log-log coordinates should be approximately -1 at the point where the curve crosses unity gain; and

(2) the phase angle of the compensated frequency response function should be no greater, negatively, than 150° at the frequency at which the gain (in criterion 1) becomes unity.

These rules are depicted in Figure 10.4.

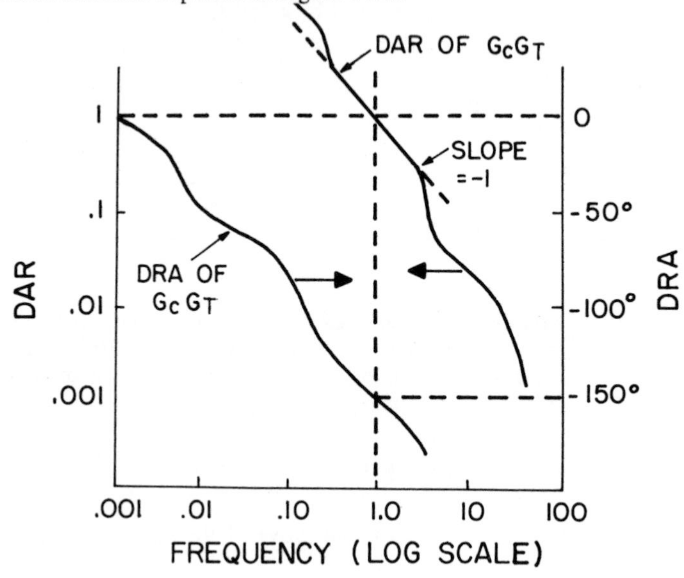

Figure 10.4. Illustration of Bode's rules.

Refinements to these rules have been made by Oldenburger (*10*), but there appears to be little to be gained by their application to most process control system design.

The shape of the open loop process frequency response curve of the form

$$\frac{K(1+\tau_4 s)}{(1+\tau_1 s)(1+\tau_2 s)(1+\tau_3 s)}$$

will depend upon the values of the various time constants (τ's). (If τ_4 is present, experience has shown its value generally lies between two of the denominator time constants.) In any event, if all terms are present, the system assumes the characteristics of a second order system at sufficiently high frequency. That is, the slope of the frequency response curve on log-log coordinates (Bode plot) approaches -2. To satisfy Bode's amplitude rule (Rule 1), requires that the compensation provided by the controller increase the slope by one, from -2 to -1. A control function having a +1 slope of its Bode amplitude plot in the frequency range of interest would be required.

In the case where τ_4 is missing, the process curve takes on the properties of a third order system. The slope of a corresponding Bode plot approaches -3, which indicates that the controller amplitude function should possess a +2 slope in the frequency range of interest.

The function commonly available for high frequency compensation in fixed configuration electronic controllers has the form

$$\frac{1 + \alpha\tau_d s}{1 + \tau_d s} .$$

The value of α usually lies between 10 and 15. A Bode plot of this function for $\alpha = 10$ is shown in Figure 10.5 where ω_1 and ω_2 are the break point frequencies for the numerator and denominator terms, respectively.

Since the maximum slope of the amplitude curve is +1, it is ob-

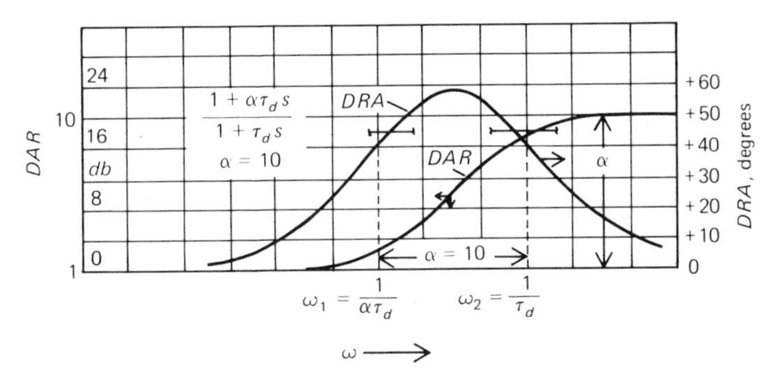

Figure 10.5. Frequency response diagram for the function $\dfrac{1 + \alpha\tau_d s}{1 + \tau_d s}$ with $\alpha = 10$.

vious that such a function cannot compensate a third order (or higher) process if the criterion of Bode's Rule 1 is to be met.

Controller functions for high frequency compensation of the form

$$\left(\frac{1+\alpha\tau_d s}{1+\tau_d s}\right)^2 \quad \text{or} \quad \left(\frac{1+\alpha_1\tau_1 s}{1+\tau_1 s}\right)\left(\frac{1+\alpha_2\tau_2 s}{1+\tau_2 s}\right)$$

can be used and have been found to give superior results. In practice, however, it appears that improvements which can be achieved with the added complexity have not been considered warranted by either vendors of control hardware or users.

Electronic circuits which produce the form $\left(\frac{1+\alpha\tau s}{1+\tau s}\right)^2$ are easy to fabricate, and the inclusion of this added capability into packaged controllers would not appear to be unreasonable.

Controller design implies the selection of at least the parameters τ_i, τ_d and K_C such that criteria relevant to the compensated open loop function are satisfied. That is, K_C and G_C must be chosen so that the function $K_C G_C \cdot K_T G_T$ has appropriate characteristics. Here the complete controller function is, for example,

$$K_C\left(\frac{1+\tau_i s}{\tau_i s}\right)\left(\frac{1+\alpha\tau_d s}{1+\tau_d s}\right) = K_C G_C$$

and $K_T G_T$ is of the form

$$K_T\frac{(1+\tau_4 s)}{(1+\tau_1 s)(1+\tau_2 s)(1+\tau_3 s)} \quad .$$

That is, K_C and K_T are the gains or frequency independent portions, and G_C and G_T are the frequency dependent portions of the controller and overall process, respectively.

For the high frequency region, Bode's rules are usually satisfactory. Compensation in the low frequency region, although not so critical, does require thought. The general rule is to make τ_i as small as possible and yet not introduce undue phase lag in the high frequency region from the integral component. Selection amounts to more than cancelling a 'zero' with a 'pole' which would occur if $\tau_i = \tau_1$, for example (assuming $\tau_1 > \tau_2, \tau_3, \tau_4$ in the generalized process model.)

Fitting the integral component, $\left(\frac{1 + \tau_i s}{\tau_i s}\right)$, and the high frequency component, $\left(\frac{1 + \alpha\tau_d s}{1 + \tau_d s}\right)$, is an operation unique to each particular process function, since the 'positioning' of the controller function components in the frequency domain to achieve best results certainly depends upon the various apparent time constants of the process.

Controller Adjustments The design procedure for determining τ_i and τ_d may be viewed as shifting the controller functions on a Bode plot in such a way that the combination satisfies desired closed loop performance criteria. Since closed loop performance depends upon the gain, K_C, introduced by the controller, as well as upon the choice of τ_i and τ_d, a trial and error approach is indicated.

The following procedure is recommended for determining the best controller adjustments.

1. Construct on translucent paper the frequency response curves for the process, with unity gain, as a Bode plot. If the general form for the process is assumed, this amounts to having a plot of

$$G_T = \frac{(1 + \tau_4 s)}{(1 + \tau_1 s)(1 + \tau_2 s)(1 + \tau_3 s)}$$

although the individual apparent time constants usually are not known.

2. Construct on a separate sheet of paper, with the same scales, the Bode plot of the integral function, $\frac{1 + \tau_i s}{\tau_i s}$ or $\frac{1 + \tau_i s}{1 + \beta_i \tau_i s}$. This set of curves will be used as an underlay. (Figure 10.3 shows the Bode plots for these functions ($\beta_i = 10$).

3. Construct on a separate sheet of paper, with the same scales, the Bode plot of the derivative function $\left[\frac{(1 + \alpha\tau_d s)}{(1 + \tau_d s)}\right]^n$. This set of curves will also be used as an underlay. Figure 10.5 shows the function for the case where $n=1$ and $\alpha = 10$.

4. With the integral curves (step 2) as an underlay and with the unity amplitude axes coinciding, shift the curves until the amplitude curve of the integral component when combined (added on log scale) with the amplitude of the process blends in smoothly to yield

a curve with a slope of about −1 extending as far as possible to the right.

5. With the derivative curves as an underlay and with the unity amplitude axes coinciding, shift the curves until the sum of the pro-

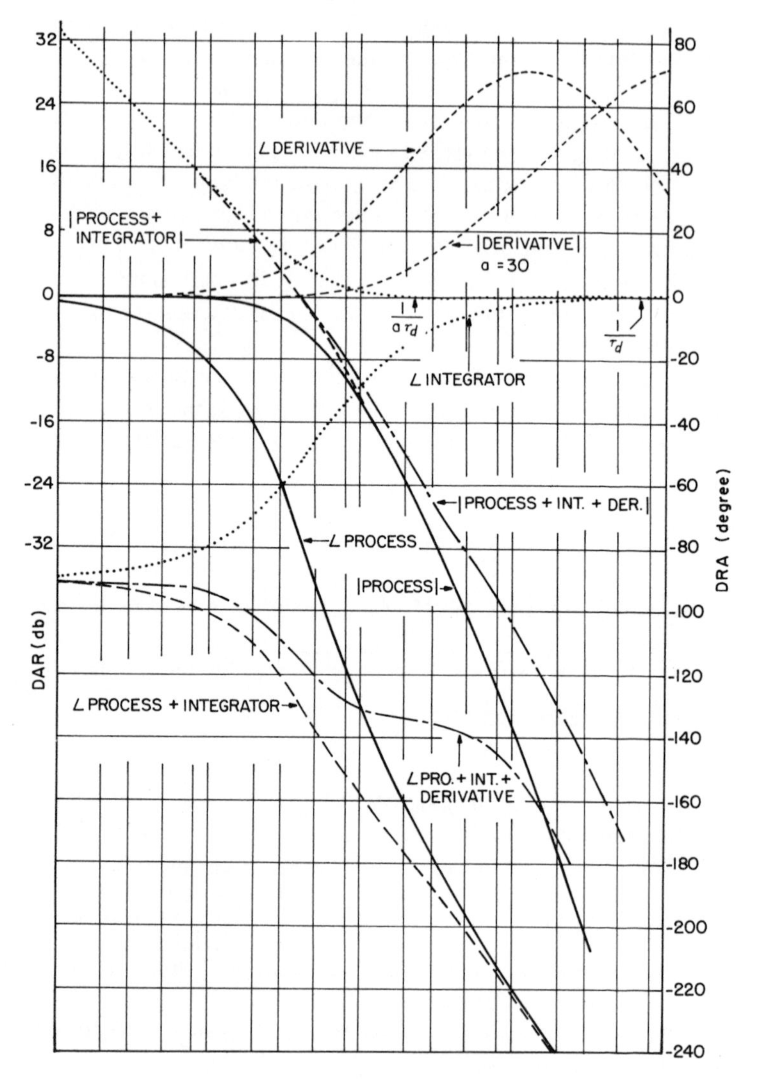

Figure 10.6. Graphical technique of achieving dynamic compensation using standard controller functions.

cess phase angle and the maximum phase angle contributed by the derivative function is about $-150°$.

6. Sketch the amplitude and phase curves of the combined results to yield the Bode plot of

$$G_C G_T = \left(\frac{1+\tau_i s}{\tau_i s}\right)\left(\frac{1+\alpha\tau_d s}{1+\tau_d s}\right)^n G_T.$$

Figure 10.6 is illustrative. In this example, α was chosen as 30 and n as unity.

7. Plot the frequency response of the combined open loop function (with unity gain) on the Nichols chart shown in Figure 10.7. On this figure, the frequency response of the closed loop may be obtained from the open loop curve. That is, the frequency response of $\frac{G}{1+G}$ is found from the graph of G drawn on Figure 10.7.

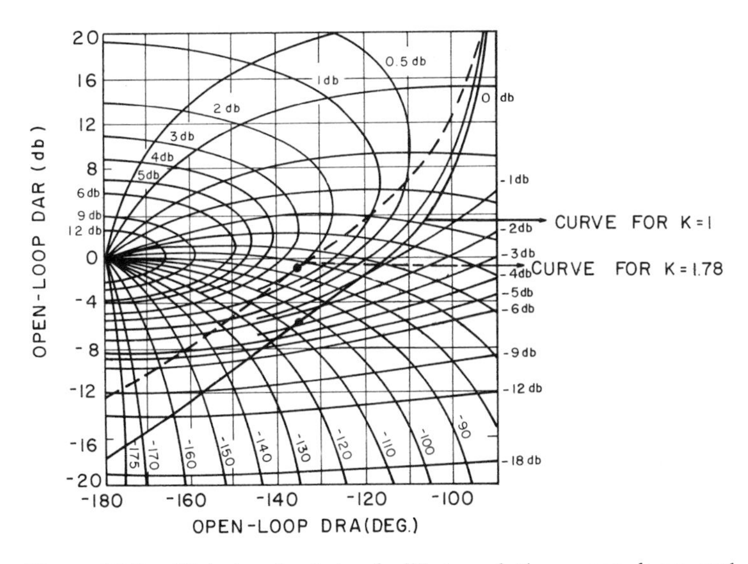

Figure 10.7. Nichols chart to facilitate relating open loop and closed loop frequency response.

8. Determine the vertical translation (in decibels) required to bring the curve for G (i.e. $G_C G_T$, with all gains unity) tangent to the closed loop amplitude curve corresponding to 2 db. This means that the closed loop amplitude will reach a maximum of 2 db when the

total feedforward gain of the system, $K_c K_T$, is equal to K. Thus, if the vertical translation required to achieve tangency to the 2 db closed loop locus is 5, then 20 log K = 5 or $K = 10^{5/20} = 1.78$ (See Figure 10.7.)

Since K_T (overall process gain) is known, the gain to be contributed by the controller is found as $K_c = K/K_T$.

9. Plot the frequency response of the translated open loop curve (gain = K) taken from the Nichols chart on log-log coordinates for both amplitude and phase angle; i.e. make a Bode plot of the translated open loop curve. Use information only in the region where the translated open loop amplitude curve crosses unity gain. Inspect this new curve, and see if the frequency at which gain cross-over (point where gain becomes unity) can be shifted farther to the right by adjusting the position of the derivative function (sometimes adjustments in the integration function must also be considered). At the same time, the phase angle of the open loop must not exceed, negatively, 150°, at the frequency corresponding to gain cross-over.

10. If appreciable adjustments were possible at this point, replot the new information on the Nichols chart and determine a new overall gain and new estimate of allowable controller gain. Rarely are more than two trials required.

From the position of the controller functions with reference to the frequency response of the process, the controller dynamic parameters can be found from the relations

$$\frac{1}{\tau_i} = \omega_i \text{ or } \tau_i = \frac{1}{\omega_i},$$

and

$$\frac{1}{\alpha\tau_d} = \omega_d \text{ or } \tau_d = \frac{1}{\alpha\omega_d},$$

where ω_i and ω_d are the break point frequencies associated with the integral and derivative components of the controller function, respectively, as shown in Figures 10.3 and 10.5.

Then, from a correlation of the control function adjustment with the appropriate time constant, the desired adjustment is determined. Typical correlations are shown in Figures 9.11, 9.12 and 9.13.

It is good practice to plot the frequency response of the final closed loop system in the region of the peak in order to verify results.

The selection of 2 db as the desired maximum closed loop amplitude is rather arbitrary and usually results in a system having a transient response approximating a second order system with a damping coefficient of about 0.5. This may be more oscillatory than desired in which case a lower maximum—1.5 or even 1 db, for example—may be chosen.

The objective is to design a system with predictable performance. The selection of performance best suited for the particular problem must ultimately be the responsibility of the designer. The above procedure guarantees an organized and rational approach toward that end.

Polar coordinate representation is useful to clarify the role of Bode's rules. The loci on such a plot of the open loop frequency response of a system with various gains is shown in Figure 10.8. This is usually referred to as a Nyquist diagram.

As mentioned previously, if the open loop locus on such a plot encircles the 1, −180° point, closed loop instability ensues. The speci-

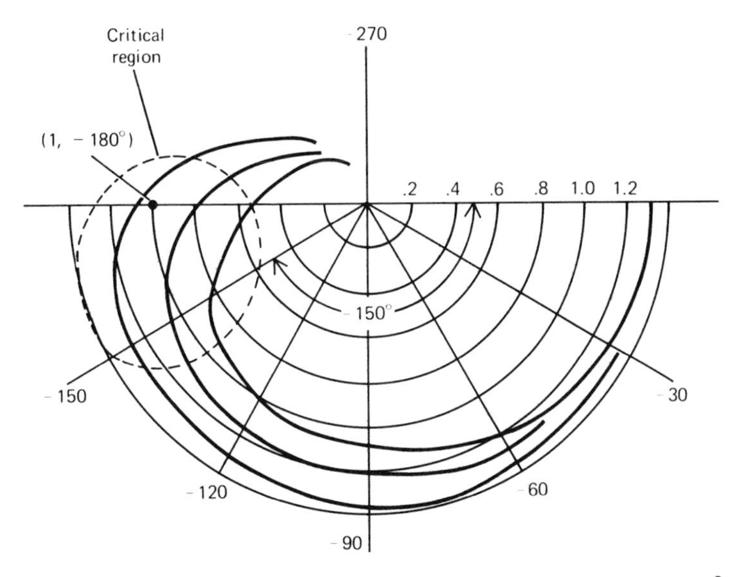

Figure 10.8. Nyquist diagram showing encirclement of 1, −180° point as locus is altered.

fication that the open loop locus be less than unity for all phase angles more negative than 150° gives assurance that the 1, −180° point is avoided by a safe margin. The specification that the slope of the amplitude-frequency relation in the region of unity gain of the compensated open loop should be about −1 indicates that the *shape* of the Nyquist plot in this region is important. The rule specifies that, as the amplitude passes through unity, the amplitude should be changing with frequency such that

$$\frac{d \log A}{d \log \omega} \cong -1$$

or that

$$\frac{dA}{d\omega} \cong \frac{A}{\omega}$$

so that, at the point where $A = 1, \dfrac{dA}{d\omega} \cong \dfrac{1}{\omega}$, where A is the amplitude.

Because of the apparent simplicity, recognized or not, of the dynamic behavior of processing systems, it is not surprising that several empirical methods of determining appropriate controller functions have been suggested. (See References *1-7*.) These methods have for the most part been based on transient response records–i.e., upon performance in the time domain. It is difficult to assess the efficacy of these methods because of the lack of satisfactory descriptions of the controllers employed and the accuracy and sensitivity of the experimental data.

The Bode method, based on frequency response data, has always proved adequate but has the disadvantage that process and controller performance must be known in terms of frequency response.

Frequency response information derived by pulse testing a large variety of processes and components has indicated that the frequency dependence of these systems can be described by the apparent linear form

$$\frac{K_T(1 + \tau_4 s)}{(1 + \tau_1 s)(1 + \tau_2 s)(1 + \tau_3 s)}.$$

It has also been previously indicated that a controller function of the following form will be adequate in most cases:

$$K_c \frac{(1+\tau_i s)}{\tau_i s} \left(\frac{1+\alpha\tau_d s}{1+\tau_d s}\right)^n,$$

where n is either 1 or 2.

The values of τ_i, τ_d, α and n will be unique for every process in which τ_1, τ_2, τ_3 and τ_4 differ. K_c is also dependent upon these values as well as upon the gain of the process, K_T.

A systematic study of this problem was made in which the best values of the controller parameters were determined for systems with various values of process time constants. In this study, it was assumed that α could take on values of 10 or 30 and that n could take on values of 1 or 2. K_T was taken as unity. Results are summarized in Table 10.1. Gains are given in decibels (db) and is the constant amplification required to produce the response called for from Bode's rules. In some cases, approximate values for closed loop

TABLE 10.1a Simple 2nd-Order Systems; α = 10, 30.

Process: $\dfrac{1}{(1+\tau_1 s)(1+\tau_2 s)}$ *Controller:* $K_c\left(\dfrac{1+\tau_i s}{\tau_i s}\right)\left(\dfrac{1+\alpha\tau_d s}{1+\tau_d s}\right)$

System parameters				*Controller parameters found via XDS-930*						*Closed-loop system response characteristics*		
τ_1	τ_2	τ_3	τ_4	α	n	τ_i	τ_d	K_{db}	$K_{(gain)}$	ω_p	ω_{co}	ω_{-150}
10	10	0	0	10	1	10	.3	40.5	106	6		
10	5	0	0	10	1	9	.15	43.4	148	8		
10	2	0	0	10	1	7	.06	52	400	15	18	40
10	1	0	0	10	1	6	.03	59	900	25	30	60
10	.5	0	0	10	1	5	.015	66.5	2060	46	66	120
10	.2	0	0	10	1	2	.006	74.5	5400	–		
10	.1	0	0	10	1	1	.003	80.5	10,500	–		
10	10	0	0	30	1	10	.09	54	500	8	10	20
10	5	0	0	30	1	9	.05	57	700	15	19	30
10	3	0	0	30	1	8	.03	62.5	1340	22	30	60
10	2	0	0	30	1	8	.018	68	2250	41	60	100
10	1	0	0	30	1	7	.009	75	5600	80	101	250
10	.5	0	0	30	1	6	.005	80	10,000	160	260	450
10	.3	0	0	30	1	6	.003	82	12,800	290	460	850

TABLE 10.1b 3rd-Order Systems $\alpha = 10$, n = 1

Process: $\dfrac{1}{(1+\tau_1 s)(1+\tau_2 s)(1+\tau_3 s)}$ *Controller:* $K_c\left(\dfrac{1+\tau_i s}{\tau_i s}\right)\left(\dfrac{1+10\tau_d s}{1+\tau_d s}\right)$

System parameters				*Controller parameters found via XDS-930*						*Closed-loop system response characteristics*		
τ_1	τ_2	τ_3	τ_4	α	n	τ_i	τ_d	K_{db}	$K_{(gain)}$	ω_p	ω_{co}	ω_{-150}
10	10	10	0	10	1	30	.1	10	3.2	.15		
10	10	5	0	10	1	30	.2	12	4.0	.15		
10	10	2	0	10	1	30	.3	14.5	5.3	3.2		
10	10	1	0	10	1	30	.5	21.2	11.5	6.0		
10	5	5	0	10	1	25	.08	7.3	2.3	.16		
10	5	2	0	10	1	20	.5	14.5	5.3	.7		
10	5	1	0	10	1	20	.5	17.5	7.5	.9		
10	2	1	0	10	1	15	.3	18.5	8.4	9.0		
10	1	1	0	10	1	10	.2	20.3	10.4	2.0		

TABLE 10.1c 3rd-Order Systems; $\alpha = 30$, n = 1

Process: $\dfrac{1}{(1+\tau_1 s)(1+\tau_2 s)(1+\tau_3 s)}$ *Controller:* $K_c\left(\dfrac{1+\tau_i s}{\tau_i s}\right)\left(\dfrac{1+30\tau_d s}{1+\tau_d s}\right)$

System parameters				*Controller parameters found via XDS-930*						*Closed-loop system response characteristics*		
τ_1	τ_2	τ_3	τ_4	α	n	τ_i	τ_d	K_{db}	$K_{(gain)}$	ω_p	ω_{co}	ω_{-150}
10	10	10	0	30	1	10	.8	2	1.26	1	2.5	4
10	10	5	0	30	1	12	.5	8	2.5	3	3.7	5
10	10	2	0	30	1	10	.4	10.2	3.2	4.2	5.8	7
10	10	1	0	30	1	15	.18	23	14.	6	9	15
10	5	5	0	30	1	12	.35	9.5	3	3.1	4	5.5
10	5	2	0	30	1	13	.25	14	5	5.3	6	9
10	5	1	0	30	1	10	.2	15	5.6	8	11	14
10	2	1	0	30	1	10	.14	18.5	8.4	9	12	20
10	1	1	0	30	1	8	.06	22.7	13.6	14	20	25

TABLE 10.1d 3rd-Order Systems; $\alpha = 10$, n = 2

Process: $\dfrac{1}{(1+\tau_1 s)(1+\tau_2 s)(1+\tau_3 s)}$ Controller: $K_c \left(\dfrac{1+\tau_i s}{\tau_i s}\right)\left(\dfrac{1+10\tau_d s}{1+\tau_d s}\right)^2$

System parameters				Controller parameters found via XDS-930						Closed-loop system response characteristics		
τ_1	τ_2	τ_3	τ_4	α	n	τ_i	τ_d	K_{db}	$K_{(gain)}$	ω_p	ω_{co}	ω_{-150}
10	10	10	0	10	2	30	.8	17	7.1	6.5	8	9
10	10	5	0	10	2	25	.5	24.5	16.8	7	11	17
10	10	2	0	10	2	20	.3	36	32	15	20	25
10	10	1	0	10	2	15	.18	38	80	25	35	45
10	5	5	0	10	2	13	.37	25	17.8	10	15	19
10	5	3	0	10	2	13	.28	28	25	12	17	23
10	5	2	0	10	2	13	.2	31	35	12	20	30
10	5	1	0	10	2	11	.2	30	32	23	30	36
10	2	1	0	10	2	7	.1	36	64	34	42	50
10	1	1	0	10	2	8	.09	39	90	45	54	70

TABLE 10.1e 1st Over 3rd-Order Systems; $\alpha = 10$, n = 1

Process: $\dfrac{(1+\tau_4 s)}{(1+\tau_1 s)(1+\tau_2 s)(1+\tau_3 s)}$ Controller: $K_c \left(\dfrac{1+\tau_i s}{\tau_i s}\right)\left(\dfrac{1+10\tau_d s}{1+\tau_d s}\right)$

System parameters				Controller parameters found via XDS-930						Closed-loop system response characteristics		
τ_1	τ_2	τ_3	τ_4	α	n	τ_i	τ_d	K_{db}	$K_{(gain)}$	ω_p	ω_{co}	ω_{-150}
10	10	10	15	10	1	50	.12	53	450			
10	10	10	5	10	1	35	.3	46	200			
10	10	5	7	10	1	30	.4	35	56	28	35	65
10	10	3	7	10	1	30	.1	52.5	350	72	100	120
10	10	2	7	10	1	7	.07	55	560	100	140	290
10	10	2	5	10	1	7	.11	51	350	80	100	190
10	5	5	7	10	1	40	.08	54.5	503			
10	5	5	3	10	1	40	.15	51	350			
10	5	5	1	10	1	35	.45	18.6	8.5			
10	5	5	.7	10	1	25	.5	15.6	6.0			
10	5	5	.5	10	1	25	.4	13.8	4.9			
10	5	2	7	10	1	20	.045	56.5	670			
10	5	2	3	10	1	10	.09	52	400			
10	5	1	7	10	1	10	.027	59.5	950	24	38	70
10	5	.5	7	10	1	8	.014	64.6	1700	44	68	125
10	5	.5	2	10	1	9	.02	69.5	3000	28	40	80
10	3	1	7	10	1	10	.03					
10	1.25	1	2	10	1	4	.025	60	1000			
10	1.25	.5	2	10	1	4	.015	62.6	1350			
10	1.25	.3	2	10	1	3	.008	69	2800			
10	1.25	.1	2	10	1	2	.003	76.5	6800			

TABLE 10.1f 1st Over 3rd-Order Systems; $\alpha = 30$, n = 1

Process: $\dfrac{(1+\tau_4 s)}{(1+\tau_1 s)(1+\tau_2 s)(1+\tau_3 s)}$ *Controller:* $K_c\left(\dfrac{1+\tau_i s}{\tau_i s}\right)\left(\dfrac{1+30\tau_d s}{1+\tau_d s}\right)$

System parameters				*Controller parameters found via XDS-930*						*Closed-loop system response characteristics*		
τ_1	τ_2	τ_3	τ_4	α	n	τ_i	τ_d	K_{db}	$K_{(gain)}$	ω_p	ω_{co}	ω_{-150}
10	10	5	7	30	1	20	.05	61	1150	180	460	700
10	10	3	7	30	1	10	.035	63	1400	270	400	650
10	10	2	7	30	1	7	.025	65	1800	320	470	900
10	10	2	5	30	1	7	.04	60	1000	210	400	300
10	10	1	7	30	1	5	.01	75	2800	92	120	225
10	10	1	5	30	1	5	.045	53	450	180	250	500
10	5	5	7	30	1	6	.04	59	900	190	290	550
10	5	2	3	30	1	8	.03	63.3	1500	260	400	720
10	5	1	3	30	1	12	.01			89	130	230
10	5	.5	7	30	1	20	.005	79	9000	160	200	330
10	5	.5	2	30	1	10	.006			98	135	250
10	3	1	7	30	1	5	.006	74.8	5500	125	200	300
10	3	1	5	30	1	5	.009	69.4	3000	72	96	190
10	1	1	7	30	1	1	.01	55	506	80	105	
10	1	1	5	30	1	4	.005	70	3200	130	190	320
10	1	1	2	30	1	7	.006	75	5060	150	200	300

properties are given. These are defined as follows:

ω_p = frequency at which the closed loop amplitude is a maximum,

ω_{co} = frequency at which the closed loop amplitude first crosses unity (following ω_p), and

ω_{-150} = frequency at which the closed loop phase angle becomes -150 degrees.

In some instances, the minimum value of τ_i has been determined with great accuracy. It usually is true that τ_i (somewhat larger than the minimum) does not appreciably affect the closed loop frequency response. However, for best transient response, the minimum allowable τ_i is required.

The limited number of combinations of α and n is based on the conclusion that values of α in excess of 30 with $n = 1$ and in excess of 10 with $n = 2$ were impractical. The maximum amplitude and

TABLE 10.2 Controller Function Properties for Selected Parameter Combinations.

Controller function	*Maximum amplitude*	*Maximum phase angle*
$\left(\dfrac{1 + 10\tau_d s}{1 + \tau_d s}\right)$	10	54
$\left(\dfrac{1 + 30\tau_d s}{1 + \tau_d s}\right)^2$	30	68
$\left(\dfrac{1 + 10\tau_d s}{1 + \tau_d s}\right)^2$	100	108

phase lead contributions from the 'derivative' component of the controller for these three combinations are listed in Table 10.2. Table 10.1 enables a rapid selection of controller functions once the frequency response of the process has been obtained and approximated by the generalized linear form.

A specific controller function will, in general, be optimum only over a narrow range of process operation. A given set of controller parameters cannot be expected to serve a broad spectrum of processes. Where this is attempted, control criteria must be severely relaxed. The use of such a large number of simple, fixed parameter controllers on existing processes suggests that either the controller is not exercising any appreciable control or that criteria are far from being exacting.

The data upon which Table 10.1 is based were procured by digital computation using the XDS-930 computer with interactive CRT display. The design procedure, based on Bode's rules and utilizing Bode plot representation and Nichol chart plots, is entirely implemented via a keyboard. Values of τ_1, τ_2, τ_3, τ_4, α and n are chosen and, by using the interactive CRT display, the synthesis is carried out, as in steps 1-10 above. The trial-and-error type of computation can be executed very rapidly until that combination of τ_i and τ_d is found which permits the highest value of controller gain K_c for given values of α and n. The result can be verified by displaying the closed loop frequency response of the final system. The method is described in a recent publication (*11*) and thesis (*12*).

Where pure delay time (or dead time) exists, the problem of controller function selection becomes more difficult. If the pure delay time does not exceed more than 10 percent of the dominant time constant (τ_1 in the generalized model), the procedures outlined above are quite satisfactory if the phase angle due to pure delay time is included. One result of pure delay time is to shift the acceptable position of the derivative controller component to the left (toward lower frequency) which decreases the allowable controller gain. While it is usually possible to achieve the desired maximum for the frequency response amplitude of the closed loop (1-2 db), this will occur at a frequency lower than if no dead time were present and the transient recovery time—to a step input, for example—will be increased. As pure delay time increases, the controller becomes increasingly ineffective.

Correlations of Controller Parameters In those cases where the experimental frequency response data are approximated, correlations can be developed which permit rapid estimation of three-term controller parameters.

Assuming the controller function to be of the form

$$\frac{K_c(1 + \tau_i s)}{\tau_i s} \left(\frac{1 + \alpha\tau_d s}{1 + \tau_d s}\right),$$

these results are summarized as follows.

First-Order Systems. If the process dynamics can be approximated by the form

$$\left(\frac{K_p}{1 + \tau_1 s}\right),$$

the control problem is trivial. In this case, no high frequency compensation needs to be used and τ_i is set equal to τ_1. The closed loop function becomes

$$\frac{C}{Ref} = \frac{K_c K_p/\tau_i s}{1 + \dfrac{K_c K_p'}{\tau_i s}} = \frac{1}{1 + \dfrac{\tau_i s}{K_c K_p}} = \frac{1}{1 + \tau s.}$$

Since K_c can be adjusted, it is possible to achieve a first order system with as small a time constant as desired without fear of instability.

Second-Order Systems. In order to satisfy Bode's rules in the high frequency region, the 'derivative' function is required, and the open loop function becomes

$$K_c \frac{(1+\tau_i s)}{(\tau_i s)} \frac{(1+\alpha\tau_d s)}{(1+\tau_d s)} \left(\frac{K_p}{(1+\tau_1 s)(1+\tau_2 s)}\right).$$

This, too, is a special case because, in the high frequency region, this function behaves as a second-order system and instability is not a problem. However, the system can become oscillatory as the phase angle approaches $-180°$.

Because the 'integrating' function $\left(\frac{1+\tau_i s}{\tau_i s}\right)$ contributes a negative phase angle (becoming less negative as frequency increases), it is possible to realize phase angles in excess of $-180°$ if the controller adjustments are grossly in error. Also, inspection of the Nichols chart shows that tangency to the 2-db closed loop locus can occur whenever the open loop function has a phase angle more negative than $-128°$. For second-order systems and with a three-term controller function, it is possible to obtain an open loop function that appears on a Nichols chart as shown as curve 1 in Figure 10.7. That is, points A, B or C can become tangent to the 2-db locus by shifting the open loop curve vertically an appropriate amount. Obviously, the most responsive system results at the highest gain which occurs if the point C becomes tangent to the 2-db locus.

In order that tangency is assured only for the case of maximum gain, the open loop phase angle must not exceed $-128°$ until the frequency corresponding to that in the region of C is exceeded. This means that, for such systems, the compensated open loop curve should appear somewhat as curve 2 in Figure 10.9.

This situation makes pure second-order systems, along with first-order systems, somewhat unique.

With these restrictions in mind, a systematic study of second-order systems was conducted in which the combination of parameters, τ_i, τ_d and K_c were obtained which would yield the highest undamped natural angular frequency with a closed loop maximum amplitude ratio of 2 db.

These results which appear in Table 10.1a are simply summarized as follows for the case where $\alpha = 10$. Set τ_i such that

$$\frac{\tau_i}{\tau_1} = \left(\frac{\tau_2}{\tau_1}\right)^{0.22}$$

Set τ_d equal to 0.03 τ_2; set $K_c = 100/(\tau_2/\tau_1) = 100\ [(\tau_1/\tau_2)]$, where τ_1 is the larger time constant of the second-order system.

In respect to τ_i, this means that, if both system time constants are equal, τ_i is set equal to this time constant with the result that $(1 + \tau_i s)$ cancels one of the $(1 + \tau s)$ terms in the demonimator, and the open loop function becomes

$$\frac{K_c}{\tau_i s} \frac{(1 + \alpha\tau_d s)}{(1 + \tau_d s)} \frac{K_p}{(1 + \tau_1 s)}.$$

As τ_2 begins to move away from τ_1, if τ_2 is assumed to be smaller, τ_i also moves away from τ_1—with the optimum location lying somewhere between the two process time constants.

When this procedure is followed, evidently the optimum value of τ_d becomes largely dependent upon τ_2 and the optimum value of K_c depends largely on the ratio of process time constants.

If a higher value of α is chosen, there appears to be little change in τ_i required to produce the best transient response (see Table 10.1a). However, as expected, considerable improvement in high frequency response can be attained as α is increased. Again τ_d is largely dependent upon τ_2, the smaller time constant of the second-order process. For $\alpha = 30$ to achieve maximum closed loop frequency response, it was found that $\tau_d = 0.01\ \tau_2$. That is, by increasing α from 10 to 30, a three-fold decrease in τ_d can be made. At the same time, a five-fold increase in gain is permissible. Substantial extensions ot the "band pass" or increase in apparent undamped natural frequency and frequency of peak closed loop dynamic amplitude ratio are achieved as α is increased from 10 to 30.

For purely third-order systems with $\alpha = 10$ and $n = 1$, the following relation predicts a satisfactory value for τ_i:

$$\frac{\tau_i}{\tau_1} = 1 + 2\left(\frac{\tau_2}{\tau_1}\right).$$

When $\alpha = 30$ and $n = 1$, the relation becomes

$$\frac{\tau_i}{\tau_1} = 0.5 + 1.5\left(\frac{\tau_2}{\tau_1}\right).$$

With $\alpha = 10$ and $n = 2$,

$$\frac{\tau_i}{\tau_1} = 1 + \left(\frac{\tau_2}{\tau_1}\right).$$

For this latter case, a relation from which τ_d may be approximated is

$$\frac{\tau_3}{\tau_d} = 14\left(\frac{\tau_3}{\tau_2}\right)^{0.43}$$

or

$$\frac{\tau_d}{\tau_3} = 0.07\left(\frac{\tau_2}{\tau_3}\right)^{0.43}$$

These latter correlations have not been extended to include τ_i and K_c but can probably be developed using the results presented in Table 10.1c.

It should be pointed out that, for purely third-order systems, Bode's rules cannot be fulfilled using a control function with $n = 1$.

Table 10.1d gives results for third-order systems using $n = 2$ as required by Bode's rules. As expected, response characteristics are substantially improved as compared with those shown in Table 10.1c.

Some preliminary work has been done with first- over third-order systems using a controller function employing $\alpha = 10$ and 30 and $n = 1$. This is presented in Tables 10.1e and 10.1f.

References

1. Ziegler, J. G. and N. B. Nichols. Optimum Settings for Controllers. *Trans. ASME* **64** (1942), p. 759.
2. Ziegler, J. G. and N. B. Nichols. Process Lags in Automatic Control Circuits. *Trans. ASME* **65** (1943), p. 433.
3. Cohen, G. H. and G. A. Coon. Theoretical Considerations of Retarded Control. *Trans. ASME* **75** (1953), p. 827.
4. Coon, G. A. Frequency Response Methods. *ISA J.* **11**, no. 9 (1964), p. 77.

5. Coon, G. A. Frequency Response Methods. *ISA J.* **11**, no. 10 (1964), p. 87.
6. Coon, G. A. Control Charts for Proportional Action. *ISA J.* **11** (1964), p. 81.
7. Merrill, Paul W. and Cecil L. Smith. Controller, Set Them Right. *Hydrocarbon Process.* **45**, no. 2 (February 1966).
8. Couhanowr, D. R. and L. B. Koppel. *Process Systems Analysis and Control.* McGraw Hill Book Co., New York, 1965.
9. Bode, H. W. *Network Analysis and Feedback Amplifier Design.* Van Nostrand Co., New York, 1945.
10. Oldenburger, Rufus. *Frequency Response.* The Macmillan Co., New York, 1956.
11. Hougen, J. O. and Tadashi Kado. *Interactive graphic computer technique for synthesis of simple feedback control systems*, Vol. 1, pp 339-344. Summer Computer Simulation Conference, 1970.
12. Kado, Tadashi. *Computer assisted design procedures for process control systems.* M. S. thesis, Dept. of Chemical Engineering, University of Texas, January 1970.

Appendix 1
Complex Numbers

A complex number is usually written as $a + jb$ where a and b are real numbers and j, called the imaginary unit, is defined such that $j^2 = -1$. The part a is called the real part and b the imaginary part of the complex number.

The complex number $a - jb$ is called the *conjugate* of $a + jb$. The product of a complex number and its conjugate is a real number.

$$(a + jb)(a - jb) = a^2 + b^2.$$

Two complex numbers are equal if, and only if, the real parts and imaginary parts are identically equal.

Addition and subtraction follow the rule that the sum or difference is found by adding the real and imaginary parts separately.

$$(a + jb) + (c + jd) = (a + c) + j(b + d)$$

or

$$(a + jb) - (c + jd) = (a - c) + j(b - d).$$

Multiplication is conducted in the usual manner:

$$(a + jb)(c + jd) = ac + jbc + jad - bd$$

$$= (ac - bd) + j(bc + ad).$$

The same is true with division, with the added feature that multiplication and division by the conjugate of the denominator gives the quotient in more easily recognized form:

$$\frac{a + jb}{c + jd} = \frac{a + jb}{c + jd} \times \frac{c - jd}{c - jd} = \frac{(ac + bd) + j(bc - ad)}{c^2 + d^2}$$

$$= \frac{ac + bd}{c^2 + d^2} + j\frac{bc - ad}{c^2 + d^2} = A + jB.$$

The complex number $P = a + jb$ can be represented on a rectilinear plane (called an Argand diagram) as shown in Figure A1.1. The real

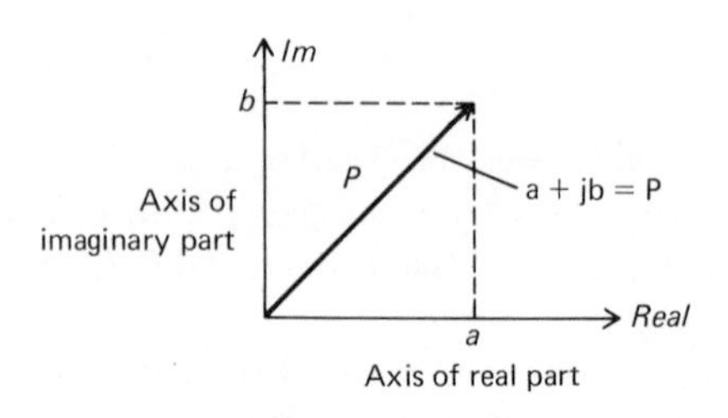

Figure A1.1. Argand diagram for representing complex numbers.

part is represented by a vector lying along the real axis and the imaginary part lying along the imaginary (j) axis. Thus the complex number can be interpreted as a vector of magnitude $\sqrt{a^2 + b^2}$. Also the effect of multiplying a real number by j is to rotate the vector representing the real number 90° (or $\pi/2$ radians) so that the vector now lies along the imaginary axis.

Alternately, the complex number can be represented in polar coordinates as a vector of magnitude $\sqrt{a^2 + b^2}$ directed at an angle of θ with the real axis where $\theta = \tan^{-1} b/a = \tan^{-1} \dfrac{\text{Imag. Part}}{\text{Real Part}}$. (See Figure A1.2). Since $a = P \cos\theta$ and $b = P \sin\theta$, it follows that

$$a + jb = P(\cos\theta + j \sin\theta)$$

where $P = \sqrt{a^2 + b^2}$.

Two of Euler's identities are useful:

$$e^{j\theta} = \cos\theta + j\sin\theta, \text{ and}$$

$$e^{-j\theta} = \cos\theta - j\sin\theta.$$

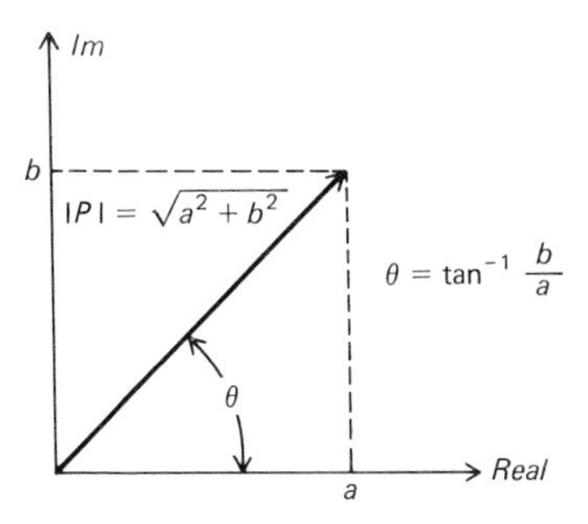

Figure A1.2. Representation of a complex number in polar coordinates.

The complex number may now be written in imaginary exponential form:

$$a + jb = P(\cos\theta + j\sin\theta) = Pe^{j\theta} .$$

The three forms in which a complex number may be written should be noted. From the Euler relations, above, it follows that

$$\sin\theta = \frac{e^{j\theta} - e^{-j\theta}}{2j} \text{ and}$$

$$\cos\theta = \frac{e^{j\theta} + e^{-j\theta}}{2}$$

Also, from the polar representation, the purely imaginary number jb can be written as

$$be^{j\pi/2}$$

and the unity imaginary number j as merely $e^{j\pi/2} - e^{-j\pi/2}$. More generally, $j = e^{j(2\pi n + \pi/2)}$ where $n = 0, 1, 2, \cdots$.

Similarly $$-j = e^{-j\pi/2} \doteq e^{j(2\pi n - \pi/2)} .$$

Through the use of Euler's relations, it is easy to show that

$$A\cos\theta + B\sin\theta = \sqrt{A^2 + B^2}\cos(\theta - \psi),$$

where $\psi = \tan^{-1} B/A$.

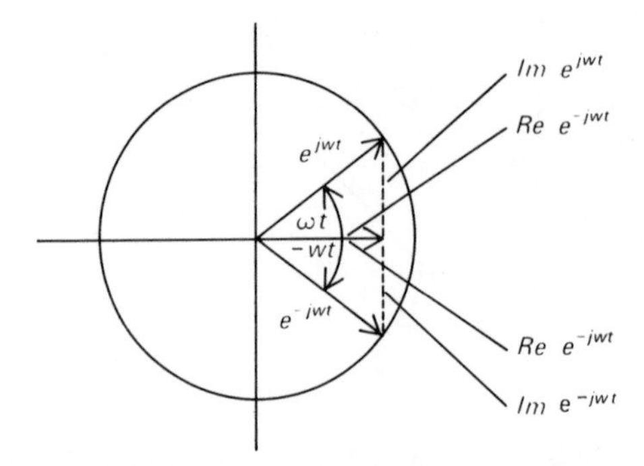

Figure A1.3. Resolution of the complex number $e^{j\omega t}$ into real and imaginary parts.

Consider the complex number, $e^{j\omega t} = \cos \omega t + j \sin \omega t$ where t is the running variable and ω is an assigned constant. As t increases, the angle of the unity vector increases. Thus, the end of the vector will trace out a circle of unit radius around the origin. The projection on the real axis traces out $\cos \omega t$ while the projection on the imaginary axis traces out $\sin \omega t$. The real and imaginary parts change with ωt such that, for all values of t, $\sqrt{(\text{Re})^2 + (\text{Im})^2} = 1$. Figure A1.3 illustrates the concepts.

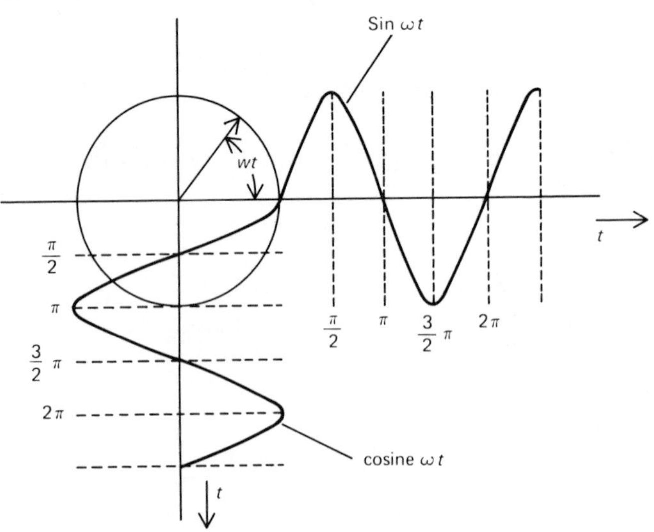

Figure A1.4. Graphical representation of conjugate imaginary numbers.

Next consider the sum of two complex conjugate numbers written as

$$e^{j\omega t} + e^{-j\omega t} .$$

For a given value of ωt, this sum will appear as a pair of oppositely rotating vectors of unit length, one making an angle of $+\omega t$ radians with the positive real axis and the other making an angle of $-\omega t$ radians. Figure A1.4 shows a typical pair and identifies the imaginary and real part of each vector. In particular, it should be noted that

$$\mathrm{Re}\,[e^{j\omega t}] + \mathrm{Re}\,[e^{-j\omega t}] = 2\mathrm{Re}\; e^{j\omega t} = 2\mathrm{Re}\; e^{-j\omega t}$$ and that

$$\mathrm{Im}\,[e^{j\omega t}] + \mathrm{Im}\,[e^{-j\omega t}] = 0.$$

Appendix 2
Table of Laplace Transforms

	$f(s)$	$f(t)$
1.	1	$\delta(t)$
2.	A/s	A
3.	$1/s + a$	e^{-at}
4.	$\dfrac{1}{(s+a)(s+b)}$	$\dfrac{e^{-at} - e^{-bt}}{(b-a)}$
5.	$\dfrac{1}{s(s+a)(s+b)}$	$\dfrac{1}{ab} + \dfrac{be^{-at} - ae^{-bt}}{ab(a-b)}$
6.	$\dfrac{1}{s^2 + a^2}$	$\dfrac{1}{a} \sin at$
7.	$\dfrac{1}{s^2 - a^2}$	$\dfrac{1}{a} \sinh at$
8.	$\dfrac{s}{s^2 + a^2}$	$\cos at$
9.	$\dfrac{s}{s^2 - a^2}$	$\cosh at$
10.	$\dfrac{1}{(s+a)^2 + b^2}$	$\dfrac{1}{b} e^{-at} \sin bt$

	$f(s)$	$f(t)$
11.	$\dfrac{(s+a)}{(s+a)^2+b^2}$	$e^{-at}\cos bt$
12.	$\dfrac{A}{s^2}$	At
13.	$\dfrac{1}{s^n}$	$\dfrac{1}{(n-1)!}t^{n-1}$
14.	$\dfrac{1}{(s+a)^2}$	te^{-at}
15.	$\dfrac{1}{s(s+a)^2}$	$\dfrac{1-(1+at)e^{-at}}{a^2}$
16.	$ln\dfrac{s+b}{s+a}$	$\dfrac{e^{-at}-e^{-bt}}{t}$
17.	$\dfrac{1}{s(s^2+a^2)}$	$\dfrac{1}{a^2}(1-\cos at)$
18.	$\dfrac{1}{\sqrt{s^2+a^2}}$	$J_0(at)$

References

Extensive tables of Laplace transform pairs are found in the following publications.

1. Kaplan, Wilfred. *Operational Methods for Linear Systems.* Addison-Wesley Pub. Co., Inc., Reading, Mass., 1962.
2. Gardner, M. F. and J. L. Barnes. *Transients in Linear Systems,* vol. 1. John Wiley & Sons, New York, 1942.
3. Grabbe, E. M., S. Ramo and E. D. Wooldridge, eds. *Handbook of Automation, Computation and Control.* John Wiley & Sons, New York, 1958.

Appendix 3
Numerical Computation of the Fourier Transform of an Arbitrary Pulse Function

It is usually inconvenient to make the forcing conform to a given mathematical form when testing a process for dynamic characteristics. In principle, it is only necessary to compute the Fourier Transform of the forcing function. The same is true for the time response which depends not only on the forcing but upon the nature of the system.

A method by which the time histories of the forcing and response functions are processed to yield their respective Fourier transforms and the ratio, the performance function, is outlined below.

Since the most satisfactory forcing for determining process dynamics is the pulse function, only that type will be considered.

A pulse, for the purpose here, will be defined as a continuous function of a bounded variation which returns to its initial value after a finite time and remains so as time progresses.

Depending upon the system being excited, the response to a pulse will also be pulse-like. Sometimes the output or response will not return to its initial value. Such responses are called *non-closing pulses*.

The procedure used to convert any arbitrary closed pulse function in the time domain to the frequency domain is to divide the time history into a number of small increments, compute the Fourier Transform of each section of the curve in the given increment, and then sum the results of each piecewise computation.

Response functions usually exhibit rapid variations early in their time histories and become smoother as time progresses. Usually, then, smaller increments are required in order to resolve the early part, while in the later portion larger increments are adequate. For this reason, it is convenient to design the computational routine to accommodate two increment widths.

Figure A3.1 gives the notation and illustrates the use of increments of two widths in approximating a pulse function. The approxima-

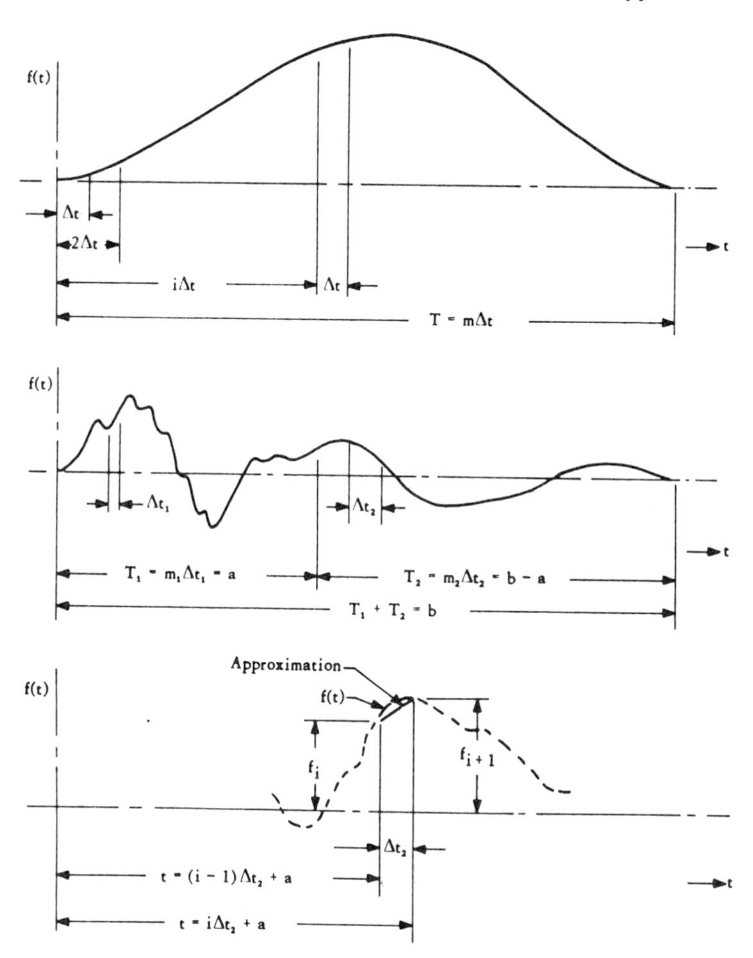

Figure A3.1. Notation for trapezoidal approximation to the Fourier transform (designated TAFT) for a typical time function. Computer program should allow for use of Δt_1 and Δt_2 for convenience and a maximum of about 400 time ordinates.

tion to the curve is considered to be the top portion of a series of trapezoids formed between the edges of the time increments. The pulse is divided into two large sections, the first described by the shorter time increments of width Δt_1 and the second by the larger increments Δt_2. The length of the first section is $T_1 = a$, the length of the second section is T_2, and the total duration of the complete pulse is $T_1 + T_2 = b$. There are m_1 increments in the first section and m_2 in the second. Therefore, $T_1 = a = m_1 \Delta t_1$ and $T_2 = b - a = m_2 \Delta t_2$.

The time elapsed to the leading edge of an increment is $t_1 = (i - 1)\Delta t + a$; the time elapsed to the trailing edge of an increment is $t_2 = i\Delta t + a$.

If two increment widths are used, $\Delta t = \Delta t_1$ for the first section during which a is zero. In the section beyond a, $\Delta t = \Delta t_2$, and a is retained in computing time. The value of the function on corresponding edges of an increment are designated as f_i and f_{i+1}. It will be noted that, when $i = 1$, $t = 0$ so that $f_1 = f(0)$, the initial value of the pulse. That is, f_1 is the value of the function at the leading edge of the first increment.

The line segment representing the top of a given trapezoidal approximation will have the form

$$f(t) = Mt + B\,.$$

The slope M is

$$\left(\frac{f_{i+1} - f_i}{\Delta t}\right),$$

so that, if f_i is known, any value of $f(t)$ within the increment is estimated as

$$f(t) = f_i + \left(\frac{f_{i+1} - f_i}{\Delta t}\right)(t - T_1).$$

Since $T_1 = (i - 1)\Delta t + a$

$$f(t) = f_i + \left(\frac{f_{i+1} - f_i}{\Delta t}\right)(t - a - (i - 1)\Delta t)$$

$$= f_i\left[i + \frac{a}{\Delta t} - \frac{t}{\Delta t}\right] + f_{i+1}\left[\frac{t}{\Delta t} + 1 - i - \frac{a}{\Delta t}\right]$$

$$= \left[\left(i + \frac{a}{\Delta t}\right) f_i + \left(1 - i - \frac{a}{\Delta t}\right) f_{i+1}\right] + \left(\frac{f_{i+1} - f_i}{\Delta t}\right) t.$$

For convenience, let

$$\left(i + \frac{a}{\Delta t}\right) f_i + \left(1 - i - \frac{a}{\Delta t}\right) f_{i+1} = \left[\frac{t_2}{\Delta t} f_i - \frac{t_1}{\Delta t} f_{i+1}\right] \equiv B$$

and

$$\left(\frac{f_{i+1} - f_i}{\Delta t}\right) \equiv M.$$

The objective is to compute the Fourier transform of each section of the curve and then to obtain an expression for the sum.

For a typical section, the result will be denoted as $[TAFT]_i$, the Trapezoidal Approximation of the Fourier Transform, for the ith interval. Thus

$$[TAFT]_i = B \int_{t_1}^{t_2} e^{-j\omega t} dt + M \int_{t_1}^{t_2} t e^{-j\omega t} dt = I_1 + I_2$$

where

$$t_1 = (i - 1)\Delta t + a$$

and

$$t_2 = i\Delta t + a .$$

The first integral becomes

$$I_1 = B \int_{t_1}^{t_2} e^{-j\omega t}\, dt = \left[B \; \frac{e^{-j\omega t_1} - e^{-j\omega t_2}}{j\omega}\right].$$

After integrating by parts where $dv \equiv e^{-j\omega t} dt$ and $u \equiv t$, the second integral is

$$I_2 = M \int_{t_1}^{t_2} t e^{-j\omega t} dt = M \int_{t_1}^{t_2} u dv = M [uv] \Big|_{t_1}^{t_2} - M \int_{t_1}^{t_2} v du$$

$$= M\left[\frac{te^{-j\omega t}}{-j\omega}\right]\Bigg|_{t_1}^{t_2} - M\left[\frac{e^{-j\omega t}}{(-j\omega)(-j\omega)}\right]\Bigg|_{t_1}^{t_2}$$

$$= M\left[\frac{t_1 e^{-j\omega t_1} - t_2 e^{-j\omega t_2}}{j\omega}\right] + M\left[\frac{e^{-j\omega t_2} - e^{-j\omega t_1}}{\omega^2}\right].$$

Therefore

$[TAFT]_i$

$$= B\left[\frac{e^{-j\omega t_1} - e^{-j\omega t_2}}{j\omega}\right] + M\left[\frac{t_1 e^{-j\omega t_1} - t_2 e^{-j\omega t_2}}{j\omega}\right] + M\left[\frac{e^{-j\omega t_2} - e^{-j\omega t_1}}{\omega^2}\right]$$

$$= \underbrace{j\omega B\left[\frac{e^{-j\omega t_2} - e^{-j\omega t_1}}{\omega^2}\right]}_{①} + \underbrace{j\omega M\left[\frac{t_2 e^{-j\omega t_2} - t_1 e^{-j\omega t_1}}{\omega_2}\right]}_{②} + \underbrace{M\left[\frac{e^{-j\omega t_2} - e^{-j\omega t_1}}{\omega_2}\right]}_{③}.$$

Recall that

$$B = \left[\frac{t_2}{\Delta t} f_i - \frac{t_1}{\Delta t} f_{i+1}\right]$$

and

$$M = \left(\frac{f_{i+1} - f_i}{\Delta t}\right);$$

then terms 1 and 3 may be written as

$$(j\omega B + M)\left[\frac{e^{-j\omega t_2} - e^{-j\omega t_1}}{\omega^2}\right]$$

$$= \left[j\omega\left(\frac{t_2}{\Delta t} f_i - \frac{t_1}{\Delta t} f_{i+1}\right) + \left(\frac{f_{i+1} - f_i}{\Delta t}\right)\left(\frac{e^{-j\omega t_2} - e^{-j\omega t_1}}{\omega^2}\right)\right]$$

$$= \frac{f_i j}{\omega}\left[\frac{t_2 e^{-j\omega t_2}}{\Delta t} - \frac{e^{-j\omega t_2}}{j\omega\Delta t} - \frac{t_2 e^{-j\omega t_1}}{\Delta t} + \frac{e^{-j\omega t_1}}{j\omega\Delta t}\right]$$

$$+ \frac{f_{i+1} j}{\omega}\left[\frac{t_1 e^{-j\omega t_1}}{\Delta t} - \frac{e^{-j\omega t_1}}{j\omega\Delta t} - \frac{t_1 e^{-j\omega t_2}}{\Delta t} + \frac{e^{-j\omega t_2}}{j\omega\Delta t}\right].$$

Term 2 becomes

$$j\omega M\left[\frac{t_2 e^{-j\omega t_2} - t_1 e^{-j\omega t_1}}{\omega^2}\right] = j\omega\left(\frac{f_{i+1} - f_i}{\Delta t}\right)\left[\frac{t_2 e^{-j\omega t_2} - t_1 e^{-j\omega t_1}}{\omega^2}\right]$$

$$= \frac{f_{i+1} j}{\omega}\left[\frac{t_2 e^{-j\omega t_2}}{\Delta t} - \frac{t_1 e^{-j\omega t_1}}{\Delta t}\right] - \frac{f_i j}{\omega}\left[\frac{t_2 e^{-j\omega t_2}}{\Delta t} - \frac{t_1 e^{-j\omega t_1}}{\Delta t}\right].$$

Combining terms 1, 2, and 3 gives

$$[TAFT]_i = \frac{f_i j}{\omega}\left[\frac{e^{-j\omega t_1}}{j\omega\Delta t} - \frac{e^{-j\omega t_2}}{j\omega\Delta t} - \frac{(t_2 - t_1)}{\Delta t} e^{-j\omega t_1}\right]$$

$$+ \frac{f_{i+1} j}{\omega}\left[\frac{e^{-j\omega t_2}}{j\omega\Delta t} - \frac{e^{-j\omega t_1}}{j\omega\Delta t} + \frac{(t_2 - t_1)}{\Delta t} e^{-j\omega t_2}\right]$$

$$= \frac{f_i j}{\omega}\left[\frac{j e^{-j\omega t_2}}{j\omega\Delta t} - \left(\frac{j}{\omega\Delta t} + 1\right) e^{-j\omega t_1}\right]$$

$$+ \frac{f_{i+1} j}{\omega}\left[\frac{j e^{-j\omega t_1}}{\omega\Delta t} + \left(1 - \frac{j}{\omega\Delta t}\right) e^{-j\omega t_2}\right],$$

where

$$t_1 = (i - 1)\Delta t + a$$

and

$$t_2 = i\Delta t + a .$$

In order to see how the summation develops, consider a pulse divided into N increments of equal width, Δt, for convenience. Then since $a = 0$,

$$[TAFT]_1 = \frac{f_1 j}{\omega}\left[\frac{j}{\omega\Delta t} e^{-j\omega\Delta t} - \left(\frac{j}{\omega\Delta t} + 1\right) e^{-j\omega(0)}\right]$$

$$+ \frac{f_2 j}{\omega}\left[\left(1 - \frac{j}{\omega\Delta t}\right) e^{-j\omega\Delta t} + \frac{j}{\omega\Delta t} e^{-j\omega(0)}\right]$$

$$[TAFT]_2 = \frac{f_2 j}{\omega}\left[\frac{j}{\omega\Delta t}\, e^{-j\omega 2\Delta t} - \left(\frac{j}{\omega\Delta t}+1\right) e^{-j\omega\Delta t}\right] + \frac{f_3 j}{\omega}\left[\left(1-\frac{j}{\omega\Delta t}\right) e^{-j\omega 2\Delta t} + \frac{j e^{-j\omega\Delta t}}{\omega\Delta t}\right]$$

$$[TAFT]_3 = \frac{f_3 j}{\omega}\left[\frac{j e^{-j\omega 3\Delta t}}{\omega\Delta t} - \left(\frac{j}{\omega\Delta t}+1\right) e^{-j\omega 2\Delta t}\right] + \frac{f_4 j}{\omega}\left[\left(1-\frac{j}{\omega\Delta t}\right) e^{-j\omega 3\Delta t} + \frac{j e^{-j\omega 2\Delta t}}{\omega\Delta t}\right]$$

$$[TAFT]_N = \frac{f_N j}{\omega}\left[\frac{j e^{-j\omega N\Delta t}}{\omega\Delta t} - \left(\frac{j}{\omega\Delta t}+1\right) e^{-j\omega(N-1)\Delta t}\right] + \frac{f_{N+1} j}{\omega}\left[\left(1-\frac{j}{\omega\Delta t}\right) e^{-j\omega N\Delta t} + \frac{j e^{-j\omega(N-1)\Delta t}}{\omega\Delta t}\right].$$

The approximation for the entire pulse composed of equal increments can, therefore, be written where the first and second terms are the first and last terms of the previous set and the summations include the remaining terms:

$$[TAFT] = \frac{f_1 j}{\omega}\left[\frac{j e^{-j\omega\Delta t}}{\omega\Delta t} - \left(\frac{j}{\omega\Delta t}+1\right) e^{-j\omega(0)}\right] + \frac{f_{N+1} j}{\omega}\left[\left(1-\frac{j}{\omega\Delta t}\right) e^{-j\omega N\Delta t} + \frac{j e^{-j\omega(N-1)\Delta t}}{\omega\Delta t}\right]$$
$$+ \sum_{i=2}^{N}\frac{f_i j}{\omega}\left[\frac{j e^{-j\omega i\Delta t}}{\omega\Delta t} - \left(\frac{j}{\omega\Delta t}+1\right) e^{-j\omega(i-1)\Delta t}\right] + \sum_{i=2}^{N}\frac{f_i j}{\omega}\left[\left(1-\frac{j}{\omega\Delta t}\right) e^{-j\omega[(i-1)\Delta t]} + \frac{j e^{-j\omega[(i-2)\Delta t]}}{\omega\Delta t}\right].$$

If the pulse is divided into two sections, the approximation is as shown below. For the first section, a is zero; after t exceeds T_1, a is included.

$$[TAFT] = \frac{f_1 j}{\omega}\left[\frac{j\,e^{-j\omega(\Delta t+a)}}{\omega\Delta t} - \left(\frac{j}{\omega\Delta t}+1\right)e^{-j\omega a}\right]$$
$$+\frac{f_{N+1}j}{\omega}\left[\left(1-\frac{j}{\omega\Delta t}\right)e^{-j\omega(N\Delta t+a)} + \frac{j\,e^{-j\omega[(N-1)\Delta t+a]}}{\omega\Delta t}\right]$$
$$+\sum_{i=2}^{N}\frac{f_i j}{\omega}\left[\frac{j\,e^{-j\omega(i\Delta t+a)}}{\omega\Delta t} - \left(\frac{j}{\omega\Delta t}+1\right)e^{-j\omega[(i-1)\Delta t+a]}\right]$$
$$+\sum_{i=2}^{N}\frac{f_i j}{\omega}\left[\left(1-\frac{j}{\omega\Delta t}\right)e^{-j\omega[(i-1)\Delta t+a]} + \frac{j\,e^{-j\omega[(i-2)\Delta t+a]}}{\omega\Delta t}\right].$$

The next step is to obtain expressions which are convenient for computation.

The initial term can be altered, using the identity $e^{j\theta} = \cos\theta + j\sin\theta$.

$$\frac{f_i j}{\omega}\left[\frac{j\,e^{-j\omega(\Delta t+a)}}{\omega\Delta t} - \left(\frac{j}{\omega\Delta t}+1\right)e^{-j\omega a}\right]$$
$$= \Delta t f_1\left[\frac{-e^{-j\omega\Delta t}\cdot e^{-j\omega a}}{(\omega\Delta t)^2} + \frac{e^{-j\omega a}}{(\omega\Delta t)^2} - \frac{j\,e^{-j\omega a}}{\omega\Delta t}\right]$$
$$= \Delta t f_1\left[-\frac{(\cos\omega\Delta t - j\sin\omega\Delta t)(\cos\omega a - j\sin\omega a)}{(\omega\Delta t)^2}\right.$$
$$\left. + \frac{(\cos\omega a - j\sin\omega a}{(\omega\Delta t)^2} - j\,\frac{(\cos\omega a - j\sin\omega a)}{(\omega\Delta t)}\right]$$
$$= \Delta t f_1\left[\left(\frac{\sin\omega\Delta t\sin\omega a}{(\omega\Delta t)^2} - \frac{\cos\omega\Delta t\cos\omega a}{(\omega\Delta t)^2}\right.\right.$$
$$\left. + \frac{\cos\omega a}{(\omega\Delta t)^2} - \frac{\sin\omega a}{(\omega\Delta t)}\right) + j\left(\frac{\cos\omega a\sin\omega\Delta t}{(\omega\Delta t)^2} + \frac{\cos\omega\Delta t\sin\omega a}{(\omega\Delta t)^2}\right.$$
$$\left.\left. - \frac{\sin\omega a}{(\omega\Delta t)^2} - \frac{\cos\omega a}{(\omega\Delta t)}\right)\right]$$
$$= \Delta t f_1\left\{\left[\left(\frac{\sin\omega\Delta t}{\omega\Delta t} - 1\right)\frac{\sin\omega a}{\omega\Delta t} - (\cos\omega\Delta t - 1)\frac{\cos\omega a}{(\omega\Delta t)^2}\right]\right.$$
$$\left. + j\left[\left(\frac{\sin\omega\Delta t}{\omega\Delta t} - 1\right)\frac{\cos\omega a}{\omega\Delta t} + (\cos\omega\Delta t - 1)\frac{\sin\omega a}{(\omega\Delta t)^2}\right]\right\}.$$

Then, since $\cos 2A = 1 - 2\sin^2 A$,

$$\cos \omega\Delta t - 1 = -2 \sin^2 \frac{\omega\Delta t}{2} \text{ or } \left(\frac{\cos \omega\Delta t - 1}{(\omega\Delta t)^2}\right) = -\frac{1}{2}\left[\frac{\sin \frac{\omega\Delta t}{2}}{\frac{\omega\Delta t}{2}}\right]^2 .$$

Thus, the first term becomes

$$\Delta t f_1 \left\{\left[\frac{1}{2}\left(\frac{\sin \frac{\omega\Delta t}{2}}{\frac{\omega\Delta t}{2}}\right)^2 \cos \omega a - \frac{1}{\omega\Delta t}\left(1 - \frac{\sin \omega\Delta t}{\omega\Delta t}\right) \sin \omega a\right]\right.$$
$$\left. + j\left[-\frac{1}{2}\left(\frac{\sin \frac{\omega\Delta t}{2}}{\frac{\omega\Delta t}{2}}\right)^2 \sin \omega a - \frac{1}{\omega\Delta t}\left(1 - \frac{\sin \omega\Delta t}{\omega\Delta t}\right) \cos \omega a\right]\right\} .$$

Similarly, the second term becomes

$$\frac{f_{N+1}\, j}{\omega}\left[\left(1 - \frac{j}{\omega\Delta t}\right) e^{-j\omega[N\Delta t + a]} + \left(\frac{j}{\omega\Delta t}\right) e^{-j\omega[N\Delta t + a - \Delta t]}\right]$$

$$= \Delta t f_{N+1}\left[\frac{e^{-j\omega[N\Delta t + a]}}{(\omega\Delta t)^2} - \frac{e^{-j\omega[N\Delta t + a]} \cdot e^{j\omega\Delta t}}{(\omega\Delta t)^2}\right.$$
$$\left. + j\frac{e^{-j\omega[N\Delta t + a]}}{(\omega\Delta t)}\right]$$

$$= \Delta t f_{N+1}\left[\frac{\cos \omega[N\Delta t + a] - j \sin \omega[N\Delta t + a]}{(\omega\Delta t)^2}\right.$$
$$- \frac{(\cos \omega[N\Delta t + a] - j \sin \omega[N\Delta t + a])(\cos \omega\Delta t + j \sin \omega\Delta t)}{(\omega\Delta t)^2}$$
$$\left. + j\frac{(\cos \omega[N\Delta t + a] - j \sin \omega[N\Delta t + a])}{\omega\Delta t}\right]$$

$$= \Delta t f_{N+1} \left\{ \left[(1 - \cos \omega\Delta t) \frac{\cos \omega[N\Delta t + a]}{(\omega\Delta t)^2} \right. \right.$$

$$\left. + \left(1 - \frac{\sin \omega\Delta t}{\omega\Delta t}\right) \frac{\sin \omega[N\Delta t + a]}{\omega\Delta t} \right]$$

$$+ j \left[\left(\cos \omega[N\Delta t + a] - 1\right) \frac{\sin \omega[N\Delta t + a]}{(\omega\Delta t)^2} \right.$$

$$\left. \left. + \left(1 - \frac{\sin \omega\Delta t}{(\omega\Delta t)}\right) \frac{\cos \omega[N\Delta t + a]}{(\omega\Delta t)} \right] \right\}$$

$$= \Delta t f_{N+1} \left\{ \left[\frac{1}{2} \left(\frac{\sin \frac{\omega\Delta t}{2}}{\frac{\omega\Delta t}{2}} \right)^2 \cos \omega[N\Delta t + a] \right. \right.$$

$$\left. + \left(1 - \frac{\sin \omega\Delta t}{\omega\Delta t}\right) \frac{\sin \omega[N\Delta t + a]}{(\omega\Delta t)} \right]$$

$$+ j \left[- \frac{1}{2} \left(\frac{\sin \frac{\omega\Delta t}{2}}{\frac{\omega\Delta t}{2}} \right)^2 \sin \omega[N\Delta t + a] \right.$$

$$\left. \left. + \left(1 - \frac{\sin \omega\Delta t}{\omega\Delta t}\right) \frac{\cos \omega[N\Delta t + a]}{(\omega\Delta t)} \right] \right\}.$$

Finally, the two summations are handled as follows:

$$\sum_{i=2}^{N} \frac{f_i j}{\omega} \left[\frac{j e^{-j\omega(i\Delta t + a)}}{\omega\Delta t} - \left(\frac{j}{\omega\Delta t} + 1\right) e^{-j\omega[(i-1)\Delta t + a]} \right.$$

$$\left. + \left(1 - \frac{j}{\omega\Delta t}\right) e^{-j\omega[(i-1)\Delta t + a]} + j \frac{e^{-j\omega[(i-2)\Delta t + a]}}{\omega\Delta t} \right]$$

$$=\sum_{i=2}^{N}\frac{f_i j}{\omega}\left[\frac{j\,e^{-j\omega[(i-1)\Delta t+a+\Delta t]}}{\omega\Delta t}-j\,\frac{e^{-j\omega[(i-1)\Delta t+a]}}{\omega\Delta t}\right.$$

$$-\,e^{-j\omega[(i-1)\Delta t+a]}+e^{-j\omega[(i-1)\Delta t+a]}-j\,\frac{e^{-j\omega[(i-1)\Delta t+a]}}{\omega\Delta t}$$

$$\left.+j\,\frac{e^{-j\omega[(i-1)\Delta t+a-\Delta t]}}{\omega\Delta t}\right]$$

$$=\sum_{i=2}^{N}\frac{f_i j}{\omega}\left[\frac{j\,e^{-j\omega[(i-1)\Delta t+a+\Delta t]}}{\omega\Delta t}-2j\,\frac{e^{-j\omega[(i-1)\Delta t+a]}}{\omega\Delta t}\right.$$

$$\left.+j\,\frac{e^{-j\omega[(i-1)\Delta t+a-\Delta t]}}{\omega\Delta t}\right]$$

$$=\sum_{i=2}^{N}\frac{f_i j^2}{\omega^2\Delta t}\left[e^{-j\omega[(i-1)\Delta t+a]}\cdot e^{-j\omega\Delta t}-2e^{-j\omega[(i-1)\Delta t+a]}\right.$$

$$\left.+\,e^{-j\omega[(i-1)\Delta t+a]}+e^{j\omega\Delta t}\right]$$

$$=\sum_{i=2}^{N}-\frac{f_i}{\omega^2\Delta t}\,[e^{-j\omega\Delta t}+e^{j\omega\Delta t}-2]\,e^{-j\omega[(i-1)\Delta t+a]}\,.$$

Now

$$[e^{-j\omega\Delta t}+e^{j\omega\Delta t}-2]=\cos\omega\Delta t-j\sin\omega\Delta t+\cos\omega\Delta t$$

$$+j\sin\omega\Delta t-2$$

$$=2\cos\omega\Delta t-2=2(\cos\omega\Delta t-1)$$

$$=2\left(-2\sin^2\frac{\omega\Delta t}{2}\right)$$

and

$$\left(4\,\frac{\sin^2\dfrac{\omega\Delta t}{2}}{\omega^2\Delta t}\right)=\left(\Delta t\,\frac{\sin\dfrac{\omega\Delta t}{2}}{\dfrac{\omega\Delta t}{2}}\right)^2.$$

Also

$$e^{-j\omega[(i-1)\Delta t+a]} = \cos\omega[(i-1)\Delta t+a] - j\sin[\omega(i-1)\Delta t+a].$$

Therefore, the summation becomes

$$\sum_{i=2}^{N} f_i \Delta t \left[\left(\frac{\sin\frac{\omega\Delta t}{2}}{\frac{\omega\Delta t}{2}}\right)^2 (\cos\omega[(i-1)\Delta t+a]) - j\,\Delta t\left(\frac{\sin\frac{\omega\Delta t}{2}}{\frac{\omega\Delta t}{2}}\right)^2 (\sin\omega[(i-1)\Delta t+a])\right].$$

The complete expression, suitable for computation is

$$\begin{aligned}[TAFT](j\omega) = \Bigg\{ &\Delta t\, f_1 \left[\frac{1}{2}\left(\frac{\sin\frac{\omega\Delta t}{2}}{\frac{\omega\Delta t}{2}}\right)^2 \cos\omega a - \frac{1}{\omega\Delta t}\left(1-\frac{\sin\omega\Delta t}{\omega\Delta t}\right)\sin\omega a\right] \\ &+ \Delta t\left(\frac{\sin\frac{\omega\Delta t}{2}}{\frac{\omega\Delta t}{2}}\right)^2 \sum_{i=2}^{N} f_i \cos\omega[(i-1)\Delta t+a] \\ &+ \Delta t\, f_{N+1}\left[\frac{1}{2}\left(\frac{\sin\frac{\omega\Delta t}{2}}{\frac{\omega\Delta t}{2}}\right)^2 \cos\omega[N\Delta t+a] + \frac{1}{\omega\Delta t}\left(1-\frac{\sin\omega\Delta t}{\omega\Delta t}\right)\sin\omega[N\Delta t+a]\right]\Bigg\}\end{aligned}$$

$$+j\left\{\Delta t f_1\left[-\frac{1}{2}\left(\frac{\sin\frac{\omega\Delta t}{2}}{\frac{\omega\Delta t}{2}}\right)^2\sin\omega a\right.\right.$$

$$\left.-\frac{1}{\omega\Delta t}\left(1-\frac{\sin\omega\Delta t}{\omega\Delta t}\right)\cos\omega a\right]$$

$$+\Delta t\left(\frac{\sin\frac{\omega\Delta t}{2}}{\frac{\omega\Delta t}{2}}\right)^2\sum_{i=2}^{N} f_i(-\sin\omega[(i-1)\Delta t+a])$$

$$+\Delta t f_{N+1}\left[-\frac{1}{2}\left(\frac{\sin\frac{\omega\Delta t}{2}}{\frac{\omega\Delta t}{2}}\right)^2\sin\omega[N\Delta t+a]\right.$$

$$\left.\left.+\frac{1}{\omega\Delta t}\left(1-\frac{\sin\omega\Delta t}{\omega\Delta t}\right)\cos\omega[N\Delta t+a]\right]\right\}.$$

Values of the functions $\frac{\sin x}{x}$ and $\left(\frac{\sin x}{x}\right)^2$ for various values of the argument, x, have been compiled. For example, see *Tables of Functions* by E. Janke and F. Emde.

When $\omega = 0$, the approximation reduces to

$$[TAFT]_{\omega=0} = \Delta t f_1\left(\frac{1}{2}\right) + \Delta t\sum_{i=2}^{N} f_i + \Delta t f_{N+1}\left(\frac{1}{2}\right).$$

If the pulse closes (as is assumed), then

$$f_{N+1} = f_1 \qquad \text{and} \qquad \frac{\Delta t f_1}{2} + \frac{\Delta t f_{N+1}}{2} = \Delta t f_1 \ .$$

Obviously, the summation, with $\omega = 0$, gives a real number which is an approximation of the area under the curve. Moreover, the approximation is made up from a summation of rectangles rather than

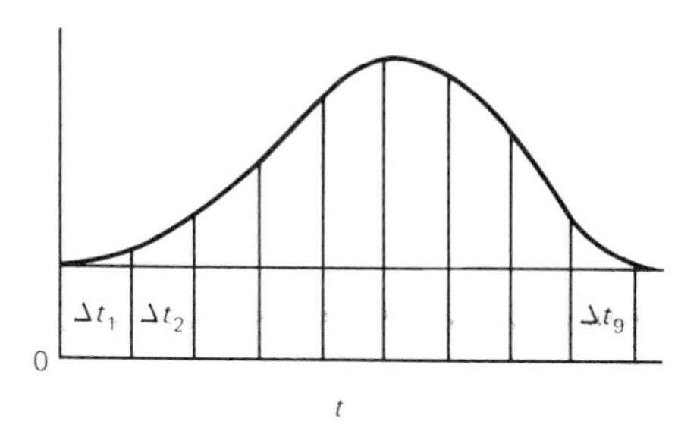

Pulse function divided into 9 increments

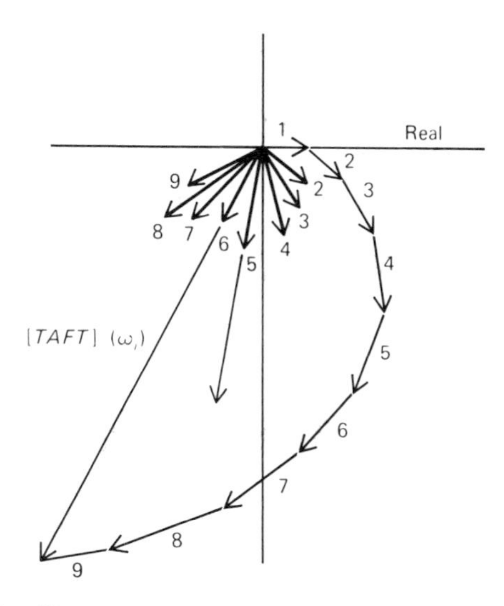

Figure A3.2. Illustration of Fourier approximation for a pulse divided into 9 increments.

trapezoids. As frequency assumes positive values, the coefficients of the trigonometric functions (which are, in turn, trigonometric functions) take on values different from either unity or zero, and these are unique to the trapezoidal approximation.

Draper, McKay and Lees (*1*) show that if the time functions are approximated by the tops of rectangles of the same width, the Fourier Transform approximation is

$$[RAFT]\ (j\omega) = \left(\frac{\sin \frac{\omega \Delta t}{2}}{\frac{\omega \Delta t}{2}} \right) \Delta t \sum_{i=0}^{N+1} f_i(i\Delta t) e^{-j\omega\Delta t}.$$

The coefficient

$$\left(\frac{sin \frac{\omega \Delta t}{2}}{\frac{\omega \Delta t}{2}} \right) = \frac{e^{+j\frac{\omega\Delta t}{2}} - e^{-j\frac{\omega\Delta t}{2}}}{2j\left(\frac{\omega\Delta t}{2}\right)}$$

is the Fourier transform of a rectangle of unity height with zero time located at the center of its base. When the trapezoidal approximation is used, the square of this coefficient appears.

As frequency increases from zero, the approximation produces an imaginary part so that the result is a complex number for each selected frequency. At a given frequency, the Fourier transform is approximated for each interval, and the resulting complex numbers are summed. The procedure is indicated in Figure A3.2 for a 9-increment approximation.

An example is worked out in detail by Draper, McKay and Lees. An alternate derivation for the trapezoidal approximation is also given therein.

References

1. Draper, C. S., Walter McKay and Sidney Lees. Instrument Engineering, vol. II. McGraw-Hill Book Co., New York, 1953.

Appendix 4
Non-Technical Aspects of Engineering—Some Practical Suggestions

Successful execution of in-plant testing programs demands more than technical competence, effective procedures and demonstrated performance. All members of the test crew must be aware of the personal factors and interactions of people with widely different and frequently conflicting points of view. Because of the wide range of training, objectives and motivations of the different people who become involved, personnel relations can become complex indeed. Yet, unless the major conflicts can be resolved and a modicum of common goals established, the entire effort may come to naught despite the technical excellence of the engineering.

If the test work is conducted entirely under the auspices of the plant (i.e., handled by a technical service group located at and associated with a given manufacturing facility), subsidiary people problems are usually minimum. Such a group should have already developed healthy relations with both the plant management and plant operating personnel. The nature of the problem should be well-known and common objectives fairly well defined.

If the work is to be implemented by a central engineering group, the situation becomes more difficult. Such groups almost always are suspect by plant people who naturally resent intrusions into their areas of competence and who do not want others to uncover or probe into areas of ignorance.

The most difficult situation occurs when the plant study is undertaken by a central staff group and especially when the services of this group are requested by another centrally located group which has responsibility for plant engineering. The central group requesting the work naturally wants a simple answer in a very short time and, moreover, an answer which does not reflect inferior performance on their part for past or present actions. They are not likely to applaud a result which unequivocally indicates poor engineering or judgment regardless of the ultimate improvements which would acrue. As a matter of fact, the greater the improvements, potential or achieved, the greater the efforts may be to frustrate or discredit the work, for ineffectiveness of one group may be measured by the degree of improvement which can be achieved by another.

In view of the fact that the test crew cannot possibly conduct its work with a full knowledge of all the company politics and since good engineering probably is impossible if political concessions must be made, the best policy would appear to be one of forthright honesty and complete dedication to solution of the problem with no compromise of convictions. The neophyte should realize, however, that winning friends and earning respect may be diametrically opposed in the industrial environment.

A number of principles relevant to plant test programs may be helpful.

(1) Develop as concise a qualitative description of the problem as is possible.

(2) Try to establish current overall performance records of plant production with statements as to how the data were obtained and how performance is, and will be, evaluated; i.e., establish a status quo if possible.

(3) Obtain the opinions of engineers and operators concerning the nature of the problem and possible courses of action to obtain a solution. Listen respectfully to all sources, but do not take undue credence of any because very few indisputable hard facts will be known and much of what will be said will be based on hearsay and faulty intuition.

(4) Plan the proposed testing program as carefully as possible in the light of the information considered reliable. Do not compromise on what data should be obtained or the instrumentation required to get it.

(5) As knowledge of the plant behavior increases, the nature or source of problems will begin to emerge and these may differ from those originally visualized. For this reason, be willing to alter plans of attack or testing procedures and to make compromises as to scope and objectives.

(6) Know the plant thoroughly. The details of all processing systems and apparata must be familiar to the test crew. Their function, principles of operation and possible malfunctions should be thoroughly understood. The test personnel should be able to visualize the operation of the complete ensemble being tested without the aid of flow diagrams and should be able to identify every important item in the plant. This cannot be overemphasized!

(7) With the test instrumentation installed, collect data typical of "normal" operations as well as of behavior during occasions when difficulties are encountered, especially if these are associated with the immediate problem. This will, in part, constitute a documentation of the status quo.

(8) Be sure plant personnel, including plant manager, production supervisor, technical service manager, and operators are aware of the test program and are in agreement with the test procedures and objectives.

(9) Keep your own management informed on all matters of importance so that they can speak knowledgeably about your work to their peers. Their confidence in your work should be sufficient to persuade them to assist you in implementing the warranted changes which are indicated by the study. Nothing is more enervating than an uncertain management which vacillates until the fruits of your work are lost. An ideal manager backs up his people and insists that plant test results which show promise are thoroughly reviewed and recommendations given a fair hearing. The test engineer must so condition his management that they will respond in this manner.

(10) Remember that the overall behavior of a plant or subsystem is usually quite simple. If it were complicated, few plants would be operating. Also remember that, since almost no quantitative design goes into present-day process feedback control systems, the control problems cannot for the most part be very difficult. Thus, if a plant is operating at all, it is almost a certainty that it can be made to operate better.

(11) Simplify, vitalize and personalize your applications of engineering.

Index